George J. Bart

BLAKISTON BOOKS ON AGRICULTURE

GILBEART H. COLLINGS, PH.D., *Consulting Editor*

THE NATURE AND PREVENTION

OF

PLANT DISEASES

The goal of plant pathology,—production of high quality crops with inherent disease resistance.

Golden Cross Bantam sweet corn, seen in this disease-free hybrid seed field, has been bred for resistance to the bacterial wilt disease. The widespread adoption of this and other wilt-resistant varieties has almost eliminated this once-destructive disease as a loss factor in the American crop. (Courtesy of the Corneli Seed Co.)

THE NATURE
AND
PREVENTION
OF
PLANT DISEASES

By K. STARR CHESTER

Department of Botany and Plant Pathology,
Oklahoma Agricultural Experiment Station

THE BLAKISTON COMPANY

Philadelphia

PRINTED IN U. S. A.
BY THE MAPLE PRESS COMPANY, YORK, PA.

PREFACE

The subject matter of this book and the manner of treatment have been largely dictated by the needs of students to whom an elementary course in plant pathology is a part of the background fitting them for useful work in agriculture. It has evolved and been used in mimeographed form as the basis for my elementary course for several score college juniors and seniors, most of whom are majoring in field crops, horticulture, soils, entomology, and related fields. These students bring to class a rich experience in practical agriculture often resting on a somewhat limited base of training in botany, chemistry, and bacteriology. Their interest primarily concerns the practical side of plant disease control. The book has the dual purpose of introducing the student to the essential features of the science, as exemplified in important diseases of our leading crops, and of providing him with a work to which he may refer for detailed and specific directions on plant disease control. Wherever possible, there have been included lists of disease-resistant crop varieties, trade names as well as compositions of fungicides, and working directions for putting theory into practice.

In the selection of diseases for detailed treatment, it was recognized that agricultural students are motivated largely by the economic importance of each disease and the crop in which it occurs. This has led both to a selection of major diseases of leading crops, and to emphasis on the nature and amounts of the losses they occasion. A second type of emphasis prevailing through the book has to do with the environment as it conditions the development of contagious disease, and with the epiphytological peculiarities of plant diseases. Proportionately less space is devoted to mycological detail or to parasitism *per se*. I have tried to select for detailed study diseases that are of considerable economic importance over a broad area in the United States, that represent all of the leading categories of plant disease, that have been investigated sufficiently to permit a fairly complete account, and that illustrate the leading

v

principles of plant pathology. I have attempted to rectify the past neglect of diseases of southern and prairie crops and of the modifications in epiphytology of plant diseases under warm climate and dry land conditions. An innovation is seen in the treatment of certain complex pathological syndromes, such as the corn root, stalk, and ear rots, the cotton seedling disease and boll rot problem, and the stalk- and root-rots of sorghums. In spite of their great economic importance such complex syndromes have been somewhat neglected in the past and for this reason they are treated in proportionately greater detail than other diseases more commonly included in textbooks.

It will be noticed that the arrangement of chapters is quite different from that employed in other elementary textbooks of plant pathology. The conventional series of chapters devoted to general principles is reserved for the latter part of the book. This arrangement is advantageous in commanding the early attention of students who, from the nature of their whole course of study, are interested primarily in specific diseases and their control. The synthesis of general principles at the end of the course is more economical of time, since the student has already become familiar with the leading principles. It finds the student more receptive to generalization and theory, and it serves to summarize and fix in his mind the essential principles that he has gleaned, one by one, from a study of individual diseases. This arrangement also makes the book more flexible in relation to the instructor's available time, since if time is limited certain of the last chapters could be omitted without destroying the unity of the book.

In the order of chapters, the more usual phylogenetic arrangement has been abandoned as of little importance to the student in comparison with other, more practical arrangements. The rusts, which are first treated in the book, are of such general importance in all types of crops and of such fascinating etiology that they offer the student an absorbing starting point regardless of his particular crop interest. Their complex but well-defined life histories and their exquisite adaptations give the student a healthy respect for etiology and epiphytology, and prepare him for thoroughness in studying less complex and well-defined diseases later on. However, the chapters are sufficiently independent that their consideration in modified order would result in no serious difficulty. Such a minor matter as the availability of fresh laboratory materials, is sufficient justification for taking up chapters out of order.

The choice of references was dictated by several considerations. References, however valuable, in foreign languages were omitted as beyond the linguistic ability of most agricultural undergraduates. Of the few references included, some were selected because they represent thorough treatments of individual diseases, others because of their fundamental or classic importance. They are limited to papers or bulletins generally available in agricultural libraries, and wherever possible they represent the latest comprehensive studies. Attention has been called to more extensive bibliographies, and the works cited in this book are intended merely as illustrative supplementary reading.

I am grateful for the many helpful suggestions that were received from colleagues who kindly contributed their time in criticizing the manuscript. Among those who have read certain chapters most pertinent to their own fields of interest are: Dr. H. D. Barker, Mr. H. P. Barss, Dr. G. H. Collings, Mr. A. C. Dillman, Dr. H. A. Edson, Dr. John Ehrlich, Dr. G. H. Godfrey, Dr. R. W. Goss, Dr. H. D. Güssow, Dr. Donald Hoffmaster, Mr. C. O. Johnston, Dr. L. O. Kunkel, Dr. Julian H. Miller, Dr. W. W. Ray, Dr. A. J. Riker, Mr. O. S. Schultz, Dr. Neil E. Stevens, Dr. J. C. Walker, and Dr. G. L. Zundel. Further suggestions and criticisms that will be useful in improving the book in the future, from those who may have occasion to use it, will be welcome at any time.

For those illustrations which are not original, the sources are indicated. I wish to express thanks to the many colleagues who made these illustrations available, and in particular to my associate, Dr. Donald Hoffmaster, who furnished many of the original negatives.

K. Starr Chester,

Dept. of Botany and Plant Pathology,
Stillwater, Oklahoma,   Oklahoma Agriculture Experiment Station.
Feb. 1, 1942.

CONTENTS

ix

CHAPTER 14

Diseases due to unfavorable soil conditions: Lack of necessary chemical substances; excess of soil chemicals; water deficiency; excess of water and irregularity of water supply. *Diseases due to unfavorable air relationships:* Lack of oxygen; poisonous gases. *Diseases due to unfavorable temperatures:* Heat injury; cold injury. *Diseases due to unfavorable light conditions:* Insufficient light; excessive light; photoperiodism.

CHAPTER 15

Field observations; plant disease surveys; collections; preservation of specimens; laboratory examination of specimens; identification of organisms; investigating the causes of diseases; studies on epiphytology; studies on disease control; literature review.

CHAPTER 16

Effect of temperature on parasitic disease; effect of moisture on parasitic disease; effect of wind on parasitic disease; effect of light on parasitic disease; effect of soil on parasitic disease.

CHAPTER 17

Etiology: The names, history, and life-history of pathogenic organisms. *Epiphytology:* Epiphytotics due primarily to weather conditions; to unnatural culture; to the introduction of disease. The grand cycle of disease; the origin of plant diseases; the prediction of epiphytotics.

CHAPTER 18

Control procedures; the biological aspects of quarantines; the economic aspects of quarantines; the mechanism of plant quarantines; present day quarantines; the efficacy of quarantines.

CHAPTER 19

The economic significance of the development of disease resistant crop varieties. Some basic concepts of plant immunology. The nature of disease resistance and immunity: mechanical defenses; chemical defenses; functional defenses; hypersensitivity; acquired immunity; complexity of the factors that determine resistance.
The control of plant diseases through the use of resistant varieties: the need for this type of disease control; requirements for an acceptable resistant variety; accomplishments in the development of disease resistant varieties; the genetics of disease resistance in plants; the limitations of breeding for resistance.

CHAPTER 20

Chapter 1

THE SIGNIFICANCE OF PLANT DISEASE IN AGRICULTURE

Waist deep in a sea of ripening wheat stand two men, and they mark a turning point in American agriculture. The man in overalls dejectedly pulls a few stalks from the soil. The stems are cracked and dried, stained with red and black streaks. He breaks off a head of grain and rubs it between his palms, and as he blows the chaff gently away there remain in his palm a few, pitifully shrivelled kernels. Many of the stalks have broken over and fallen beneath the reach of binder or combine. The field that just a few days ago gave promise of forty bushels to the acre, today will hardly yield the expense of harvesting. Perhaps it would be better to cut it for hay, or plow it under to give way to a summer crop of fodder.

This is the grim side of black stem rust, the scourge of wheat farmers in every land. The scene, which took place in 1935 or '37 or '39, is a classic scene, which had its prototypes four thousand years ago in the grain fields of the ancient Hebrews.

What will this mean to the man in overalls? Perhaps another postponement of the childrens' chance for education; perhaps failure to meet the payments on the nearly paid-up farm; perhaps this year will mark the beginning of the long, sad back-trek from combine to binder, from tractor to mules, from a square mile of rich, flat bottom land to a quarter section of eroded hillside,—on from wheat, which takes machinery to cotton or corn, which you can raise if you have a mule and a family, on to working for the insurance company or the W.P.A.

That's the dark side. But what about the other man beside the man in overalls? He is the county agricultural agent. He's saying something to this effect: "You don't need to put up with this loss another year. The men at the Experiment Stations have been working to breed varieties of wheat that are resistant to the stem-

1

rust fungus. They have been able to combine rust resistance with the other qualities we need in wheat,—high yields, drought- and cold-resistance, and good milling and baking qualities. Jim Beard, out west of town, has been growing one of these varieties, and it's making thirty seven bushels to the acre this year. You can get some of that wheat for seeding, and be ready for rust another year."

Because disasters like this occur today and often mean the difference between success and failure in agriculture and because many such disasters can be averted by timely intervention of simple preventive measures, some acquaintance with the science of plant pathology is indispensible to agricultural workers. The purposes of an introductory course in plant pathology, and the purposes of this book, are to enable you to become acquainted with the principal types of plant diseases, to learn of the principles of plant disease prevention and their practice in controlling important plant diseases that are injuring farming activity today, to have some background of understanding of the essentials of plant disease and its control, so that when you are faced with an unfamiliar problem in plant pathology you will be aided in solving it by your familiarity with related problems, and finally, to become acquainted with the yet unsolved problems of plant pathology and with the efforts the Federal Department of Agriculture and the State Experiment Stations are making to devise means for combating plant diseases.

You are studying a comparatively new science, that of plant disease. It is only a few decades since plant pathology came into being. Some of the pioneer plant pathologists, founders of the science in America, are still vigorously carrying on their warfare against plant disease, setting a stimulating example to their army of young followers. But plant diseases themselves, and their prevention by empirical or intuitive recipes, are by no means limited to problems of today. Long before the appearance of civilized man, the agents of disease were leaving petrified thumbprints in the fossils that tell us of the leaf spot diseases and other ailments of prehistoric vegetation. Among the earliest written records of man, the unmistakeable complaints of blights, mildews, and plagues show us clearly that plant disease has shadowed the agricultural path of man since he first scratched the soil with a pointed stick and

planted seed.   The Old Testament tells us of plant diseases visited
upon man in punishment of his transgressions.   Three hundred
years before Christ, Theophrastus, the Father of Botany, was well
familiar with plant diseases of his time, and in his writings we can
recognize many of our plant troubles of today, scorch, rot, scab,
and rust.   So formidable were the cereal rusts in those early days
that the Romans evolved a pair of rust Gods, Rubigus and Rubigo,
whom they annually honored as a means of rust prevention.

As ancient times gave way to the intellectual darkness of the
Middle Ages, these early sparks of understanding of plant disease
were all but extinguished by the superstition and avoidance of
reason that overshadowed that period.   Plant diseases continued
to take their toll from the European peasant and landowner, but
we learn little of them save that from time to time great epiphytotics* occurred, attended by disaster, famine, and migrations,
and historical documents of the early days tell us of entreaties to
The Deity to ward off the evil blights, of tragic suffering and death
from the "holy fire" which we now attribute to the eating of ergot-
diseased grain, of the suffering and famine in Ireland when disease
destroyed the potato crop in 1845 and drove many of the Irish
people to America, and of the powdery mildew which wiped out the
wine industry of Madeira and forced the population of that little
island back to their ancient occupations of sugar-cane growing and
cochineal gathering.

The story of the Irish potato blight is the story of a microscopic
fungus which wrought havoc in Europe equalled by few of Europe's
many wars.

It is believed that the potato was first brought to Europe by Sir
Francis Drake from the Andean hinterland of South America, where
it had long been revered, emblematic of fertility, and even been the
inspiration of mutilation and human sacrifice.   Thanks to the
efforts of Sir Walter Raleigh and many other enthusiasts, the potato
soon won its rightful place as a leading source of carbohydrate food
throughout all of Europe, from the Mediterranean to northernmost
Scandanavia, and in northeastern North America as well.   In
its migration from South America the potato had left behind its most

* The name given to a destructive outbreak of plant disease; comparable to epidemics of human disease or epizootics of animal diseases.

serious agents of disease; for two hundred years or more it enjoyed comparative freedom from disease. But in the early half of the nineteenth century, disturbing reports of potato failures began to appear. In ever-increasing intensity, a plague of potato fields was laying waste the crops of individual farmers, and of whole communities.

In 1845 the crisis was reached. With unbelievable fury the potato blight devastated millions of acres in Europe, the United States, and Canada. So sudden was the catastrophe and so complete that in only a few days fields with every promise of abundant harvest were transformed into blackened wastes of vegetation overlying foul and putrifying masses of rotten tubers. And this was not a local problem, nor limited to a few fields,—everywhere where potatoes were grown the tragedy was repeated, bringing in its wake privation, then starvation or the fever that inevitably follows malnutrition. In Ireland alone, a quarter of a million people fell victim to the famine, and many others migrated to America and became the basis of the Irish-American population of the United States. The tragedy of the potato blight is a dramatic story, well worth reading in detail as given in Rolfe and Rolfe's "Romance of the Fungus World," the novel "Famine" by Liam O'Flaherty, or Large's "Advance of the Fungi."

Like most tragic experiences of mankind, the potato blight was not without some benefit. In the nineteenth century science was rapidly throwing off its stupor of the Middle Ages; the chains of superstition that so long had bound and suppressed creative thought were rusting away. The intellectual genuises Louis Pasteur and Robert Koch were performing the first crucial experiments that were to open up the vast field of modern research on contagious disease. Charles Darwin was revolutionizing biology and philosophy with his keen deductions on organic evolution. Von Liebig was laying the foundations of modern agricultural chemistry. The stage was set for the first fundamental discoveries on the nature and control of plant disease, and the catastrophe of the potato blight forced the attention of master minds to the solution of this and related problems in plant pathology. Out of the labor pains of Europe, racked by the potato blight, was born modern plant pathology, the science of plant disease. The brilliant young German, Anton de Bary, stared at the dying potato leaves through his primitive microscope, saw the green leaf cells in the clutches of the sinuous, pallid fibers of the fungus, and its myriads of wind-driven spores, proved that the fungus was the cause, the sole cause of the blight, and paved the way for Millardet a few years later to give humanity an effective weapon against any future recurrence of the blight, Bordeaux mixture.

The story of Bordeaux mixture itself is worth the telling. According to the tale, a farmer in Médoc, France, had a vineyard that bordered the highway.   Passers-by are alike the world over, and to the despair of the farmer, the wayfarers could not resist the luscious bunches of ripening grapes, just over the fence.   In a moment of inspiration, the farmer decided to take steps.   He went to the barn, and his eye falling on a sack of lime, he made a milky broth to splash on the vines.   As the mixture didn't look repulsive enough, he threw in a shovelful of bluestone.   This accomplished, he spattered it over the vines, posted a "Poison" sign and awaited results.   History does not tell us whether the wayfarers were deterred by the farmer's ingenuity, but it does recall that Dr. Millardet came past the vineyard, noted that the sprayed grapes alone had escaped the destructive mildew disease, learned of the spray so accidentally applied, tested its efficiency against fungus diseases of the vine, and gave us the completely effective protection against future outbreaks of both vine and potato blights which we now know as Bordeaux mixture.

Man has a tendency to learn things the hard way.   It took another epiphytotic which has practically exterminated one of our finest forest trees, the American chestnut, to establish the science of plant pathology in America.   The chestnut blight fungus was a foreigner that sneaked into America from Asia.   Starting its deadly work about 1904, it spread swiftly, destroying every tree in its path.   Today there hardly remains a chestnut tree in the great forests of the East which were once dominated by this tree.   This disaster taught us what might be expected from unwelcome foreign pests; it was largely responsible for the establishment of the National Plant Quarantine Act in 1912.

Today new and potent enemies of our cultivated plants are coming to the attention of growers and scientists.   The Dutch elm disease for a while threatened to exterminate the American elm, as it had done in many parts of Europe. In the royal gardens at Versailles were long avenues of stately elms that were mature trees in the hey-day of the pre-revolution French court. Only a few years after the Dutch elm disease appeared, the avenues were lined with dead and dying trees, nearly all sacrificed to the elm disease fungus (Fig. 1). Thanks to our lesson from the chestnut blight and to energetic eradication of diseased elms in America, the elm disease has been brought under control, but any relaxation of these efforts could still release the disease in all its destructiveness. In the Northeast another fungus disease, scab, has been slowly but steadily destroying large numbers of willows. Will it reach the Middle West and be able to attack the osiers that hold back the levees of the Mississippi River? The possibility exists and with it the possibility of flood danger far exceeding the already serious loss of the trees themselves. The sycamore is threatened by another virulent disease organism. During the last few years the native persimmon in the south central states has fallen victim to a fungus which equals the chestnut-blight organism in its virulence. This may be welcome news to farm lads who have worked in the hot sun grubbing weedy persimmons out of the pasture. The editor of a leading Southern agricultural journal recently wrote: "I am delighted to hear the persimmon disease has arrived in the Southwest." But there is also much to be said in favor of the persimmon,—its delicious fruit, its value in feeding 'possums and other desirable wild life, its usefulness in preventing soil erosion, and to a limited extent the use of its exceedingly hard wood in such articles as the heads of golf clubs. Already large areas have been depleted of persimmon by the ravages of the disease and a real possibility exists that this tree may emulate the fate of the dodo, the heath hen, and the American chestnut.

Few of the main groups of crop plants are free from occasional but disastrous attacks of disease. Among the fruits may be mentioned fire blight which caused "one of the greatest industries of the San Joaquin valley to vanish like a dream" when 500,000 pear trees were killed by the disease within a few years. In the rich fruit section of New York State a new virus disease of peaches has broken out in epiphytotic form, promising to be even more destruc-

Figure 1. The threat of the Dutch elm disease. Above, a scene along an elm-shaded village street; below, as the same street would appear if the elms were destroyed. This has already happened in many parts of Europe, but prompt quarantines and energetic eradication of diseased trees has prevented the disease from becoming general in America. (*Courtesy of M. A. McKenzie, Mass. Agri. Exp. Sta.*)

tive than any of the other twelve or more virus diseases of this tree. In the tropics banana plantations cannot be permanent. Invariably they become infested with the "Panama disease" after a few years. There is no escape; the infested plantation must be abandoned, and the industry must continually push on to new plantings in virgin soil.

Among vegetables, the ravages of the potato blight are seconded by those of watermelon wilt, at first welcomed as nature's way to

Figure 2. Typical of many watermelon fields laid waste by the wilt disease, this commercial field of Dixie Queen melons shows great bare areas where plants have succumbed. Until the development of wilt-resistant varieties of watermelons, such fields were henceforth useless for the cultivation of watermelons, since the wilt fungus remains virulent in the soil for many years. *(Courtesy of M. N. Walker, Fla. Agr. Exp. Sta.)*

maintain price levels by restricting production, but soon wiping out the melon industry in important sections of Florida, Iowa, and California (Fig. 2). Within the past few years a new potato disease has appeared, bacterial ring rot. It is so dreaded that state potato inspectors have placed on the disease a tolerance of zero; a single infected tuber is sufficient to condemn a shipment. And with reason, for reports from infested counties are of this sort: "In one county the growers are becoming discouraged because of serious losses. Potato acreage and production have declined 50 per cent in the past three years"; and in another locality: "The loss in one county is estimated at 500 to 700 cars plus reduced price on several thousand cars." Other such cases among vegetables could be cited.

And in field crops the story is the same. Flax has always been a pioneer crop, moving on to virgin areas and leaving behind a trail of "flax-sick" soil, infested with the flax wilt fungus, soil upon which susceptible flax cannot again be grown for many years. Texas root rot has rendered great areas of the Southwest unsuitable for culture of cotton, alfalfa, and many other crops. The disease causes a loss in Texas of 300,000 bales of cotton a year, and in addition, attacks more than 2,000 other species of plants, aggregating a total loss from this disease, in the seven states affected, which reached $150,000,000 in 1937. In Sudan and Nigeria is another serious threat to cotton, leaf curl, a virus disease which can steal as much as 300 pounds of cotton per acre. It cannot be predicted whether this virus may be brought to America or the potentialities of its introduction, but in Africa it is regarded as highly menacing. And finally, no account of epiphytotics in field crops can omit mention of the cereal rusts. Stem rust is always with us, and now and then, when the weather is suitable, it rages northward from the Great Plains to Canada leaving in its wake millions of acres of wasted grain. These epiphytotics are coming more and more frequently. There have been three in the past five years. That of 1935 destroyed a quarter of the national wheat crop, a total of 160,000,000 bushels, and in North Dakota and Minnesota 60 per cent of the wheat crop was sacrificed to stem rust.

This is the spectacular side of plant disease, the great epiphytotics that are so often followed by privation, suffering, loss of homes and farms, even famine, migration, or abandonment of farming. Tragic as these outbreaks are, they are surpassed by the multitude of less dramatic but more prevalent ailments of plants. One would not be inclined to think of the maple tree as commonly suffering from disease. Yet, not less than 54 contagious diseases affect this tree. A conservative estimate would place the number of known diseases of wheat in America at 75, of balsam fir 54, of the potato 75, and of the apple more than 100. In the potato there have been described more than 50 virus diseases, exclusive of other types, and while this probably represents some duplication, there are doubtless from 12 to 20 such diseases of the potato in addition to many fungous and bacterial diseases.

The losses from most of these lesser troubles do not reach high percentages. Like the common cold they are always with us. They kill a plant here or there or reduce production by 1 per cent or 5 per cent, and the grower has come to look upon them as necessary evils to be accepted with philosophy as part of the gamble in farming. The average farmer is not usually concerned with any plant disease until the loss reaches 15 per cent of the crop, and he rarely takes steps to prevent it until the loss mounts to 25 per cent.

American business has learned the importance of little leaks. The only difference between the borrower and the banker is a little difference of 3 or 4 per cent. Money safely invested at 4 per cent interest is a stride toward prosperity, and a crop loss of the same amount equally represents retrogression.

And how many farmers realize that a small percentage of loss in the field represents a much larger loss, perhaps all, of the profit. To be specific, take the case of a farmer with a quarter-section in wheat, and assume that under disease-free conditions his average yield is a conservative 25 bushels to the acre, or a total of 4,000 bushels. The harvest return is divided into two elements, part, usually most of it, must be paid out to cover all the costs of production of that crop, the remainder is the farmer's profit, and may be applied to maintaining and improving his standard of living and of farming. Under normal circumstances the 4,000 bushels would be used somewhat after this fashion: use of the land, 40 per cent; seed, 3 per cent; labor, 12 per cent; machinery and maintenance, 20 per cent; insurance, 5 per cent; leaving a profit of 20 per cent based on disease-free conditions. The loss from diseases in the American wheat crop for the period 1919 to 1937 averaged slightly more than 10 per cent per year. Let us assume that our potential 4,000 bushel wheat crop was subjected to disease to this extent, and that 10 per cent or 400 bushels were lost through disease. All of the costs of production are unchanged; it still cost 3,200 bushels to produce the 3,600 bushel yield. The bills could not be paid with the diseased grain or that which failed to materialize. Ten per cent disease in the field did not strike the farmer as an unusual or serious loss; yet, the 10 per cent field loss cost him one-half of his profit.

In times of prosperity, of favorable crop weather, and high prices, such losses, needless though they may be, can be borne by the farmer without hardship and need not be a serious concern of the layman, but in the economic crisis of today they have a double significance. In the first place, the farmer's plight is apparent to all; until the outbreak of war his prosperity was only a memory or a vision in the stress that followed years of drought-ridden crops, of depleted soil, and of prices below the cost of production of the crops they purchase. War provides a temporary relief only to be followed by depression in which the farmers' burden again becomes acute. Although disease losses are felt at all levels of farm prosperity they are most acute as they affect the marginal farmer; to him the percentage of loss is the back-breaking straw, the difference between survival and failure.

We hear much today of the misfortunes of the American farmer as compared with the greater security and prosperity of the American business man. We blame this difference on many factors, but is not a part of the explanation in the differences in methods between the two? To the business man a loss of one per cent in his industry through waste is a vital loss, one to be corrected. The story is told that Mr. Rockefeller, in an inspection of one of his factories, noticed a machine dripping solder on oil cans. He asked and found that the superintendent had never tested the exact amount of solder needed. Mr. Rockefeller counted and found that the machine was applying 39 drops of solder per can. An experiment was devised on the spot; it was discovered that 38 drops would suffice. In a year's time the concern had been saved $10,000 worth of solder and time through this slight economy. No business a fraction as wasteful as the average farm could survive without subsidy in the face of its competition. When the American farmer learns to regard his farming as the business man regards his business, we venture to predict that the need for farm relief and crop subsidy will be materially decreased.

And there is added significance to preventable waste today, at a time when the nation is moving toward mobilization of all its resources, engaged in a war that takes men from farms and puts

them in factories and uniforms, and calls for an increase in agricultural production from a decreased farm population.

The various governmental and private undertakings for better-
ing farm conditions have in some instances been late in realizing
that diseases and insects may materially affect the success of these
projects, and they are now beginning to turn to plant pathologists
and entomologists in efforts to avoid the crop-pest hazard. A few
illustrations will bring out this point.

In 1936 a farmer was resettled on a rich bottom farm in the
Southwest. In 1938 the farmer called on the State Experiment
Station for information on the dying of his cotton plants. Examination of the fields showed great circular areas of dead plants
among the cotton, and rows of dead cowpeas between the rows of
tall, luxuriant corn, the ravages of Texas root rot. The farmer
had learned to know this disease in Texas. He said: "I am a
cotton farmer; I can make a good living growing cotton, but I
don't know how to handle the other crops that are resistant to root
rot. The Resettlement agent wants me to buy this farm and
settle here. But 10 miles north in this bottom I can get a farm that
is free of root rot, and I don't believe I want this one." The time
and money spent on this farmer were lost because of a failure to
recognize that the root rot fungus was a property of that soil fully
as important as its fertility or water supply. The first reaction to
these failures from root rot was to run away from them. The Soil
Conservation Service issued orders to its field men: "Keep your
nurseries outside the root rot area." The Shelterbelt Administration called in a plant pathologist to map out the area of root rot
infestation, and ordered no shelterbelts to be planted in that area
with the exception of a few miles of experimental belts. But
gradually it has become recognized that it is not enough to confine
activities to root rot-free areas. In the recent planning of the Soil
Conservation program for one of the infested counties, the county
committee have squarely faced the question of root rot, and with
the assistance of the state plant pathologist have drawn up a program of farm cropping practices that will reduce root rot to a
minimum.

Irrigation projects in root rot areas represent another point at
which farm improvement and plant disease come in conflict. One

of the projected dams in the Southwest will irrigate land within three miles of the known root rot area. This land is connected by water with a stream which first passes through the infested adjacent area. The plan for payment for the dam includes a shift to more profitable crops and assumes high yields. The closeness to the root rot area, and connection to it by water offers the hazard that the disease will spread to the irrigated section, but more hazardous is the fact that the program requires a shift from pasture grasses and cereals, which are root rot resistant, to cotton, alfalfa, fruits, and

Figure 3. Texas root destroying a stand of alfalfa at Sacaton, Ariz. in 1941. The white line of dying plants marks the steady advance of the disease, leaving behind it a few surviving alfalfa plants and a tangle of weeds. (*Photo by the Bureau of Plant Industry, U. S. Dept. of Agriculture.*)

vegetables, which are all highly susceptible to the disease. Our only effective means of checking the ravages of Texas root rot is a rotation plan in which susceptible annual crops are grown on infested land only once in four years, the other three years being devoted to corn, sorghums, and small grains. No susceptible perennial, such as alfalfa or fruit trees, can be grown on such soil. Land which could well repay the costs of irrigation through crops of vegetables, cotton, alfalfa, and fruits may be unable to support the cost of the project when these crops are withdrawn from cultivation three years out of four. The only alternative is to persist in growing the susceptible crops and suffer the losses from the disease, losses that can soon wipe out the advantages of irrigation. This does not at all imply that every irrigation project in the root rot area is doomed to failure. Each case will be determined by its own peculiarities. But in undertaking the responsibility of such a long-term investment, the farmer needs and is entitled to know the hazards that may spell failure of the project.

When watermelon wilt first appeared in Florida melon plantings a few growers reported the new disease that was killing the vines, and the Experiment Station undertook to find means of checking the disease. The attitude of some of the growers in the early 1920's savors strongly of 1940 agricultural philosophy. They said: "If this disease is eradicated, there will be a surplus of watermelons; the price will be lowered, and our profits will lessen. We do not approve of efforts to prevent wilt." But wilt is not a disease that can be trifled with. A few years after its introduction, affected land became useless for melons; losses of 90 per cent of the crop were not uncommon. The industry must move on to new land, expensive to clear. The abandoned land went back into scrub-oak, since it was not suitable for other crops.

And now a new thought crystallized in the growers' minds. A profitable industry was seriously threatened. They carried their problem to the Florida Legislature, and in 1929 funds were appropriated for a study of wilt. At the Experiment Station a watermelon wilt project was initiated, and by 1936 Dr. Walker of that Station announced that the "Leesburg," a new and desirable wilt-resistant melon, was available to the growers. Further improvements have followed, in particular the development of better shipping qualities in the resistant melons; gradually the abandoned land is being reclaimed as it again becomes attractive to the growers, and with it returns the prosperity that attaches to successful production even in a competitive field. The same story has been repeated in sandy southeastern Iowa, in California, in Texas, and in the Rush Springs area of central Oklahoma.

At this point we meet the challenge of modern agricultural philosophy. Is our farm prosperity dependent upon reducing production? And is toleration of disease losses an intelligent way of reducing over-production? As to the first question, opinions may justifiably differ. To those, who like Joseph, look forward to the seven lean years, any interference with production may ultimately work hardship.   And the others, the sponsors of reduced production, insist at the same time on uniform production, the "ever-normal granary."   So long as plant disease is out of hand, we have no control of production; the ever-normal granary is the shuttlecock of fungus and weather.

Decreased production, if it is to be equitable and to avoid hardship must divide the load of production and the profits of production as equally as possible among growers.   If plant disease subtly and evenly lowered production on all farms it might be tolerated in the interests of reduced production.   But it does not.   Each year it leaves some farms unscathed, overproductive, while others are ruined.   A short-sighted Texas wheat grower might rejoice at wheat failure in the Dakotas, feeling that he gains, through the destruction of competing crops.   Actually, the loss of a considerable part of the United States crop has less influence on the wheat price than many other factors quite unrelated to production.   Next year the reverse may be true, and it will be the Texas farmer who suffers.   In farming as in every industry, annual extremes of profit and loss are much more difficult to bear than a uniform medium level of return.   Such extremes may be due to uncontrollable factors, such as rainfall and temperature, and this is all the more reason for minimizing the production extremes due to controllable factors, such as many insects and diseases, to buffer and partly offset the suffering and waste caused by these extremes.

But consider the years of "normal production."   During those years is not a moderate percentage of plant disease useful in preventing overproduction?   Let any academician who vouchsafes to ask that question come South, close to the land in the fall.   Schools have been closed to let the children help with the cotton picking. The women, too, and the old people have wrapped their knees with burlap and crawl on hands and knees, a fifty-pound, ten-foot sack tugging at one shoulder.

Cotton diseases are causing a loss of one-fifth of the crop annually. Prevention of these diseases, many of which can be controlled, does not need to mean a 20 per cent increase in American cotton production.   Might it not better mean a 20 per cent reduction in the labor of planting, chopping, and picking, some release of children and women from this grinding drudgery, a release of 20 per cent of depleted cotton land for a program of soil restoration. Whichever philosophy we accept the moral is the same: the prevention of waste from plant disease does not mean suffering from overproduction; it means on the contrary an opportunity for improving the lot of the farmer by aiding to buffer him against the shock of sudden and unpredictable crop losses, and by giving him some measure of alleviation of the economic and social burden under which he labors.

This, then, is the challenge of American agriculture to the American scientist: "You can see our problem; we are calling on you to help us," a challenge blended of thousands of pleas to the Federal and State Experiment Stations.

And how are the scientists meeting this challenge? One of the newest branches of science, plant pathology, already has enlisted a thousand or more specialists. In Washington, at the state colleges, in private institutions and plant industries these men are devoting their lives to a crusade against plant disease. Much has been accomplished; against many destructive diseases highly effective chemicals of prevention have been found: sprays for fruit and vegetable crops, simple and inexpensive chemical dust treatments for ridding seeds of the germs of disease, tear gas for sterilizing soil, benzol vapor for protecting tobacco seedlings from mildew, fermentation acids for sterilizing tomato seeds, and a host of others. Better, because they are simpler, are the measures of disease control which depend only upon slight changes in the ways of cultivating plants: changing the date of planting to favor the plant and inhibit its parasites, rotation of crops to starve the parasites out of the soil, farm sanitation to destroy the breeding and hiding places of plant pests, to mention only a few of these. Best of all are the scores of new varieties of plants, joint contribution of the plant breeder and the plant pathologist, varieties that are innately resistant to the attack of parasites and at the same time desirable commercial types. There are, for example, the wilt-resistant Bison flax, Marglobe tomatoes, Stoneville and Rowden cottons, Stone Mountain and Hawkesbury watermelons, and Ladak alfalfa. New rust-resistant small grains are coming to the fore and enormous acreages have already been planted to some of these, such as Thatcher wheat and

Red Rustproof oats. One of the most outstanding of these recent accomplishments is the development of the Wisconsin Refugee bean which is at once immune from mosaic and rust, tolerant of two bacterial bean diseases, and resistant to two of the three races of the anthracnose fungus.

The story of this winning fight against plant disease is a gripping story of onward marching in the face of many obstacles. There have been failures, and much remains to be accomplished. Many plant diseases still resist efforts at their control. With others, we have methods for prevention but they are costly, difficult, or disagreeable. But as the American farmer moves on into the task implied by the economic stress of today, he will have in the background the hundreds of scientists, quietly working with him, providing him with the knowledge he needs to lighten his own economic load and permit him to produce the raw products that America needs, amply, efficiently, and economically.

REFERENCES

1. Large, E. C. Advance of the fungi. Henry Holt Co., New York. 1940.
2. Melhus, I. E. and G. C. Kent. Plant pathology and human affairs. Chap. 2 of "Elements of Plant Pathology." Macmillan Co., New York. 1939.
3. Millardet, P. M. A. The discovery of Bordeaux mixture. 1845. Transl. by F. J. Schneiderhan. Phytopath. Classics 3. (Amer. Phytopath. Soc.) 1933.
4. O'Flaherty, Liam. Famine. Literary Guild, Inc., New York. 1937.
5. Rolfe, R. T. and F. W. Rolfe. Romance of the fungus world. J. B. Lippencott Co., Philadelphia. 1926.
6. Stevens, N. E. and R. B. Stevens. Recent developments in plant diseases in the United States. Bot. Rev. 7: 714–736. 1941.
7. Stevens, N. E. and J. I. Wood. Recent fluctuations in plant diseases in the United States. Bot. Rev. 3: 277–306. 1937.
8. Whetzel, H. H. An outline of the history of phytopathology. W. B. Saunders Co., Philadelphia. 1918.
9. Whetzel, H. H. Relation of plant pathology to human affairs. In Mayo Foundation Lectures: 151–178. W. B. Saunders Co., Philadelphia. 1928.

Chapter 2

TYPES OF PLANT DISEASE; FUNGI

In its broadest sense, disease in a plant is any alteration that interferes with its normal structure, functions, or economic value. Thus defined, plant diseases may be classified as follows:

I. Non-parasitic plant diseases (abiotic or physiogenic diseases) caused by such environmental disturbances as deficiencies of food materials in the soil, excesses of soluble salts in the soil, unfavorable water, air, and light relations, unfavorable temperatures, injurious chemicals, and mechanical injuries.

These subjects are treated at length in courses and books on agronomy, horticulture, and plant physiology, and are here considered only very briefly. References: Sorauer: "Non-parasitic plant diseases"; Heald: "Manual of plant diseases."

II. Diseases caused by viruses, infectious principles that are invisible with the microscope, but are highly contagious, causing many diseases of animals, such as sleeping sickness, infantile paralysis, smallpox, and rabies, and important diseases of plants, such as the mosaic diseases of tomato, potato, and cucumber, the yellows diseases of peach and aster, curly top of sugar beets, and many others.

III. Diseases caused by parasitic or predatory animals:

1. *Protozoa.* Certain flagellates are found in the latex of milky plants, but important cases of parasitism by protozoa in plants are rare or lacking.

2. *Nematodes or eelworms.* A few species are responsible for important plant diseases, and are included in the field of plant pathology.

3. *Molluscs* (snails, slugs, etc.) and

4. *Arthropods,* including insects, mites, and millipedes. Treated in entomology.

5. *Vertebrates*, particularly rodents and birds. Usually considered in connection with entomology or wild-life.

IV. Diseases due to parasitic plants:

1. *Parasitic flowering plants.* (Dodder, mistletoe, and a few flowering plants parasitic on the roots of other plants).
2. *Algae and lichens.* (Rarely disease-causers, with a few pronounced exceptions.)
3. *Bacteria.* Causes of many important plant diseases, such as corn wilt, alfalfa wilt, cotton blight, fireblight of fruits, soft rot of vegetables.
4. *Fungi.* Familiar examples of *fungi* (singular *fungus*) are blue, green, and black molds common on decaying foods, mushrooms, rusts, smuts, and mildews. Of the thousands of species of fungi, most are harmless saprophytes, feeding on dead animal or plant materials, and benefiting man by breaking down these organic substances into their simpler elements and restoring them to the soil. Some fungi are parasitic on insects and nematodes, aiding in the control of these pests; others are destructive to fish; a few cause disagreeable skin diseases in man, as "athlete's foot," and "ringworm"; and many are parasitic on plants, producing the great majority of parasitic plant diseases.

The body or thallus of a fungus consists of threads (*hyphae;* singular, *hypha*); a mass of these threads is called *mycelium* (Fig. 86). These are white, less often red, brown, or yellow, but devoid of chlorophyll. They can elaborate no food but are dependent on living or dead organic matter for sustenance. Food is absorbed directly through the hyphal wall, the process often being aided by the action of powerful enzymes, secreted by the fungus. At times the hyphae join in parallel to form long, rope-like strands, or *rhizomorphs*, which aid in advancing through the soil (Figs. 38, 75). At other times the hyphae may form hard, compact, rounded masses, analogous to a tightly compressed ball of yarn, called *sclerotia* (singular, *sclerotium*), which serve as resting bodies to carry the fungus through hot, cold, or dry periods (Fig. 78).

While fungi can reproduce by means of broken-off bits of mycelium or other vegetative means, their common method of reproduction is by *spores*.   These are one- or several-celled, micro-scopic, seed-like bodies varying greatly in size, shape, color, thick-ness and structure of the spore wall, appendages, and other characters, and the classification of fungi is based on these spores and on the types of *fruiting-bodies* in which the spores are produced. Spores are usually adapted to distribution by wind, but some move about by swimming, others have no special means of spread, and usually remain imbedded in the plant or in the soil.   Because of their remote chance of reaching a susceptible host, the spores are usually produced in prodigious numbers.

Fungi reproduce either by a sexual process or by vegetative spore production, and many fungi have both methods.   The main subdivisions of the fungi are based on the methods of sexual reproduction.

The principal divisions of the fungi are phycomycetes, ascomy-cetes, basidiomycetes, and fungi imperfecti (imperfect fungi).

A. *Phycomycetes*.   Typically the multinucleate mycelium has few or no divisions into cells, is often irregular in diameter, coarse, granular, and usually exhibits vigorous streaming of the protoplasm.   Cross-walls (*septa; singular, septum*) occur mainly in connection with spore production.   This differs in the main subdivisions:

a. *Chytrids*.   Most primitive and simplest in structure of all the fungi are the *chytrids*, tiny organisms with little or no true development of mycelium.   They reproduce asexually by swimming *zoospores*, produced in sack-like *sporangia* into which all, or a large part of the thallus is transformed.   A rudimentary type of sexual reproduc-tion is seen in the occasional union of two thalli.   In the parasitic forms the entire body of the chytrid may be contained within a single cell of the host.   The chytrids are water-loving fungi.   Many are found sub-merged in water, as free-living saprophytes or as parasites on algae or other fungi, but a considerable number parasitize higher plants, often producing tumorous outgrowths or discolorations as a result. The chytrids causing brown spot of corn and club root of crucifers will be studied as examples of this lowly but important group of plant pathogens.

b. *Oomycetes*. (Downy mildews and kin). These are adapted to wet environments. Asexual reproduction is usually by swimming spores (*zoospores*) produced in round or pear-shaped *zoosporangia*, borne on stalks (*sporangiophores*). Instead of producing zoospores, the entire zoosporangium may break off and blow about, acting as a single wind-borne spore. Sexual reproduction is by the union of a round female cell (*oogonium*) with a male process (*antheridium*) to form a fertilized

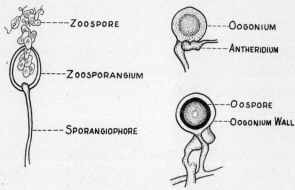

Figure 4. Reproductive structures of the oomycetes. Left: nonsexual reproduction by zoospore production; right: sexual reproduction with formation of oospores.

zygote (*oospore*) with a thick and often highly ornamented spore wall (Fig. 4).

c. *Zygomycetes*. (Bread molds and kin). These are adapted to drier environments, and lack the swimming spores. Asexual (non-sexual) reproduction is by air-borne *sporangiospores*, borne in *sporangia* (singular, *sporangium*). In sexual reproduction there is no clear cut distinction between the sexes, which are arbitrarily referred to as + and −. The thick-walled fusion cell is a *zygospore*. These structures are illustrated in Figure 5.

B. *Ascomycetes*. These include many important leaf, stem, root, and fruit pathogens. The mycelium is regular, divided by frequent cross walls into cylindrical cells often with an

indefinite number of nuclei. Asexual reproduction is by
spores known as *conidia* borne on stalks (*conidiophores*), singly,

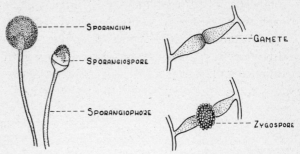

Figure 5. Reproduction in the zygomycetes, as seen in *Rhizopus nigricans*,
the common bread mold. Left: non-sexual reproduction by means of
sporangiospores; right: sexual production by zygospores.

or in bunches or chains. The conidia may occur at random
over the surface of the mycelium, or may be grouped in

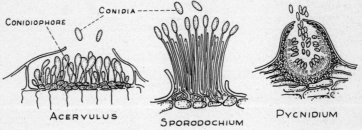

Figure 6. Types of fruiting structures seen in asexual reproduction in the
ascomycetes.

fruiting bodies, the principal types of which are shown in
Figure 6. Another type of vegetative or asexual spore,
found in ascomycetes, basidio-
mycetes, and imperfect fungi, is
the *chlamydospore*. These are
thick-walled, r e s t i n g spores
formed by the rounding off and
thickening of individual cells in
the mycelium. They may occur
singly or in chains, terminal on

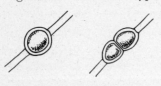

CHLAMYDOSPORES

Figure 7. Typical chlamydospores as seen in *Fusarium* species.

a hyphal tip, or at some point along a hypha (Fig. 7).

In sexual reproduction there is a transfer of nuclei in hyphal cells, which may be specialized as sexual organs, followed by the production of sack-like *asci* (singular, *ascus*), each typically containing 8 *ascospores*. In each young ascus two sexually distinct nuclei fuse and undergo reduction division, there being 3 divisions resulting in 8 haploid, uninucleate spores. The asci may be scattered over the

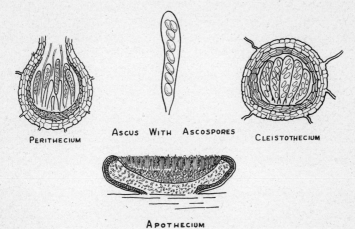

PERITHECIUM   ASCUS WITH ASCOSPORES   CLEISTOTHECIUM

APOTHECIUM

Figure 8. Types of fruiting bodies of ascomycetes, with the ascus, common structure of them all.

surface of the host plant, as in peach leaf curl, or they may be grouped in special fruiting bodies (*ascocarps*) of the types shown in Figure 8.

The main subdivisions of the ascomycetes depend on the type of ascocarp. The conidia are typically thin-walled spores, produced in great profusion, and adapted to rapid spread of the fungus during the growing period of the host. For this reason they are often called "summer spores." The ascospores are usually formed in the spring from resistant, overwintered fruiting bodies or mycelial masses, and provide the first new infections on the resumption of activity by the host.

C. *Fungi imperfecti* (imperfect fungi). In the cases of many fungi, the sexual reproductive stage is unknown or has been lost in evolution. Therefore, they cannot be properly classified as ascomycetes, phycomycetes, or basidiomycetes, although if their sexual stages were known they would be properly assigned to the one or another of these groups.   The great majority of them appear to be degenerate or inadequately known ascomycetes.   These fungi with incomplete life cycles are temporarily put in the artificial group of fungi imperfecti, and as their perfect or sexual stages are discovered they are transferred to their proper class.   This is one reason why fungi often have more than one name.   They have first been given the name of an imperfect genus; then, later when the sexual stage was discovered the fungus has been transferred to a genus of ascomycetes, etc.   If the imperfect stage is the one found commonly, the imperfect name is often commonly used, just as Mrs. Tom Brown is still known to her old friends as Mary Smith.

The imperfect fungi are responsible for many important leaf, stem, root, and fruit diseases.   The spore types in the group are the same as those described for asexual reproduction in the ascomycetes, and illustrated on page 22.

D. *Basidiomycetes*.   The mycelium is regular, divided into cells, and often shows bridge-like *clamp connections*, joining the

Figure 9.   Various types of clamp connections seen in the higher basidiomycetes.

cells.   Examples are shown in Figure 9.   Asexual conidia sometimes are found in the basidiomycetes but are relatively unimportant.   The principal method of reproduction is sexual, resulting in the production of *basidiospores*, usually borne in 4's on a club-shaped *basidium*.   The number of nuclei in the mycelium is more definite than in the ascomycetes.   There is an alternation of generations, a portion of the life cycle in which the cells are uninucleate alternating with one in which they are binucleate.   The binucleate stage arises from the fusion of hyphae having single nuclei. In the binucleate condition the nuclei of any one cell are sexually different, and they divide in pairs, conjugately, to maintain a binucleate condition.   These two nuclei finally fuse in the basidium and then undergo reduction division. The basidiospores thus receive one nucleus each of one of the two sexes.

  a. *Fleshy fungi or palisade fungi.* (Mushrooms, bracket fungi, wood decay fungi, puffballs, stinkhorns). The

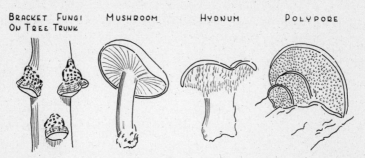

BRACKET FUNGI   MUSHROOM   HYDNUM   POLYPORE
ON TREE TRUNK

Figure 10.   Common types of fruiting bodies of the higher basidiomycetes.

abundant, club-shaped basidia line the surface of flat fungous crusts, or pores, gills, or spines. Typical fruiting bodies are shown in Figure 10. A section of the basidium-bearing layer (*hymenium*) of any of the above is illustrated in Figure 11.

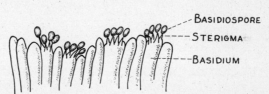

-- BASIDIOSPORE
---- STERIGMA
------ BASIDIUM

Figure 11.   Typical sexual reproduction in the higher basidio-mycetes.   These palisade-like layers clothe the gills, pores, or spines of fruiting bodies such as are shown in the preceding figure.

  b. *Smut fungi.* The mycelium is internal in affected plants and as the disease reaches its climax, each cell in the mycelium rounds off and becomes a chlamydo-spore, the dark smut masses consisting of myriads of dark chlamydospores. On germination, the thick-walled chlamydospore produces a basidium which bears several basidiospores either at the tip of the basidium (genus *Tilletia*) or along its sides (genus

Ustilago). The basidiospores are sometimes called
sporidia (singular, *sporidium*). These two methods of
chlamydospore germination are illustrated in Figure 12.
A reduction division occurs in the production of the
basidiospores, these becoming male or female, and
frequently fusing in a sexual manner.

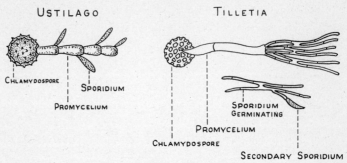

Figure 12. Chlamydospore germination in two leading genera of smuts. (*Ustilago*,
after Smith; *Tilletia*, after Heald).

c. *Rust fungi.* The rusts are *obligate parasites*, the mycelium requiring living plant cells on which to feed.
They are responsible for some of our most destructive
plant diseases, the rusts of grain crops alone causing
many millions of dollars worth of loss each year.

The rusts have the most complicated life histories
of all the fungi, often requiring two entirely distinct
types of hosts in order to pass through their complete
life cycle. There may be as many as 5 different types
of spores, each produced in a different manner, and
each with a definite function to perform.

The rust fungi will be considered in detail in the
chapter immediately following, and their complex life
cycles and numerous spore forms will be described
there.

Infection by fungi. *Infection* is the process by which a fungus spore
or hypha invades a new host tissue and produces disease in that
tissue. When rust spores are produced on a barberry leaf, you
do not say that those spores infect that leaf. They may be blown to

wheat and in that case can *infect the wheat*.   When pathogens* are
present, mixed with seed, in soil, on the surface of a plant, etc.,
ready to cause disease, but not yet producing it, we say that the seed,
soil, or plant is *infested*.   Infection implies that disease has been
produced; infestation is merely the presence of the pathogen in a
suspicious place.   If the spores are on the surface of seed, the seed is
infested.   If the fungus has grown inside the seed, it is *infected*.

When a spore is carried by a *vector* (wind, water, insects, etc.)
or its own exertions to a suitable place for infection (*infection court*),

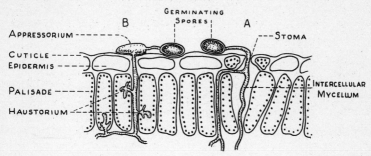

Figure 13.   Infection by fungi.   In A the infection thread has entered the plant
through a stoma and formed intercellular mycelium.   In B the infection thread formed
an appressorium, forced its way in through the cuticle and developed intercellular
mycelium, sending sucker-like haustoria into the cells.

under suitable moisture and temperature conditions it germinates as
shown in the diagram (Fig. 13).   The *infection thread* may enter the
host through a stoma or other natural opening (A) or may force its
way through the unbroken cuticle and epidermis (B).   In the latter
case, the infection thread anchors itself to the cuticle with a sucker-
like disk, the *appressorium*, then forces its way in.   Penetration may
be by mechanical force, and this is sometimes aided by powerful
enzymes that dissolve the cuticle.   Within the host, the mycelium
may feed between the cells (*intercellular*), it may send little absorbing
organs (*haustoria*) into the cells (*intracellular*) and feed on their inner
content, or the mycelium itself may penetrate to the inside of host
cells.

After a period of such feeding (*incubation period*), symptoms
appear, and we recognize from discoloration or killing of cells that

* A pathogen is any organism (bacterium, fungus, nematode, etc.) that can produce
disease.

the plant is infected.   This is usually followed by the production of spores (*sporulation*) on hyphae that force their way back out through the epidermis, or unite to form a fruiting body, and the cycle is completed.

REFERENCES

TEXTBOOKS AND OTHER GENERAL WORKS ON PLANT PATHOLOGY

1. Duggar, B. M.   Fungous diseases of plants.   Ginn and Co., New York.   1909.
2. Heald, F. D.   Manual of plant diseases.   McGraw-Hill Book Co., New York. 1933.
3. ————.   Introduction to plant pathology.   McGraw-Hill Book Co., New York. 1937.
4. Melhus, I. E. and G. C. Kent.   Elements of plant pathology.   Macmillan Co., New York.   1939.
5. Owens, C. E.   Principles of plant pathology.   John Wiley & Sons, New York. 1928.

MANUALS AND HANDBOOKS OF PLANT DISEASES

General

1. Brooks, F. T. Plant diseases.   Oxford Univ. Press, London.   1928.
2. Stevens, F. L. and J. G. Hall.   Diseases of economic plants.   Macmillan Co., New York.   1923.

Field Crops

1. Boewe, G. H.   Diseases of small grain crops in Illinois.   Ill. Nat. Hist. Surv. Cir. 35.   1939.
2. Brown, J. G. and R. B. Streets.   Diseases of field crops in Arizona.   Ariz. Agr. Exp. Sta. Bull. 148.   1934.
3. Dickson, J. G.   Outline of diseases of cereal and forage crop plants of the northern part of the United States. Burgess Publ. Co., Minneapolis.   1939.
4. Smith, R. E.   Diseases of field crops.   Calif. Agr. Ext. Serv. Cir. 121.   1941.
5. Weniger, W.   Diseases of grain and forage crops in North Dakota.   N. D. Agr. Exp. Sta. Bull. 255.   1932.

Vegetable Crops

1. Chupp, C.   Manual of vegetable garden diseases.   Macmillan Co., New York. 1925.
2. Taubenhaus, J. J.   Diseases of truck crops and their control.   E. P. Dutton & Co., New York.   1918.
3. Walker, J. C.   Diseases of vegetable crops.   Edwards Bros., Ann Arbor, Mich. 1939.

Fruit and Nut Crops

1. Anderson, H. W.   Diseases of Illinois fruits.   Ill. Agr. Exp. Sta. Cir. 241.   1920.
2. Cunningham, G. H.   Fungous diseases of fruit trees in New Zealand and their remedial treatment.   Brett Print. and Publ. Co., Auckland, N. Z.   1925.
3. Hesler, L. R. and H. H. Whetzel.   A manual of fruit diseases.   Macmillan Co., New York.   1917.

4. Smith, R. E.   Diseases of fruits and nuts.   Calif. Agr. Ext. Serv. Cir. 120.   1941.

(The various state experiment stations issue many other circulars on fruit diseases and fruit spray calendars.)

Ornamental Plants

1. Felt, E. P. and W. H. Rankin.   Insects and diseases of ornamental trees and shrubs. Macmillan Co., New York.   1938.
2. Pirone, P.   Diseases of ornamental plants.   N. J. Agr. Exp. Sta. Cir. 385.   1939.
3. Smith, R. E.   Diseases of flowers and other ornamentals.   Calif. Agr. Ext. Serv. Cir. 118.   1940.
4. Tilford, P. E.   Diseases of ornamental plants.   Ohio Agr. Exp. Sta. Bull. 511. 1932.

Greenhouse Plants

1. Bewley, W. F.   Diseases of glasshouse plants.   Ernest Benn., Ltd., London.   1923.
2. Taubenhaus, J. J.   Diseases of greenhouse crops and their control.   E. P. Dutton Co., New York.   1919.

Trees

1. Boyce, J. S.   Forest pathology.   McGraw-Hill Book Co., New York.   1938.
2. Hubert, E. E.   An outline of forest pathology.   John Wiley & Sons, Inc., New York.   1931.
3. Rankin, W. H.   Manual of tree diseases.   Macmillan Co., New York.   1918.

JOURNALS

The leading American journals reporting studies on plant disease are "Phyto-pathology," the official organ of the American Phytopathological Society, the "Plant Disease Reporter," issued by the U. S. Department of Agriculture, and the "Journal of Agricultural Research."   Phytopathological papers occasionally appear in the "American Journal of Botany," "The Botanical Gazette," and "Mycologia."

Chapter 3

DISEASES CAUSED BY BASIDIOMYCETES: RUSTS

Rusts of Field Crops

STEM RUST OF GRAINS AND GRASSES (*Puccinia graminis*).

History and distribution.   One of the best known and most important of all plant diseases, stem rust has been a major factor in small-grain production for 2000 years or more.   In France in 1660 and in Connecticut (1726) and Massachusetts (1755), long before the relation between barberry and cereal rust was known, shrewd farmers had noticed that grain suffered most severely from the rust when barberries were nearby, and laws were enacted requiring the destruction of barberry near grain fields.   De Bary (1864–65) proved the necessary connection of barberry with stem rust.

Stem rust occurs wherever wheat is grown   In North America it is most serious in the northern states and Canada, only rarely causing destructive losses in the southern Great Plains, in contrast to leaf rust, a distinct disease which is regularly more injurious than stem rust in the southern wheat areas.

Importance.   Stem rust is very dependent on weather conditions, and in some years and sections the crops will suffer no damage while at other times the disease sweeps north across the Wheat Belt in ruinous epiphytotics.   The years 1878, 1904, 1916, 1919, 1920, 1923, 1925, 1935, 1937, and 1938 were all marked by disastrous rust losses.   In 1935 stem rust reduced the nation's wheat crop by 160 million bushels, nearly one fourth of the crop, and certain states, such as Minnesota and North Dakota lost 60 per cent of their wheat from rust.   The losses are due to low yields, poor quality, shrivelled grain, and lodging caused by the disease (Fig. 19).   Stem rust attacks are sometimes followed by poorer stands in succeeding

30

crops. As seen in Figure 14, stem rust predisposes plants to winter injury.

The concentration of stem rust on wheat is measured by reference to the official scale given in Figure 15.

Figure 14. The effect of stem rust in increasing susceptibility to winter injury in oats. The upper row were rust-free plants, the lower row were infested with 85 per cent severity of stem rust. Both were subjected to an exposure of 24 hours at 20°F. with resultant killing of the rusted plants but not of the rust-free ones. (*Courtesy of H. C. Murphy, Bureau of Plant Industry, U. S. Dept. of Agriculture, and Iowa Agr. Exp. Sta.*).

The loss in the crop from stem rust is determined by noting the percentage of infection and stage of maturity of the crop, and refer-

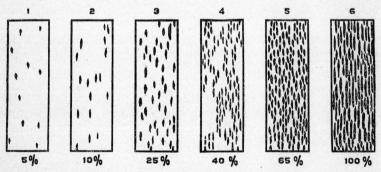

Figure 15. Scale devised by the U. S. Dept. of Agriculture and in common use for estimating the concentration of cereal rusts on leaves or stems.

ence to Table 1. The figures on rust severity refer to percentages as taken from Figure 15.

TABLE 1.—RELATION BETWEEN WHEAT RUST SEVERITY AND LOSS IN THE CROP

Stage of development of the crop						Loss from stem rust
Boot	Flower	Milk	Soft dough	Hard dough	Mature	Per cent
....	....	....	....	(tr)	5	0.0
....	....	....	(tr)	(5)	10	0.5
....	....	(tr)	(5)	(10)	25	5.
....	(tr)	(5)	(10)	(25)	40	15.
(tr)	(5)	(10)	(25)	(40)	65	50.
(5)	(10)	(25)	(40)	(65)	100	75.
(10)	(25)	(40)	(65)	(100)	100	100.

Host plants. *Puccinia graminis* is subdivided into 7 varieties, *P. graminis tritici*, principally on wheat, *P. graminis avenae*, principally on oats, *P. graminis secalis*, principally on rye, and others, largely on grasses. Each named variety in turn is subdivided into various numbered physiologic races. Thus, *P. graminis tritici* consists of more than 150 physiologic races, each being able to attack certain wheat varieties and unable to attack others. The identity of a rust race is determined by inoculating a rust collection onto each of a group of differential wheat varieties. From the type of reaction produced on each variety, the race can be identified by the use of a key. In breeding wheat for rust resistance it is necessary to know the prevalence and distribution of physiologic races in order to provide the wheat with resistance to the races peculiar to the section where the wheat is to be used.

All varieties of stem rust pass to the common barberry, a few other species of *Berberis*, and the closely related *Mahonia* for their alternate stage. The Japanese barberry (which has leaves with a smooth outline, in contrast with the spiny-leaved common barberry) is immune from stem rust (Fig. 18).

Symptoms and signs. On the grain or grass host, stem rust first appears as long, narrow streaks, largely on the stems, but also often on the leaf sheaths, leaf bases, or distal part of the leaf blade and even on the glumes and awns, and in rare cases on the grain. The streaks (*uredial sori* or *uredia*) are covered with a dark red, powdery mass of one-celled uredospores, produced from the feeding

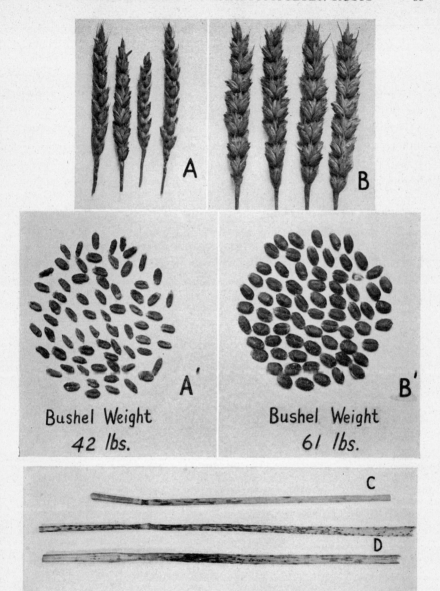

Figure 16.   Stem rust, and its effect on wheat.   Note the small heads, shrivelled grain, and low test weight of the rusted crop (A, A') in contrast to the healthy crop (B, B').   The latter was secured by sulphur dusting.   C shows a stem with an early, uredinial or red stage infection, while the two straws at D are advanced cases in the telial stage.   Straws so affected before maturity will result in grain as at A, A'.   (A, A', B, and B' courtesy of F. J. Greaney, Canada Dept. of Agriculture).

mycelium inside the stem or leaf (Fig. 16C). The epidermis is torn back to form a white collar around the sorus. Later the sori become black, as 2-celled teliospores replace the uredospores in the sori (Fig. 16D). At this stage the stems are often dried and cracked or broken over, and the grains are lacking or few in number, shrivelled, and light in weight (Fig. 16).

On the barberry the reddish lesions first show on the upper surface of the leaf, dotted with inconspicuous pimples, the pycnia (or spermagonia), and soon produce on the under surface of the same lesion a group of white cup-shaped aecia (cluster cups), filled with a yellowish, waxy layer of aeciospores (Fig. 18). No serious damage to the barberry results from the infection.

There are other rust diseases of cereals which might be confused with stem rust, and these are distinguished as shown in Table 2.

TABLE 2.—DISTINGUISHING CHARACTERS OF THE LEADING CEREAL RUSTS

	Stem rust of small grains	Leaf rust of wheat	Stripe rust of wheat and rye	Crown rust of oats
Uredospores:				
Color in mass..	Brick red	Bright orange	Yellow	Light orange
Shape and relative size.....				
Appearance of uredinium...				
Epidermis.....	Torn open	Not torn open	Not torn open	Not torn open
Teliospores:				
Color in mass..	Black	Steel gray	Black	Black
Shape and relative size.....				
Appearance of telium......	Superficial	Buried	Buried	Buried
Hosts: II–III...	Grains and grasses	Wheat (sometimes barley and grasses)	Wheat, rye, grasses	Oats, grasses
0–I........	Barberry	Meadow rue	Not known	Buckthorn
Distribution in North America....	General	General	Western Canada to Arizona and westward, Texas, Mexico	General

There is confusion in the minds of many growers regarding the rusts of wheat. The two rusts, leaf and stem, are both common and each has a red stage and a black stage. The terms "red rust" and "black rust" may apply to either leaf or stem rust and those terms should be avoided on this account. When leaf rust is abundant it produces black sori on the leaf sheaths that are often mistaken for the telial sori of stem rust, and conversely the uredial or red stage of stem rust often occurs on the leaves.

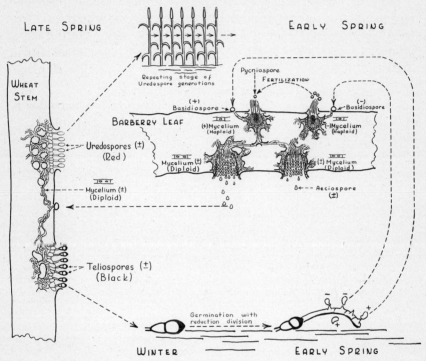

Figure 17. Diagrammatic outline of the life cycle of stem rust.

Etiology. The life cycle of *Puccinia graminis*, the stem rust organism, is indicated diagrammatically in Figure 17. About 10 days after a grain plant has become infected, masses of red uredospores appear on the stems or leaves. This stage may be referred to as the "II" stage. The uredospores are the only spores in the rust life cycle that are able to reinfect the same species of plant as that on which they are produced. On this account they are sometimes called "repeating spores." Through this ability to repeat the same type of infection every 10 days, they are the spores that are instrumental in producing rust epiphytotics.

Under favorable weather conditions, the uredospores are liberated and carried by the wind from one grain or grass plant to another.   In surface moisture (dew or rain), they germinate by sending out a hypha (infection thread) which enters the new host, establishes a feeding mycelium, and produces a new crop of uredospores all within about 10 days.   Many successive generations of uredospores may build up the infestation to epiphytotic proportions. As the grain crop approaches maturity, dark teliospores ("III" stage) begin to appear among the uredospores, in the same sori, and soon entirely replace them.   Thereafter, one of three things may occur in the case of wheat:

   a. In southern Texas and Old Mexico the rust lives through the
      winter growing on the wheat and producing uredospores.
      The teliospores are functionless.   Spring infections are the
      result of uredospores from the winter infections.
   b. In southern Kansas, Oklahoma, and northern Texas the
      barberry, which is only rarely found, plays no part in the
      spring infection, which is caused by uredospores blown in
      by south winds from southern Texas and Old Mexico.   The
      teliospores are functionless under these conditions.
   c. From the northern edge of Kansas to Canada there are two
      sources of spring infection, (1) the aeciospores from barberry,
      produced early in the season, and (2) uredospores blown up
      from the south in ever-increasing numbers later in the season.
      In the northern states the rust may overwinter as teliospores,
      which in the early spring germinate and produce basidiospores ("IV" stage), that blow to the barberry and infect it,
      there producing first pycnia ("O" stage), then aecia with
      aeciospores ("I" stage).   In grain fields that are isolated by
      mountains, as in Pennsylvania, the barberry is the only
      source of infection.

In winter wheat areas the land is fallow during the summer, and the fall infections may come from (1) rust that has oversummered in the uredospore stage in grasses or volunteer grain, (2) uredospores blown south from late harvested northern fields or volunteer grain in October and November, or (3) uredospores blown north from summer wheat cultivated in the cool regions of the Mexican mountains.

In oats the life cycle of stem rust appears to be similar to that of the wheat stem rust. The uredospores and mycelium in oats are quickly destroyed by freezing winter temperatures. Spring infection in the southern states is by means of uredospores blown northward from subtropical regions in which the winters are mild enough to permit the rust to overwinter on oats. Farther north, spring infections are due both to uredospores blown in from the more southern states, and to aeciospores from the barberry. There is some evidence that the oat stem rust can oversummer on grasses as far south as Arkansas, and then pass from the grasses to fall-sown oats.

In barley and rye stem rust outbreaks are so closely dependent on nearby infected barberry that eradication of the barberry affords a high degree of control of stem rust on these grain crops.

In passing from the grain crop to the barberry and thence back to the grain the fungus passes through a number of important activities. Each cell of the mycelium in the grain plant, each uredospore, and each cell of the young teliospore contains two nuclei. Two sexes occur in the stem rust fungus, designated not as male and female but as + and −. Of the two nuclei in a young teliospore, one is of + origin, the other of − origin. As the teliospore matures the + and − nuclei in each cell fuse to form a single nucleus containing both + and − elements. When the teliospore germinates there emerges a 4-celled basidium or promycelium and each of the 4 cells then produces a thin-walled, tiny basidiospore. The production of the 4-celled basidium is due to 2 cell divisions of the contents of the spore cell. One of these cell divisions is a reduction division in which the sexual elements become separated again, so that of the basidiospores two are + and two −. If the basidiospores chance to fall on a barberry leaf under suitable temperature and moisture conditions, they germinate, send an infection thread into the barberry tissues, develop a feeding mycelium, and after a period of feeding and growth the mycelium grows to the surface and produces flask-like fruiting bodies or pycnia on the upper side of the barberry leaf. Each pycnium contains tiny pycniospores and hyphal threads that extend out through the mouth of the pycnium (receptive hyphae). As each pycnium has developed from a single + or − basidiospore, it and its contents are entirely + or −. At this stage sexual union takes place between a pycniospore of one sex and a receptive hypha of the opposite sex. Fertilization is aided by the action of insects. The pycnia also produce a sweetish nectar, and insects, attracted by this nectar visit one pycnium after another, and as they feed they transfer pycniospores much as a honey bee carries pollen from one clover blossom to another and

Figure 18.   Stem rust on barberry; aecia (cluster cups) on the under sides of the leaves.   Note the spines on the leaves that distinguish the rust-susceptible common barberry from the smooth-leaved, rust-immune Japanese barberry.   (*Photo by U. S. Dept. of Agriculture, Bureau of Entomology and Plant Quarantine.*)

thus fertilizes them.   Without this fertilization of the pycnia, little or no further development of the rust is possible.

If a receptive hypha and a pycniospore of opposite sex come into contact, the hypha is fertilized and as a consequence binucleate or diploid mycelium develops.   This new double-sexed mycelium grows vigorously down into the barberry leaf, feeds on its cells, and finally masses together on the lower side of the leaf to produce

aecia containing aeciospores (Fig. 18). These are unable to reinfect the barberry but are wind blown to the grain or grass host,
germinate and infect the grain or grass with mycelium that in a
short time gives rise to uredospores. The aecial mycelium as well
as that in the grain plant is binucleate, and each aeciospore as well
as each uredo- and teliospore contains 2 nuclei, + and −. It is
not until the maturing of the teliospore that the sexual act occurring
in the pycnia finally reaches completion in the fusion of + and −
nuclei to form a single fusion nucleus.

In summary, the rust fungus produces 5 types of spores, each
with a distinct function to perform, the red uredospores that spread
the rust from grain plant to grain plant, the dark teliospores that
can infect nothing, but fall to the ground where they may resist
winter temperatures and the following spring germinate and
produce basidiospores, the basidiospores that can carry the rust
from the old teliospore on the ground to the barberry, the pycniospores that have only the function of sexual fusion, and the aeciospores that can carry infection from the barberry back to the grain
plant.

These different spore types differ in their ability to withstand
unfavorable temperatures and other climatic stresses. Most
delicate are the basidiospores, that can only carry the disease for
short distances. The uredospores are sufficiently resistant that
they can be carried by the wind for hundreds of miles, and then
settle down and produce infection. Aeciospores are intermediate
between these two. The distance to which a spore can be blown
without losing its infective ability is important in determining the
distance which must separate alternate hosts in order to give effective rust control.

Epiphytology. The following factors conspire to produce
destructive outbreaks of stem rust: (1) large uniform acreages of
susceptible wheat varieties, (2) presence of physiologic races of rust
that will attack those varieties, (3) mild winters in the south which
permit uredospores to overwinter more abundantly and farther
northward in Texas and possibly Oklahoma, (4) a constant succession of humid, or rainy days as the crop matures in the spring,
providing the required conditions for uredospore germination,
(5) cool temperatures (with an optimum in the vicinity of 65°–

70°F.), (6) rank, succulent growth of the crop (in general, the rusts and other obligate parasites are most destructive on the most vigorous, succulent plants, especially those in well watered soils, high in nitrogen), (7) late maturing crops which have longer exposure to the rust, (8) continuous south winds, and (9) in the northern areas, presence of barberry. The greatest losses result when these factors are combined with hot, dry conditions just before harvest, which increases the suffering of the plants already deprived of water by the inadequate functioning of the stems. Epiphytotics of stem rust are associated with a combination of most or all of the factors listed.

Control. Prevention of stem rust depends on several practices, all of which contribute to reductions in the losses from the disease:

1. *Resistant varieties.* Much effort has been expended in efforts to breed wheat and other grains resistant to stem rust. This work has largely centered in the northern states where stem-rust losses are greatest. The history of rust resistance in wheat shows some of the difficulties encountered.

Kanred wheat was a selection from a Russian wheat brought to America in 1906. In 1916, when it was being grown in Kansas, it was discovered to be stem-rust resistant. It was distributed, and by 1924 over 4,000,000 acres were planted with this variety in Kansas and adjacent states. But as years passed it began to lose its rust resistance, and became attacked more and more severely by stem rust. This weakness, together with a tendency to lodging, was such that by 1929 its acreage had dropped 20 per cent, and this drop has continued since. Kanred lost its resistance, not because of any change in the wheat, but because new physiologic races of the stem rust fungus had appeared, races that were able to attack Kanred. Meanwhile another wheat, Ceres, was coming to the fore as a stem-rust resistant wheat for northern areas. First distributed in 1926, by 1933 it occupied 5,000,000 acres in the United States and Canada, and by 1935 this had increased still further. But at the same time an obscure race of stem-rust, race 56, had been rapidly increasing, a race that could attack Ceres. With the enormous acreage of susceptible Ceres wheat and favorable weather conditions in 1935, race 56 of stem rust swept across the northern plains in the greatest rust epiphytotic of history, and destroyed one-fourth of the nation's bread grain. To replace Ceres, the rust resistant Minnesota variety, Thatcher, introduced in 1934, soon occupied the great acreages formerly devoted to Ceres. To date (1941) it has retained its stem rust resistance, but it will probably only be a matter of time before a new physiologic rust race will appear in North America capable of attacking Thatcher, and the story of Ceres will be repeated. Indeed, such a race has recently appeared in South America. Moreover Thatcher is highly susceptible to leaf rust, and suffered severely from this disease in the 1938 epiphytotic, increasing the constant need for new rust-resistant wheats. The production of rust-resistant wheat varieties remains our most important means of fighting stem rust, but the histories of Kanred and Ceres show us that the breeding work is never finished, that new resistant varieties will constantly be needed, as new physiologic races of the rust become prevalent, and that the best efforts of the wheat breeder will only succeed in keeping a few years ahead of the rust.

In the southern Great Plains no wheat variety commonly grown is highly resistant to stem rust, but a number of varieties show partial resistance or escape from the disease. Early Blackhull, largely because of its earliness, usually escapes stem-rust damage, while Blackhull, Kanred, Iobred, Kawvale, Tenmarq, Chiefkan, Iowin, and Kanhull all possess moderate resistance. Illinois No. 2 is a stem-rust resistant wheat adapted to conditions in the Ohio valley, and a number of non-commercial breeding wheats show high rust resistance.

2. *Eradication of the barberry.* In 1918 the United States Department of Agriculture in cooperation with 13 of the central states began a campaign to eradicate the common barberry over this great area. By 1936 the eradication area extended from Montana, Wyoming, and Colorado to Pennsylvania and Virginia, and over 100,000,000 bushes had been destroyed, at a cost of nearly $3,000,000 per year (Fig. 195). We now know that eradication of the barberry will not eliminate the disease because of infection by uredospores blown up from the South. There are some who feel that the eradication program has been wasted effort. But even though barberry eradication will not wipe out stem rust, there remain three good reasons for continuing the work:

a. We have seen that the efforts of the plant breeder are often thwarted by the new physiologic races of rust. In many cases these new races are the result of hybridization of older races, during sexual reproduction of the rust which takes place *on the barberry*. Eradication of the barberry aids by destroying the breeding place for new rust races.

b. The damage from stem rust depends greatly on the stage of maturity of the wheat when it is attacked. A 10 per cent rust attack (see Table 1) when the wheat is in the boot stage will result in 100 per cent loss by harvest time, while a 10 per cent attack in the hard dough stage will only produce a 5 per cent loss in the crop. The barberry brings infection to northern wheat fields much earlier than it would arrive via the south winds, hence greatly increases the rust damage.

c. In sheltered wheat sections, protected by mountains, west of the Rockies or east of the Appalachians, no uredospores blow in from the outside, and the only infection of wheat is from the barberry. In these sections barberry eradication gives 100 per cent control of the disease. The barberry is especially important in initiating local epiphytotics in rye and barley.

3. *Agronomic practices* that diminish losses from stem rust include avoidance of low, poorly-drained sites for wheat, avoidance of excessive rates of planting or excessive nitrogen fertilization, and the use of early maturing varieties.

4. *Sulphur dusting.* It has been proven for a number of years that applications of sulphur dust will control rusts (Fig. 19). Early views that this was impractical are being reconsidered in view of the recent development of airplane dusting methods (Fig. 206). Experiments in Canada, New York, Minnesota, and Australia have clearly shown that under conditions of heavy rust infestation the sulphur treatment has more than paid for itself in increased yields. It should be remembered too, that rust is most abundant in the years of ample rainfall, when potential yields are high and when the cost of the dust treatment represents a proportionately small part of the potential return. Farmers have been reluctant to undertake this treatment without more information on profit and

cost over a period of years, also because of the relatively small margin of profit. At present the experimental evidence is not extensive enough to justify recommending dusting as a general practice, but it is a desirable control measure in growing small plots of valuable grain, for seed production or for show purposes. The national defense program is providing a multitude of airplanes and aviators. When the military need for these is ended, their services

Figure 19.   The destructiveness of rust in wheat. In the rusted rows at the right note the weak, broken straw, and paucity of well-filled heads, in contrast to the rust-free plants at the left. In this case the greater part of the damage was due to stem rust; much less to leaf rust. The healthy plants are of the same variety as the rusted ones, but have been protected by dusting with sulphur. (*Courtesy of F. J. Greaney, Canada Dept. of Agriculture.*)

will be available for such peace time pursuits as crop dusting, and when that time arrives, the economics of dusting for rust control promises additional margins in favor of the cereal farmer.

LEAF RUST OF WHEAT (*Puccinia triticina*).

This rust disease, which occurs wherever wheat is grown, is more serious in the warm regions than stem rust. Each year it causes losses of a few per cent in the American crop, and it occasionally breaks out in epiphytotic force as in 1938 when it caused losses of up to 30 per cent in the various states from Texas to Canada. In many individual fields the loss was complete. Where stem rust quickly destroys the crop by cutting off the water supply, leaf rust progressively destroys the leaf tissue throughout the season, resulting in a reduced number of kernels, shrivelled grain, low test weight, and low protein content.

Host plants.   *Puccinia triticina* attacks wheat and a small number of species of grasses.   On the latter however the rust is not highly infective.   There are a number of closely related leaf rusts

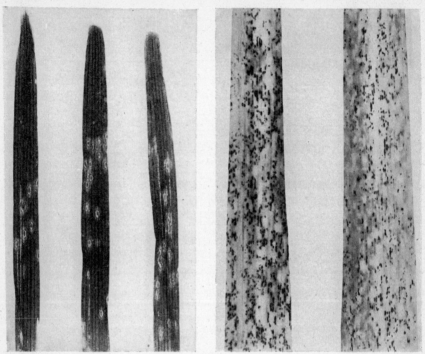

Figure 20.   Wheat leaf rust.   Leaf, seedling leaves showing uredinial pustules in an early stage of infection from artificial inoculation; right, telial stage on older leaves which have been killed by the fungus.   The teliospores are buried under the leaf epidermis.

of other grasses, but these will not attack wheat.   *P. triticina* consists of at least 112 physiologic races, each restricted to certain wheat varieties, and distinguished by their reactions on 8 or 9 differential wheat varieties.

In Europe there is an alternate, O-I stage on the meadow rue (*Thalictrum* species), but these have never been found infected in America, and apparently play no part in the life cycle of the rust under American conditions.

Symptoms and signs.   (Refer to Table 2 for a comparison with stem rust.)   Wheat leaves and leaf sheaths become covered with small, round or oval, bright orange uredial pustules (Fig. 20).   The disease begins in the lower leaves and works toward the top of the plant.   Soon after attack the leaves die, progressively upward, until in severe, early attacks every leaf may be destroyed before the heads emerge from the boot.   Later the leaves and sheaths display short, dark, lead-gray telial pustules (Fig. 20).   These are buried under the epidermis and the teliospores are not in exposed masses as in stem rust.   In heavy infestations the uredospores become so abundant that one's clothes are reddened with them, and the infested field is discolored reddish brown or yellow, when seen from a distance.   The kernels may entangle so many uredospores in the brush as to give the seed a red discoloration sometimes puzzling to farmers or millers.

Etiology.   Under American conditions the uredospore is the only functioning spore form.   The alternate host is never found infected, hence the teliospores are functionless.   The uredospores are able to endure low temperatures, and the fungus overwinters as mycelium in winter wheat, even as far north as New York State, actively producing successive crops of uredospores.   Under favorable conditions these may rapidly increase in 10-day cycles in the spring.   Although the uredospores are cold-resistant they are unable to endure high summer temperatures, and die out during hot summers in southern regions.   In such cases the fungus follows the crop northward during the summer and returns to the fall-grown wheat in the south via the north winds of October and November. In exceptionally mild summers the fungus appears to be able to oversummer on volunteer wheat even in the South.   Under suitable conditions the infestation of fall wheat may become so abundant as to injure the value of the wheat for pasture, followed by poor winter survival of the crop.

The complete life cycle as it occurs in Europe resembles that of stem rust.   The teliospores produce basidiospores or sporidia in the spring; these are borne to the meadow rue and infect it, the mycelium producing, first pycnia on the upper surface of the leaf, later aecia on the under surface, the aeciospores carrying the infection back to the wheat.

Epiphytology. The factors that favor leaf rust development are similar to those favoring stem rust, with the one exception of the presence of barberry. Epiphytotic development follows extended periods of damp weather with temperatures in the vicinity of 50°–65°F. Above 80°F. infection is erratic or does not occur. High temperatures after infection during the incubation period result in masked or symptomless infection. The uredospores are somewhat more resistant to cold and less resistant to heat than in the case of stem rust.

Control. 1. *Rust resistant varieties.* Little work has been done in breeding wheat for leaf-rust resistance, as compared with stem rust, although work in this direction is proceeding in various state agricultural experiment stations. Of the commercial winter wheats several show moderate resistance. Early Blackhull may escape the most severe damage because of its earliness. Tenmarq and Chiefkan of the hard wheats show resistance, although the latter is not recommended because of poor baking qualities. Of the soft wheats, Kawvale (also resistant to stem rust and loose smut), and Mediterranean were semi-resistant in the 1938 epiphytotic. Kanred, Kanhull, Purkov, Iobred, Hussar, Iowin, Denton, Fulcaster, and Illinois No. 2 also show some resistance. Crosses of Hope × Hussar are highly resistant and may be useful as breeding stocks on this account. Certain physiologic races of *P. triticina* that can attack Mediterranean wheat were increasing in 1939, and may ultimately cause this wheat to be placed in the susceptible group.

2. *Sulphur dusting.* (Refer to discussion under stem rust.) The two rusts, leaf and stem, often develop together as their environmental requirements are similar. Sulphur dusting would have double value in such a case. As in the case of stem rust, no general recommendation can be made, but dusting is advised in rust years on small plots of valuable seed- or show-grain.

3. *Agronomic practices* favoring rust control consist in avoiding low, undrained sites for wheat, the use of early varieties, practices which encourage earliness in the crop, and avoidance of excessive nitrogen in the soil.

4. *Biological control.* Leaf rust pustules are frequently parasitized by the imperfect fungus, *Darluca filum*, an obligate parasite on rust spores and mycelium. Thus far it has not been possible to make

practical use of *Darluca* in rust control, but in nature it undoubtedly plays a part in keeping the rust fungi in check.

STRIPE RUST OF WHEAT AND OTHER GRAMINEAE
(*Puccinia glumarum*).

Stripe rust has been known since 1892 in the northwest quarter of the United States and adjacent Canada. It has also been found at higher altitudes in Mexico, at various points in California, and in Arizona, but it had not invaded the main wheat belt of North America until 1941 when it was found to be abundant in the Experiment Station cereal nurseries at College Station, Texas. This offers a new threat to wheat, as stripe rust, wherever it occurs, is regarded as one of the most important, sometimes the most important of the cereal rusts.

Stripe rust can be distinguished from the other cereal rusts in that the uredinial stage is yellow, and the pustules occur in streak-like clusters on the leaves. Later a telial stage develops in black streaks. Glumes, necks, leaf sheaths, and even kernels are attacked resulting in poor yields and shrivelled grain of poor viability.

Wheat is the main host, although barley and rye are attacked as well as some 60 species of grasses. There are two varieties of the rust, one primarily on wheat, the other mainly on barley, with indications of physiological specialization within these varieties.

The O-I host of stripe rust is unknown, and its perpetuation is through uredospores. The conditions favoring overwintering are not fully known. Epiphytotics are favored by abundant late summer infection, winter survival, and cool spring weather with abundant moisture and sunshine. The disease is checked by hot weather.

Stripe rust can be controlled by resistant varieties of which the leading ones are:

Soft red winter wheats: Clarkan, Denton, Forward, Fulhio, Kawvale, Leap, Mediterranean, Minhardi, Penquite, Red Chief, Redhart, Red Rock, Red Russian, and Trumbull.

Hard red winter wheats: Blackhull, Cheyenne, Eagle Chief, Early Blackhull, Iowin, Kanred, Kharkov, Minturki, Purkov, Turkey, and Wisconsin Pedigree No. 2. Tenmarq varies from susceptible to resistant.

CROWN RUST OF OATS (*Puccinia coronata*).

This common leaf rust of oats with rounded, light orange uredial sori and buried telial sori, is often very destructive, the losses paralleling those from leaf rust in wheat. The alternate host is the buckthorn (*Rhamnus* species) and is important in the epiphytology of the rust from Iowa northward; but farther south crown rust survives the winter as mycelium in the oat plant. The rust is distinguished by the teliospores which are surmounted by a circle of little projections, as in a king's crown. The disease is controlled mainly by the use of resistant varieties, such as the Red Rustproof group, Bond, and Victoria oats. Forty-four physiologic races of the rust are known, and newly discovered races have been found to attack Red Rustproof and Bond varieties, but new hybrids of Bond with Lee and other oat varieties are showing a high degree of resistance to all common crown rust races. The Victoria oat is resistant to oat smuts but is a spring variety, and crosses are being made in Georgia and Kansas to combine the rust resistance of both with the smut resistance of Victoria and the winter type of Bond.

CORN RUST (*Puccinia sorghi*) with the O-I stage on Oxalis,

BARLEY LEAF RUST (*Puccinia anomala*) with the O-I stage on Star-of-Bethlehem (*Ornithogalum* spp.) in Europe only,

RYE LEAF RUST (*Puccinia dispersa*) with the O-I stage on *Anchusa*, and

SORGHUM RUST (*Puccinia purpurea*) with no O-I stage known, are all common diseases but only rarely of consequence. Little formal work has been done on their control, although there appears to be enough rust resistance in certain varieties of each of these crops to form a basis for control by selection or breeding.

FLAX RUST (*Melampsora lini*) offers a serious problem in flax culture, wherever flax is grown. It has a complete life cycle with all five spore stages occurring on flax and occurs in at least 14 physiologic races. Control is aided by rotation with other crops and removal or plowing under of flax refuse, but chiefly depends on the use of rust-resistant varieties such as Ottawa and Rio. The latter is also moderately resistant to wilt.

ALFALFA RUST (*Uromyces striatus*) is a common alfalfa leaf disease in the southern Great Plains. The aecial stage is on *Euphorbia* but poorly understood in America where it appears to have little importance, the rust evidently overwintering on the alfalfa. Losses from this rust are reduced by frequent harvesting to save the leaves before they fall from rust infection.

CLOVER RUSTS (*Uromyces elegans* and other species) are common and often quite injurious. All spore stages occur on the clovers. There is considerable resistance seen in individual plants and clover varieties, offering the basis for control by selection. Early harvesting of clover hay and burning of fields in early spring are sometimes useful as control measures, and in the case of *U. elegans* on Carolina clover an increase of 50 per cent in hay tonnage has been reported following dusting with sulphur.

Rusts of Grasses

A number of grass rusts are very common and often injurious to pasture during seasons favoring the cereal rusts (Fig. 21). Little can be offered for controlling them. Bermuda grass suffers seriously from rust at times, and when this is used as a lawn or golf grass the disease could be kept under control by reduced watering and dusting with sulphur. Little barley (*Hordeum pusillum*) may be heavily rusted under conditions favoring wheat leaf rust so that its forage value is considerably decreased. Numerous wild plants serve as the aecial hosts of the grass rusts, including members of the crowfoot, milkweed, honeysuckle, goosefoot, and primrose families and a number of others.

Rusts of Trees and Shrubs

CEDAR APPLE RUST (*Gymnosporangium juniperi-virginianae*).

This important rust is most destructive to apple (O-I stage) but at times is a nuisance in ornamental cedars (*Juniperus* species) which support the telial stage. The uredospore stage is omitted from the life cycle. Since there are no repeating spores (uredospores) on

Figure 21. This rust, *Puccinia peridermiospora*, on tall marsh grass, *Spartina pectinata*, is representative of the many rusts that affect our native grasses, sometimes being quite injurious to pasture.

either host, the disease can only persist where both hosts are present, and may be controlled by eradication of either cedar or apple.

Figure 22. Cedar apple rust. Above: left, pycnial stage on upper surface of apple leaf; right, aecial stage of the closely related hawthorn rust on hawthorn twig, showing swellings and distortion. Below: telial stage on red cedar.

Two very similar species are *G. globosum* which passes from cedars to the hawthorn, and *G. germinale* (= *G. clavipes*) which affects cedars and quince trees.

In infected apple the leaves show abundant reddish lesions, stippled with black pycnia on the upper surface and with long, funnel shaped aecial cups on the under side (Fig. 22). The walls of the aecium split at several points and roll back, giving the sorus a star-like appearance. Affected trees show serious reduction in the amount and quality of the harvested crop.

The aeciospores blow to the cedar in the summer and infect the young twigs. The infection is not obvious until the second spring after, when the lesions are seen as round galls on the twigs, ½ inch or larger in diameter. In moist weather these galls develop long, orange, jelly-like horns, which consist of masses of teliospores with long gelatinous stalks (Fig. 22). The teliospores germinate at once, producing basidiospores, which are carried by the wind to nearby apple trees and bring about the leaf infections. The fungus is tolerant of temperature within wide limits, but requires moisture for infection. It does not develop in epiphytotic proportions since there are no repeating spores.

Control is most readily accomplished by removing either host from the vicinity of the other. Twelve states have laws requiring the eradication of cedars from apple districts, the standard requirement being a cedar-free zone a mile wide around orchards. Such a wide zone is not necessary for practical control, as the basidiospores are so widely dispersed, even at a distance of a few hundred yards from cedars, to remove the danger for practical purposes. Non-commercial apple trees can be removed to protect ornamental or nursery cedars. The disease may be controlled in either host by the application of sulphur fungicides in case it is desirable to grow the two hosts near one another. A rust-resistant seedling of the common red cedar has recently been discovered in West Virginia, and the native southwestern species *Juniperus mexicana* appears to be rust-immune. Wherever they are adapted, either of these could be substituted for the common cedar in ornamental plantings near orchards.

BLISTER RUST OF FIVE-NEEDLE PINES (*Cronartium ribicola*).

The blister-rust fungus came to the United States via Europe about 1900. Since then it has caused enormous losses from New England through the Lake States, and into the virgin timber of the

Pacific Northwest.   The pycnial and aecial stages occur on the pine, and the uredial and telial stages on currants and gooseberries of the genus *Ribes*.   While blister rust has a limited distribution, it is of special interest because of the extensive federal eradication proj-

Figure 23.   Blister rust of pines.   A: Young branch canker showing typical spindle-shaped swelling; B: Merchantable pines killed by the rust; C: Trunk canker showing aecia, pycnial scars, and region of bark discoloration; D: Uredinial stage showing pustules on under side of *Ribes* leaf; E: Telial stage showing columnal development on under side of *Ribes* leaf.   (*From Leaflet 26 published for the New England Section of the Society of American Foresters*).

ect which resulted in the extermination of *Ribes* from over 6,000,000 acres in a 10-year period.

The fungus is perennial in the pine, and once a tree is infected, the mycelium gradually spreads until the tree is destroyed. Affected trees show dead branches ("flags"), slight swelling of the bark, tiny yellow droplets of ooze from the pycnia, and white, thin walled blisters, the aecia, filled with yellow aeciospores.   Bleeding of resin is common. The aeciospores carry the fungus to the currants or gooseberries, and infect the leaves, producing orange-yellow uredial pustules and columns of teliospores on the leaf lesions. This is a serious disease on the currant and gooseberry bushes as well as on the pines.

Large amounts of money have been spent on the government control program of *Ribes* eradication, but the program has been successful in protecting the eradicated areas. Since there is no repeating spore on the pine, the *Ribes* need be removed no more than a few hundred yards from pine in order that the pine be protected. Eradication has been by means of fire, by hand, by chemicals (Fig. 195), and by a system of forest management which does not favor the establishment of *Ribes*. Eradication is a local problem, and its practical value varies from one locality to another according to the type and distribution of the *Ribes*, and the abundance and value of the pines. The problem of eradication in the Pacific Northwest is the most serious one at present, because the infested areas are remote from settlements, inaccessible, and huge areas are involved if the valuable pines of the west coast are to be saved.

There are many other coniferous rusts with the aecial stage producing white, columnar sori on the needles. A common example is the needle rust of pines, *Coleosporium solidaginis* with the II-III stage on many species of asters. While these are ordinarily unimportant on either host, they are occasionally destructive in coniferous nurseries. Removal of the alternate host, usually a weed, is the preferred means of control.

RUST OF STONE FRUITS (*Tranzschelia pruni-spinosae*) is common on plums and related fruits and is often quite harmful in the latter part of the growing season, the leaves being covered with extensive brown uredial and telial spore masses. The alternate hosts are members of the crowfoot family: anemone, hepatica, buttercups, and meadow rue. Fungicidal spraying affords the best means of control.

ORANGE RUST OF CANE FRUITS (*Gymnoconia interstitialis*) is a familiar and very conspicuous disease of black and purple raspberries, blackberries, and dewberries, the leaves becoming covered with brilliant orange uredial spore masses. The rust has an unusual life history. The orange uredospores blow to raspberry leaves and cause local infections resulting in the production of brown telial sori.   On germination of the overwintered teliospores in the spring the basidiospores infect the buds at the tips of the canes and this infection becomes systemic, the rust mycelium invading the entire plant and then producing great numbers of orange uredospores in midsummer. The plants become practically worthless.   Due to the systemic nature of the disease, control measures include propagation from rust-free plantations, and in cases of light infestation, cutting out and burning the rusted canes.   Superficial examination of incoming plants of unknown source is of little value because the mycelium within infected stocks cannot be seen except by careful microscopic examination.

Figure 24. Asparagus rust. Telial pustules on asparagus stem, enlarged about 3x.

Rusts of Vegetables

ASPARAGUS RUST (*Puccinia asparagi*) at one time was a serious menace to asparagus culture in America, and almost eliminated this crop in important areas.   Today it is so generally controlled by planting of the popular rust-resistant varieties Mary Washington and Martha Washington that it is no longer a major problem.   All spore stages occur on asparagus leaves and stems. The telial stage is illustrated in Figure 24.

BEAN RUST (*Uromyces appendiculatus*) occurs on common and lima beans and cowpeas wherever these crops are grown and is often quite destructive.   All spore stages occur on the leguminous host (Fig. 25).   The green snap bean, Wisconsin Refugee, and certain selections of pole beans of the Kentucky Wonder type are resistant to some of the races of bean rust and doubtless a search would bring out resistant varieties or strains of lima beans and cowpeas. The true bean rust should be distinguished from bean anthracnose (page 203) and bacterial blight of beans (page 297) which are often loosely called "rust" but are not caused by rust fungi.

SWEET POTATO RUST (*Coleosporium Ipomoeae*) is rare in commercial sweet potato plantings except in the tropics but occurs commonly on the wild sweet potato *Ipomoea hederacea*. The O-I stage on pine trees is sometimes quite destructive in southern nurseries, in which case eradication of the weed host is suggested.

Figure 25. Bean rust. (*Courtesy of S. A. Wingard, Va. Agr. Exp. Sta.*).

Rusts of Ornamentals

CARNATION RUST (*Uromyces caryophyllinus*) is one of the commonest diseases of carnations, especially in the greenhouse. Typical brown powdery lesions disfigure the leaves (Fig. 26C). Control is accomplished by avoidance of syringing (often used for red spider control), dusting with sulphur before blooming time, maintaining relatively dry air in the greenhouse, and taking cuttings only from rust-free plants.

SNAPDRAGON RUST (*Puccinia antirrhini*) commonly causes dark brown powdery sori on all green parts of the host (Fig. 26A). It often requires control in the greenhouse, the methods being those used for carnation rust with the addition that numerous rust-resistant snapdragon varieties are available.

HOLLYHOCK RUST (*Puccinia malvacearum*) is exceedingly common, the undersurfaces of leaves often being almost wholly covered with tan to purplish telial sori (Fig. 26B). The rust is unusual in that all spore stages are lacking except the teliospores and basidiospores. Control depends on fall burning of the old hollyhock and mallow debris, and sulphur dusting in the spring.

OTHER RUSTS OF ORNAMENTALS.   Many other ornamental species suffer from rust diseases and because the value of ornamentals depends on their appearance, rust attacks too light

Figure 26.   Rusts of ornamental plants: A, snapdragon rust; B, hollyhock rust; and C, carnation rust.   (*A, courtesy of P. E. Tilford, Ohio Agr. Exp. Sta.; B and C, courtesy of P. P. Pirone, N. J. Agr. Exp. Sta.*).

to devitalize the plant may still impair its aesthetic value.   The commoner ornamentals with rust diseases include roses, violets, clematis, phlox, morning glory, sunflowers, pansies, and verbena. Control in nearly all cases is a matter of fall sanitation and preventive applications of standard fungicides in the spring.

REFERENCES

On the nature and biology of the rusts.

1. Arthur, J. C.   The plant rusts.   John Wiley & Sons, Inc., New York.   1929.

On identification and host relationships of the rusts.

1. Arthur, J. C.   Manual of the rusts in United States and Canada. Purdue Res. Found., Lafayette, Ind.   1934.

On pathology and control of specific rust diseases.

1. Anon.   Asparagus rust.   N. J. Agr. Exp. Sta. Pl. Dis. Notes 15: 26–33.   1937.
2. Craigie, J. H.   Stem rust of cereals.   Canada Dept. Agr. Farm. Bull. 84.   1940.
3. Doran, W. L.   Rust of Antirrhinum.   Mass. Agr. Exp. Sta. Bull. 202.   1921.
4. Harter, L. L.   Studies on bean rust caused by *Uromyces phaseoli typica*.   Jour. Agr. Res. 50: 737–759.   1935.
5. Henry, A. W.   Flax rust and its control.   Minn. Agr. Exp. Sta. Tech. Bull. 36.   1926.
6. Humphrey, H. B. et al.   Stripe rust (*Puccinia glumarum*) of cereals and grasses in the United States.   Jour. Agr. Res. 29: 209–227.   1924.
7. Humphrey, H. B. et al.   The rusts of cereal crops.   U. S. Dept. Agr. Circ. 341.   1935.
8. Melhus, I. E. and L. W. Durrell.   Studies on the crown rust of oats.   Iowa Agr. Exp. Sta. Res. Bull. 49: 115–144.   1919.
9. Smith, R. E.   Asparagus and asparagus rust in California.   Calif. Agr. Exp. Sta. Bull. 165.   1906.
10. Spaulding, Perley.   Investigations of the white pine blister rust.   U. S. Dept. Agr. Bull. 957.   1922.
11. Thomas, H. E. and W. D. Mills.   Three rust diseases of the apple.   N. Y. (Cornell) Agr. Exp. Sta. Memoir 123.   1929.

Chapter 4

DISEASES CAUSED BY BASIDIOMYCETES: SMUTS

Nature of the Smuts

Like the rusts, the smuts are basidiomycetes, but their life histories are much simpler than in the rusts. Only two types of spores are concerned, the *chlamydospores* which are usually in abundant black masses, and the *basidiospores* or *sporidia* which are produced by the chlamydospores much as in the case of germinating rust teliospores.

TABLE 3.—CHARACTERISTICS OF THE THREE TYPES OF SMUT DISEASES

	Seedling infection type	Blossom infection type	Local infection type
Place of primary infection........	Seedling	Blossom	Leaves, etc.
Nature of infection.....	Systemic	Systemic	Local
Transmitted from crop to crop............	On the seed	In the seed	In the soil
Principal control measures............	Seed dusting with fungicides	Hot water seed treatment	Sanitation, rotation
Examples............	Bunt of wheat Covered smut of oats Loose smut of oats Covered smut of barley Black loose smut of barley Covered smut of sorghums Millet smut Stem smut of rye Flag smut of wheat	Loose smut of wheat Brown loose smut of barley	Corn smut Head smut of corn and sorghums White smuts of spinach and ornamentals Onion smut

The smuts are primarily a grain- and grass-inhabiting group, although there are a few exceptions, as the onion smut and the white smuts of dahlia, water lily and a few other dicotyledons. In nature the smuts appear to live as obligate parasites, developing only on the living host plant, however they may be grown experimentally on nutrient media.

Control of the smuts depends on their life histories, and there are three distinct types of life history to be found among them, as indicated in Table 3.

Some smuts show features of more than one type, as flag smut of wheat, which is of the seedling infection group, but in which the spores survive between crops both on the seed and in the soil, necessitating additional control measures.

The leading smut genera considered here are *Ustilago* with basidiospores borne at the sides of the promycelia, and three genera producing the basidiospores at the tip of the promycelium, *Tilletia* with simple, dusty chlamydospores, *Entyloma* with simple chlamydospores buried in the host tissues, and *Urocystis* in which the dusty chlamydospores each consist of one or more central fertile cells ordinarily surrounded by a coat of sterile, protective cells. *Ustilago* and *Tilletia* are figured on page 26.

SEEDLING INFECTION SMUTS: BUNT OF WHEAT (*Tilletia tritici* and *T. laevis*).

History and distribution. Bunt, also called covered smut or stinking smut, occurs wherever wheat is grown, and is one of the major diseases of this crop. It is particularly damaging in the southern Great Plains, probably because of the frequent cool temperatures at planting time, and in the Pacific Northwest where the survival of bunt spores in the soil creates a difficulty in control. Before Prévost discovered in 1807 that the disease is due to fungi, it was commonly believed that bunt was due to unfavorable environmental influences, and it had undoubtedly been known as a major pest of wheat since ancient times. Even today there are many farmers who are unacquainted with its contagious nature. The scientific farmer, Julius Kühn was the first to use bunt spores in infection experiments thus showing the parasitic nature of the fungus. The use of seed disinfestation for bunt control is said to trace back to 1670 when a wheat ship was wrecked off the coast of Bristol, England, and the salt-soaked grain was salvaged for seed

and found to produce a bunt-free crop.   In recent years studies on
bunt have been largely concerned with its control by seed treatments and breeding for bunt-resistant varieties, the effect of
environmental factors in bunt development, and physiologic
specialization of the bunt fungi.

Importance.   Bunt causes important losses in several ways.
The field loss of grain is directly proportional to the percentage of
bunt in the field which in severe cases may reach 20 per cent or
higher.   The smutty grain is then considered inferior in quality
and its price is lower than that for smut-free grain.   Wheat is
graded "light smutty" if an 8 oz. sample contains 14 or more smut
balls and "smutty" if it contains 32 or more smut balls or equivalent
discoloration.   The dockage varies from one to ten cents per bushel
depending on the amount of smut and the prevailing price of wheat.
This dockage is due to the difficulty in making a good grade of
white flour from the discolored and foul smelling grain, and to the
explosion hazard in elevators and mills handling smutty wheat.
The loss from bunt in the national wheat crop has progressively
decreased from 4 per cent in 1926 to about 1 per cent at the present
time, due mainly to increasing adoption of seed treatments.
Fluctuations in the annual losses, which may be very considerable,
are largely due to prevailing temperatures at planting time.
Indirectly the supply of moisture may be the deciding factor, not
through any direct effect on infection, but because the availability
of moisture is paramount in determining the planting date each
season.   In winter wheat areas, a dry fall will greatly increase the
acreage of late-planted wheat, in which bunt would be favored by
the cool temperatures then prevailing.   There appears to be no
indication that smutty wheat is either unpalatable or poisonous to
livestock, and this also applies to corn and other grains which may
be smutted.

Host plants.   Other than wheat, rye is the only crop attacked
by either of the bunt fungi, but on rye the disease is of no consequence. Among the wheats all conditions are found from complete
susceptibility to complete freedom from smut.   All of the leading
species of wheat are attacked to some degree. Varietal resistance
in wheat is most important in the Pacific Northwest where seed
treatment is ineffective in control because of soil- and air-borne

infestation.   Here the bunt-resistant variety Relief is an outstanding development from recent breeding efforts.   In hard red winter
wheat areas, varietal resistance is less important since simple seed
treatments give complete bunt control.   Some strains of the Turkey
variety are highly bunt resistant, but most of the other commercial
hard red winter wheats are quite
susceptible.

Symptoms and signs.   No conspicuous indication of the disease is
seen until just before harvest, when
the grains are found to be transformed into balls of black chlamydospores, at first greasy, later
powdery (Fig. 27).   Affected heads
give off a foul odor, likened to that
of decaying fish.   The plants may
be much stunted in height ("low
smut," *Tilletia tritici*) or may be of
normal size ("high smut," *T.
laevis*).   Affected heads can often
be quickly recognized in the field
by the presence of small, shiny,
black beetles which feed on the
fungus material.   The awns of
affected heads often stand out from
the head at irregular angles, and
the glumes also have a tendency to
stand out, giving the head a loose
appearance.   Affected heads are a
more bluish green than normal

Figure 27.   The head smuts of
wheat.   Left: healthy head and grain;
center: bunted head and bunt balls;
right: loose smut head with the smut
spores mostly blown away.   (*Courtesy
of Benjamin Koehler, Ill. Agr. Exp. Sta.*).

ones.   Threshed grain containing an appreciable amount of bunt
has the characteristic bunt odor, and the grains are darkened by
presence of smut spores especially in the crease and brush.   Mixed
with the grain will be found the short, thick bunt balls, filled with
chlamydospores.

Etiology.   The two fungi causing bunt, *Tilletia tritici* and *T.
laevis*, are similar in most respects, with no essential differences in
life history and control.   When a smutty crop is harvested or

stored, many of the bunt balls break, and the chlamydospores come to rest on the healthy grains. Here they lie dormant until the seed is planted. When the seed germinates, if temperatures are suitable, the smut spores also germinate, each chlamydospore producing a short, thick promycelium on the tip of which are borne 8 thread-like sporidia which unite in pairs, producing 4 H-shaped sporidia (basidiospores) (Fig. 12). These in turn germinate by producing an infection thread that enters the wheat coleoptile, or by producing short, curved secondary sporidia that in turn germinate by means of an infection thread which enters the wheat seedling. As the seedling develops, the smut mycelium ramifies through the tissues, enters the blossom primordium, and replaces the ovary with mycelium which segments, each cell becoming transformed into a chlamydospore.

The bunt fungi exhibit physiologic specialization; there are 20 or more physiologic races, each capable of attacking a distinct group of wheat varieties.

Epiphytology. Bunt spores require cool soil for germination and infection, 41°–65°F. with optimum infection at 45°–55°F. Little or no infection occurs in warm soils at 70°F. or higher. Thus, smutty wheat which germinates in warm soil may escape the disease. Moderate soil moisture is favorable to bunt infection, the amount of infection increasing as soil moisture increases, up to 22 per cent of the water-holding capacity of the soil, but decreasing again with excessive soil moisture. When wheat grows rapidly under exceptionally favorable conditions, the bunt fungus inside is sometimes unable to grow rapidly enough to invade the head completely, resulting in a partially smutted head or even in complete escape from the disease. Clay soils are more conducive to bunt than sandy soils, and acid soils are unfavorable to the disease.

The heaviest bunt losses are associated with late planting of fall wheat or early planting of spring wheat, abundant inoculum on the seed, moderate soil moisture, average growing conditions, and lack of seed treatment, or persistence of the spores in the soil, as in the Pacific Northwest.

Control. It has long been known that *seed treatments* are effective in controlling bunt. Since the disease is carried from one crop to the next by the spores on the surface of the seed, any chemical which would destroy the spores without injuring the seed might be expected to control the disease.   Formerly it was the practice to dip wheat seed in a solution of formaldehyde or copper sulfate in order to destroy the spores.   More recently it has been discovered that the same result may be obtained more cheaply and easily by dusting the seed with disinfestant dusts, and today the dust method is almost exclusively practiced for the control of bunt. Various chemicals may be used for dusting seed.   Among the cheapest and best, however, are copper carbonate and ethyl mercury phosphate ("New Improved Ceresan").   The general prevalence of bunt, together with the added advantages of dusting wheat seed in improving the stand, indicate that wheat seed dusting is worth while and profitable as a routine practice.   To be sure, untreated seed will sometimes escape the disease, but a cost of 2 or 3 cents per acre will provide disease-insurance against those years in which bunt would take a heavy toll of the wheat crop.   The dusting is best accomplished by the following procedure:

Before using either seed treatment it is necessary to clean and grade the seed, by using a fanning mill and screens, in case any bunt balls are present.   Seed treatments will give only partial control if bunt balls are mixed with the grain.   The cost of cleaning equipment is not excessive, and the cleaning and grading will remove many smut balls, weed seeds, and shrivelled kernels.   Cleaned and graded seed produces cleaner, stronger plants.

For the dust treatment use either 50 per cent grade copper carbonate dust (2 oz. per bushel of seed) or "New Improved Ceresan" (½ oz. per bushel of seed).   Since no difference has been observed in the effectiveness of 50 per cent copper carbonate and "Ceresan," growers may take advantage of any difference in price in these products in their local markets, remembering that the prices must be compared on the basis of cost per bushel of grain treated, not cost per pound of chemical.   ("Ceresan," while more expensive per pound, may be cheaper in the long run because of the small amount of dust required per bushel of grain.)   In any case the cost for chemical will be in the neighborhood of 1 to 2 cents per bushel of grain.   The dusting may be quickly and continuously carried out by using a gravity mixer of either of the types shown in Figure 28.

Either of these treaters can be made at home for about $3 and either is a great improvement over the older revolving barrel type. In using either type, pour in a bushel of seed, add the necessary amount of dust, stir in the dust for a moment, and then allow the

A

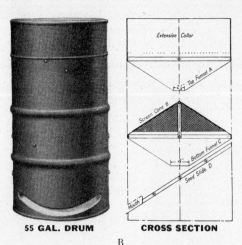

55 GAL. DRUM   **CROSS SECTION**

B

Figure 28.   See next page for descriptive legend.

seed to run through into the receiving sack by raising the hopper (Fig. 28C) or pulling the plug (Fig. 28B).   With "Ceresan" dust either type of treater may be used, but with copper carbonate the wooden type (Fig. 28C) is preferred.

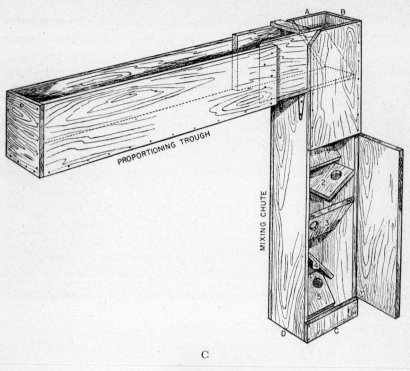

C

D

Figure 28. A and B, types of treaters used in dusting field crop seed. A, commer-cleaner-grader-duster suitable for treating 300–500 bushels of grain seed per day. B–D, homemade treaters. B and C, gravity types; D, revolving barrel type. The oil barrel treater, B, designed by the Bayer-Semesan Co., is convenient for treating hull-less small grain seed with organic mercury dusts, while the Minnesota seed treater (C) is suitable for all cereal seed and for applying either copper carbonate or organic mercury dusts. D, which originated at the Pennsylvania State College, is the only one of these types that can be used for treating fuzzy cotton seed.

Several types of manufactured seed treaters are available such as those manufactured by:

Calkins Mfg. Co., Hutchinson, Kan. (Combination cleaner-grader-treater).

Ben Gustafson Seed Grain Machinery Co., Fargo, N. Dak.

Clow-Winter Mfg. Co., 1117 Metropolitan Life Bldg., Minneapolis, Minn.

The United States Department of Agriculture has issued a circular (No. 415) describing the commercial treaters. Wheat seed treatment on a community basis has proven successful in a number of states, the machine being owned by a farm group or owned and operated on a custom basis by a single farmer, 4-H member, or Future Farmer.

Note the following *precautions* in dusting seed:

a. The dusts are poisonous. The operator should tie a cloth across mouth and nose, wear gloves, and work out of doors.
b. Dusted grain is poisonous and should be stored where livestock will not feed on it.
c. Dusted seed begins to deteriorate after 1 to 2 months. It should be treated not longer than 1 month before planting.
d. Copper carbonate has a tendency to clog the drill. After using it the drill should be carefully cleaned out. This trouble does not apply to "Ceresan."

Wheats differ in susceptibility to bunt, and in the Pacific Northwest where soil-borne bunt is common and seed treatment ineffective, the use of *resistant varieties* is the leading control measure. Here Relief, a hard red winter wheat, has come into general use for bunt control. Among the other winter wheats, the following are bunt resistant: certain Fultz-Hungarian hybrids, Hungarian, Hussar and some of its hybrids, Kruse, Ashkov, Cooperatorka, Ioturk, Marmin, Minturki, Nebred, Oro and some of its hybrids, Regal, Ridit, Rio, Sherman, Sibley 81, certain Turkey selections, and Yogo. As most of the important commercial varieties are susceptible and chemical control is simple and inexpensive, the use of resistant varieties in bunt control is largely limited to areas of soil-borne infestation.

OTHER SEEDLING INFECTION SMUTS

Insofar as life history and control are concerned there are few differences between bunt and the other seedling-infection smuts listed on page 58, but certain of these differences are worthy of mention.

Oat and barley seeds are protected by a husk. The seedling-infection smut fungi attacking these crops (Fig. 29) may penetrate

Figure 29. Loose smut of oats. The spikelets may be almost entirely converted into black spore masses, or in many cases, as at the right, the glumes are only partially destroyed. (*Courtesy of Illinois Natural History Survey*).

the husks and live between crops not as spores on the seed surfaces but as mycelium within the husks. On germination of the seed, this mycelium starts into activity and grows into the seedling. A chemical that is not volatile, such as copper carbonate, fails to penetrate the space between husk and seed, and hence does not protect the seed. For this reason volatile fungicides, such as formaldehyde or "New Improved Ceresan" are required with these smuts. Formaldehyde treatments have long been used, but more recently Ceresan is replacing formaldehyde to a considerable degree.   The dust is applied as in the case of bunt, except that the wooden, gravity type of treater or the rotating barrel type are preferred to the oil-barrel gravity treater which does not allow a free flow of seed.   If formaldehyde is used it may be applied in any one of three ways.   In all three cases the same amount of formaldehyde is used; namely, one pint to fifty bushels of seed.

Figure 30.   Spraying oats with formaldehyde for controlling loose and covered smuts.   (*Courtesy of R. S. Kirby, Pa. Agr. Ext. Service.*)

a. Mix 1 pint of commercial formaldehyde with 1 pint of water. Apply this mixture uniformly with a sprayer at the rate of 1 quart of the mixture to 50 bushels of seed as it leaves the grain spout or as it is being shoveled from one pile to another on a clean floor or canvas, or in a tight wagon box (Fig. 30). Bin it or pile and cover with canvas, blankets, or disinfested sacks for 4 to 8 hours. Then sow immediately or run through a fanning mill or otherwise expose to air before storing for any length of time.   If treated grain is stored in an elevator it should be moved and aerated, preferably by running through a fanning mill, within 4 to 8 hours after treatment.

b. Mix 1 pint of commercial formaldehyde with 40 gallons of water in a barrel or tank.   For best results the temperature of the water should be about 60° to 70°F.   Dip loosely filled burlap sacks of grain in this solution until the grain is thoroughly wet.   Drain and dry 2 hours, or over night. Then sow immediately.   If the sowing must be delayed, spread out the treated seed to dry and sow as soon as possible.   Treated seed should not be allowed to freeze while it is damp or wet.   If the grain is moist, increase the seeding rate about one-fourth.

c. Mix 1 pint of commercial formaldehyde with 20 to 30 gallons of water at a temperature of 60° to 70°F., and with a sprinkling can, sprinkle it uniformly on 50 bushels of seed grain as it is being shoveled from one pile to another on a clean floor or canvas, or in a tight wagon box.   Shovel until all of the seed is uniformly moist.   Pile and cover with canvas, blankets, or disinfested sacks for at least 4 hours, or over night.   Then sow immediately.   If the sowing must be delayed, spread out the treated seed to dry and sow as soon as possible.   Treated seed should not be allowed to freeze while it is damp or wet.   If the grain is moist, increase the seeding rate about one-fourth.

Sorghum seed are somewhat more susceptible to disinfestant seed injury than those of the other grains, and here it is important to avoid overdosage of the dust.   Copper carbonate is often preferred to Ceresan for sorghum on this account.

Flag smut of wheat (*Urocystis tritici*) which is primarily a leaf and stem disease, persists between crops both on the seed and in the soil.   For this reason seed treatments are not sufficient for control, and this is accomplished by the combination of seed treatments, the use of flag-smut resistant varieties (compulsory in the area of infestation in the Central States), and crop rotation.   Flag smut is a very destructive disease but fortunately is limited, in the United States, to a small area in the Central States and the Pacific Northwest.   There is a quarantine on Australian wheat designed to protect American growers from further introductions of flag smut.

Rye is affected by both the wheat bunt and loose smut organisms but only rarely. The more common and serious smut of rye is a stem and leaf disease caused by *Urocystis occulta*, kin to the flag smut and onion smut fungi. The disease is recognized as black, elongated sori on stems, leaves, and heads, ending in destruction of the entire plant with complete loss of bearing. For the most part the inoculum survives on the seed where it is amenable to chemical disinfestation, although in some localities and dry seasons, soil-survival may occur, calling for crop rotation as a supplementary control measure.

BLOSSOM-INFECTION SMUTS: LOOSE SMUT OF WHEAT
(*Ustilago tritici*).

History and distribution. Loose smut or "blackheads" of wheat, is worldwide in its distribution, being most serious in regions with humid weather during the blossoming period, regardless of the total annual rainfall. The disease has been known since early times, but it is only during the past 50 years that the distinction between loose smut of wheat and those of oats and barley has been recognized, and that the life history and control of loose smut have been worked out, beginning with the separation of two of the barley smuts by Jensen in Copenhagen (1888). The important discovery of blossom and internal seed infection was made by Maddox in Tasmania (1895–1897) and at once confirmed by several Japanese workers. Jensen, recognizing with others that chemical seed treatments were ineffective for loose smut control in wheat and barley, first suggested a hot water treatment for this purpose (1887–1889). Recent work has largely concerned varietal resistance toward loose smut, genetics and specialization of the fungi involved, and improvements in the hot water treatment.

Importance. While loose smut is a major disease of wheat, in past years the estimates of its damage have ranged somewhat lower than those for bunt, the national loose smut losses usually being between .5 and 1 per cent of the crop. However, bunt has been progressively decreasing in importance during the past decade, thanks largely to widespread adoption of seed dusting, while loose smut has constantly increased until its importance is equalling or even exceeding that of bunt in many areas. While average loose smut losses in the main Wheat Belt range from 1 to 4 per cent, individual fields with 5 per cent or more are not uncommon, and fields with as much as 40 per cent infestation have been recently observed in this area. As in the case of bunt, affected plants are usually a total loss, and the percentage loss in yield closely agrees with the percentage of infestation in the field. Loose smut infection has also been shown to increase winter killing. The grower is inclined to underestimate the loose smut loss or attach little importance to it because the disease is inconspicuous at harvest time and the harvested grain is uninjured in quality. For the latter reason, the elevator operator, who is largely responsible for the bunt control program, enforced by dockage penalties, puts no pressure on the grower with regard to loose smut.

Host plants. *Ustilago tritici* is only important on wheat, although rye can be attacked by this fungus. Various degrees of resistance and susceptibility occur in different wheat varieties. While many of the commercial varieties are highly susceptible, some degree of resistance has been seen in the varieties Kawvale, Early Blackhull, Bacska, Forward, Fulcaster, Leap, Ridit, Trumbull, Fulhio, Illinois No. 2, Red Chief, Redhart, Valprize, Cooperatorka, Kanhull, and Hope-Hussar hybrids.

Symptoms and signs. The disease is most apparent in the field at the blossoming period, when affected heads become transformed into dark, powdery masses of fungous spores (Fig. 27). All parts of the head are destroyed, and the spores soon shatter away, leaving only the naked rachis, which is inconspicuous at harvest time. Affected stems are usually shorter than normal ones. Generally, but not always, all stems from a single stool are affected. The harvested grain from fields containing loose smut is not discolored nor lowered in quality; the loss is entirely one of yield and value for planting purposes.

Etiology. The chlamydospores of *Ustilago tritici*, the fungus that causes loose smut, mature on the affected heads as adjacent normal heads are blossoming. They are carried by wind to the healthy heads, where they lodge on the feathery stigmas and germinate much as a pollen grain. The infection thread grows down through the style into the ovule, and as the ovule develops into a seed the fungus mycelium occupies the embryo, where it lies dormant until the seed germinates.   Infected seed are indistinguishable from normal seed in appearance.   As the seed germinates, the fungus resumes activity, grows up inside the developing head, reaches and invades the flower primordia, and replaces the floral parts with masses of chlamydospores.   By a nice adaptation, the infected heads emerge just before normal heads, so that dusty masses of spores are available to infect the normal heads as they emerge.

Thus the smutty heads observed this year came from normal looking seeds that were infected at blossoming time last year but gave no evidence of their infection until a full year after infection occurred.   Spores in the soil or on the surface of seed are of no consequence in the life history of this smut; they are delicate and soon die.

Ustilago tritici consists of 7 or more physiologic races, each of which is limited in its attack to certain varieties of wheat.

Epiphytology.   Loose smut is most prevalent during years when moisture was adequate at blossoming time the previous year. From this, its severity can be predicted a year in advance with reasonable accuracy.   The structure of the blossom appears to have little correlation with susceptibility, although in barley loose smut escape is correlated with the closed type of flower.   Time of planting appears to have an effect on the amount of infection in winter wheat, late planted wheat showing the least infection, while the greatest infection is seen in wheat planted at normal planting dates.   Heald explains this on the assumption that in late plantings, at low temperatures, the fungus fails to come out of its dormant state when the seed germinates, and the plant thus "runs away from the fungus."   Rapidly growing wheat may escape injury, even though infected, if the fungus inside is unable to develop fast enough to reach the floral parts.

Control.   Since the loose smut fungus is *inside* the seed, dusting or any other method of sterilizing seed on the surface will not control it.   The only effective method of disinfecting wheat seed which contain the loose smut fungus, is to heat the seed to a temperature that will destroy the fungus inside the seed without injuring the seed itself. Since the treatment requires considerable care, it is suggested that growers plan to treat only enough seed for a seed-production block (5 to 10 per cent of the main wheat acreage), and harvest the grain from this treated block for seeding the main acreage the following year. The most effective plan is for growers to cooperate in the treatment, rather than to carry out the treatment independently on individual farms.

Where special equipment for hot-water seed treatment is not available, the following method can be used.

Before treating, the grain should be well cleaned and graded. Put the seed into coarse burlap sacks, filling them about one-half full. Tie the sacks at the ends so as to give the seed ample room for swelling. It is a good practice to put a measured bushel of dry seed into each sack, if the seed is to be sown wet. The seed will swell considerably and this will make it easier to sow at the desired rate. Provide water in containers, such as water tanks or other large vessels. A pond with hard bottom and clean water or a river may be used, provided the water is deep enough to cover the sacks well. Lay the sacks in the water on their sides, not on end, and leave them to soak 4 or 5 hours. Caking of the grain when it begins to swell should be avoided by moving the sacks so as to stir the grain after it has been in the water 2 or $2\frac{1}{2}$ hours.

The following equipment is required: three barrels or other containers such as tanks or tubs, two containers for heating water, a heater or a supply of live steam from an engine or boiler, and a reliable thermometer; one which will float is most convenient. Also it is well to have some sort of a pulley arrangement over the barrels or containers for lifting the sacks from one bath to another. The arrangement is shown in Figure 31.

Fill the first barrel about two-thirds full of warm water at 120°F. Fill the second barrel two-thirds full of hot water at 129°. Then fill the third barrel almost full of cold water. If live steam is not available keep a reserve supply of boiling hot water, about 10 gallons, for pouring into the first two barrels from time to time, as they cool below the required temperatures. It is well also to have at hand a supply of cold water for cooling the water in these barrels, if this should be necessary. If a rope and pulley are used, tie the rope to the top of one of the sacks of grain which has been soaked and drained and tie another short rope, 3 or 4 feet long, to one of the lower corners of the sack.   Plunge the sack into the first barrel, containing the warm water and leave it in about a minute. This will warm the seed and prevent cooling the water too much in the next barrel.   Move the sack about while in the water in order that the seed at the middle of the bulk will be reached by the process.   This may best be done by lifting with first one rope and then with the other.   The water in the second barrel will be too hot for the hands and stirring of the seed will be impossible

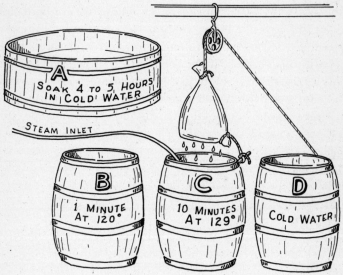

Figure 31.   A simple arrangement for the hot-water treatment of seed wheat for loose smut control.   (*After Brentzel.*)

unless the ropes are used.   Lift the seed from the first barrel or warming bath, drain for a few seconds and plunge it into the second barrel which contains the hot water.   Here it should be moved about, as in the first barrel, and left exactly 10 minutes.   The temperature throughout this 10-minute period must be held as near the 129 degree mark as possible.   As the water cools it will be necessary to add hot water or steam and to stir well.   If the temperature should drop to 124 degrees the addition of 1 gallon of boiling water would raise the temperature almost 2 degrees. At this ratio it would be necessary to add about 2½ gallons of boiling water to bring the temperature up to the 129 degree mark. When the seed has been in the hot water exactly 10 minutes draw it out and plunge it immediately into the third barrel which contains the cold water. This will stop the action of the heat and thereby avoid injury to the seed which would be sure to occur if the process were prolonged. If the grain can be spread out in a thin layer immediately upon coming from the hot water it will not be necessary to cool it by dipping it into the cold water.

Figure 32. Oklahoma hot water equipment for treating wheat and barley seed grain for loose smut control. Preheating tank in foreground, main tank at the rear. Each basket holds a bushel of grain. An electric motor (right) activates endless belts at the bottom of the tank, which move the baskets the length of the tank in 10 minutes (wheat) or 13 minutes (barley), giving automatic time control. The water is heated by free steam manually controlled by the ball valve at the left.

As in the case of dusting, the hot water treatment for wheat seed has worked out very well on a community basis, which minimizes the investment in equipment and keeps the cost of treatment down to a small amount. The principal features of the equipment are a boiler and tanks, and various communities have worked out ingenious methods of obtaining this equipment, such as the use of a steam tractor, or adapting a creamery, cotton gin, mill, or laundry to the seed-treatment work. Since hot-water-treated seed does not deteriorate in storage the treatment can be carried out at any time in the off-season.

To simplify the hot water treatment a hot water seed treatment machine has been developed at the Oklahoma Agricultural Experiment Station and put into practical operation (Fig. 32). The machine has a capacity of treating 500 bushels of seed grain per day, and combines the advantages of automatic time control, semi-automatic temperature control, efficient penetration of heat, and portability. It is transported from one community to another, serviced with steam, electricity, and water from cotton gins, elevators, creameries and the like, and operated on a self-sustaining custom basis, at a charge of 5 to 10 cents per bushel of grain treated. The grain is presoaked by the farmers and after treatment is dried on roped-off pavement or on the farm.

Control of loose smut is also effected by the use of the more resistant wheat varieties, several of which are listed on page 71. It must be borne in mind that with any organism, such as this, which exhibits physiologic specialization, resistant varieties may from time to time become attacked by new physiologic races of the pathogen, which limits their period of usefulness and necessitates constant efforts at their replacement with newer resistant varieties.

BLOSSOM INFECTION SMUTS: BROWN LOOSE SMUT OF BARLEY (*Ustilago nuda*).

Barley is subject to three smut diseases: covered smut (*Ustilago hordei*) black loose smut (*U. medians* or *U. nigra*) and brown loose smut (*U. nuda*). The first two are similar to bunt and are controlled by seed dusting. Brown loose smut has a life cycle similar to that of loose smut of wheat and requires a hot water treatment for control. As barley seed is somewhat more susceptible to heat injury than wheat seed, barley is treated at 126°F. for 13 minutes instead of at 129° for 10 minutes as in wheat. It is not easy to distinguish the two loose smuts of barley and their intergrades in the field, and as a practical control measure, it is recommended to growers of smutty barley that they first try dusting their seed with a disinfestant dust. If this fails to solve their smut problem, then the hot water treatment must be used or new seed secured.

LOCAL INFECTION SMUTS: COMMON SMUT OF CORN (*Ustilago Zeae*).

History and distribution. There are several smut diseases of corn of which common or boil smut is by far the most important.

The head smut of sorghums also attacks corn but is much rarer than common smut. The common smut is world wide in its distribution wherever corn is grown except in Australia where it has been eradicated. The disease has been known since very early times and has probably existed in America for centuries. At first it was thought that smut was an exudation of superfluous sap from highly nourished plants; in the last half of the past century its parasitic nature was realized but it was thought to be seed-borne; and it was not until 1895 that it was finally recognized that corn smut differs from the other smuts in not being seed borne, and is distinguished by the fact that infections are local and not systemic. Recent work on corn smut has largely concerned attempts at breeding smut-resistant varieties of corn.

Importance. Wherever corn is grown in America, smut is a major problem. Average annual losses for the United States are usually from 3 to 5 per cent, or 50 to 80 million bushels, the losses in individual states ranging up to 10 per cent and in individual fields up to nearly 100 per cent. Both field and sweet corn are severely attacked. The losses from smut are difficult to estimate because of the nature of the disease, attacking any aboveground portion of the plant, but the damage includes yield reduction through sterility, destruction of the ears, lodging, reduction of the amount of fodder, and lowering of the carbohydrate content. Smutted stalks yield about ⅓ less grain than healthy stalks. In sweet corn the loss is increased by the fact that an ear which is smutted to only a minor extent is still a total loss for use as a roasting ear.

Host plants. The corn smut fungus attacks only corn and the closely related teosinte. While there is considerable variation in susceptibility among the different varieties of corn, relatively little use has been made of this in controlling smut because of the difficulties arising through physiologic specialization of the smut fungus, and because in many cases resistance has been found to be correlated with lack of vigor in the corn plant, and this is even less desirable than smut susceptibility. Sweet corn is most susceptible, field corn next, and pop corn least of all. Of the field corns, the flint varieties are more susceptible than the dent varieties, and some of the commercial hybrids of the Corn Belt are relatively resistant.

Symptoms and signs.   The fungus causing common smut can
attack any aboveground organ of the corn plant: stalk, prop roots,
leaf, tassel, husk, or ear.   The disease is readily identified by the
boils or masses of black chlamydospores, which are often very large
on ears or stalks and much smaller on leaves or tassels (Fig. 33).
At first the boils are covered with a greenish-white, firm, glistening

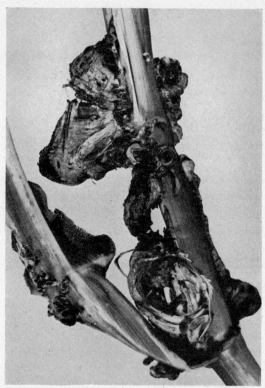

Figure 33.   Corn smut.   Boils like these appear on any above-ground part of the
plant, often lowering the yield of affected plants by 50 per cent or more.

membrane. In this stage they are edible, and are sometimes
served, boiled or fried, as a rustic delicacy.   As the boil matures,
the membrane dries and weathers away releasing myriads of dark
spores.   In ears or tassels, only a part of the organ is involved in
the boil, in contrast with head smut.   The plant is often remarkably distorted or abnormal.   A boil at a node may result in a stem
that bends at a right angle and becomes horizontal.   Infected

tassels often develop normal kernels, the central spike of the tassel resembling a small ear.   However, there is no production of leafy shoots from the tassel, and the ear boils do not contain a mass of stringy fibers, exposed as the spores shatter away, characteristic of head smut.   This last characteristic effectively distinguishes head smut from common smut.

Etiology.   Common smut is caused by the fungus *Ustilago Zeae*. Distinct from most of the smut fungi, *U. Zeae* causes only local infections; it does not pervade the entire plant, and each boil results from a separate, distinct infection.   The fungus is not seed borne and does not infect the germinating seedling.   The chlamydospores overwinter in the soil, in corn debris, or in manure or litter from livestock that have fed on smutty corn.   Under favorable conditions the chlamydospores germinate and produce sporidia, which in turn can multiply by budding to produce secondary sporidia (Fig. 34).   When the corn plant is 1 to 3 feet high, some of these sporidia are carried by the wind and other agencies to the younger tissues of the corn plant, especially the moist funnels at the leaf bases, and here germinate to produce infection hyphae which penetrate the corn tissues.   Mycelium from spores of two sexes must be present if the fungus is to develop actively.   As the infection progresses, the boil appears, at first permeated with mycelium, later filled with chlamydospores formed by the rounding off and separation of individual cells of the hyphae.   The membrane dries and ruptures, and the spores are liberated.   They may be blown about or may germinate at once, in the boil, producing sporidia which initiate new infections, especially in the ears. Eventually the chlamydospores are returned to the soil, where they lie dormant during the winter.   The smut fungus exists in several physiologic races, each capable of attacking only certain varieties of corn.   Sexual reproduction occurs which enables these races to hybridize with one another, and mutant races are constantly appearing, to give a great variety of distinct smut lines or races.

Epiphytology.   Corn smut is adapted to warm weather.   The optimum temperature for spore germination is 80° to 92°F., which is considerably higher than for many other smuts.   Heaviest infection occurs when scant rainfall in the early stages of corn development is followed by moderate rainfall as the crop approaches

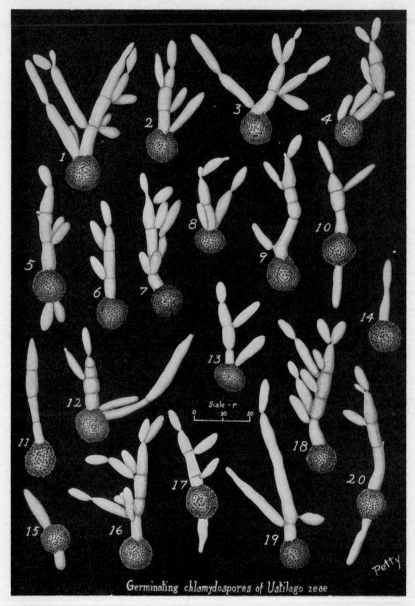

Figure 34. Germinating chlamydospores of corn smut, illustrating deviations from the normal 4-cell promycelium. (*Courtesy of M. F. Kernkamp and M. A. Petty, Minn. Agr. Exp. Sta.*)

maturity; the least infection is associated with heavy rain in the early part of the season followed by dry weather.   Light, but evenly distributed rains throughout the growing season usually result in moderate infection.

Spore germination in the soil is favored by an acid soil reaction, the optimum being pH 4.9.   Susceptibility to smut is increased in weak plants of low vigor, by stimulating their growth with fertilization or cultivation, but the most vigorous, rapidly growing plants, while highly susceptible to smut, may largely escape its most serious effects through their rapid growth.   Corn varieties with tight, long husks are less affected by smut than varieties with loose, open husks.

The thick walled chlamydospores are quite resistant to ageing, and will retain their viability for as much as 5 to 7 years.   They are destroyed by digestive juices of the alimentary tract or by the acids which accumulate in silage.   The sporidia, on the other hand, are thin-walled and less resistant than the chlamydospores.

Smut is reported to be less serious in well spaced hills with 2 or 3 plants per hill than in closely spaced hills, or hills with more or fewer stalks per hill.

On the whole, corn smut is a type of disease which appears fairly regularly in about the same extent, year after year, and is not subject to marked fluctuations in importance from one year to another.

Control.   No seed treatment is effective against corn smut. The general use of "New Improved Semesan Jr." on corn seed has to do with seedling disease and stalk, root, and ear rots, rather than with smut.   Despite extensive corn breeding programs in many states, there has been relatively little progress in developing smut-resistant corn varieties.   This is not due to lack of effort, but to the great variability in the corn smut fungus, and to a tendency for smut resistance to be associated with weak types of corn. Several investigators have found smut resistance consistently present in certain inbred lines of corn, but at present smut-resistant varieties are not available for general planting, although progress is being made in incorporating smut resistance in the newer hybrids.

For controlling this disease, the grower must turn to cultural methods,—rotation and sanitation.   These will not give complete control, but will materially aid in reducing losses from corn smut. A three year rotation is normally recommended, using any crop other than corn two years out of three. Stalks of smutty corn should be either harvested or plowed under in the fall. Manure

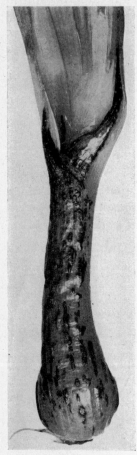

from animals that have fed on smutty corn will contain an abundance of smut spores, and this should not be returned to corn fields. Ensilage is a good means of disposing of smutty corn stalks, as the spores are killed within a few weeks in the silo. Collecting and burning the smut boils as soon as they appear is helpful in small sweet corn plantings, but usually regarded as impractical on large field-corn acreages, however this point is open to question.

LOCAL INFECTION SMUTS: ONION SMUT (*Urocystis cepulae*).

While this is a disease of importance only in onions grown from seed in cool climates, it is introduced because of its unusual method of control. The disease causes a smutty disintegration of bulbs and leaves (Fig. 35). The causal organism, *Urocystis cepulae*, is capable of living in the soil for many years, but can attack only seedlings, not the plants developing from onion sets. Effective control is obtained by treating the soil with formaldehyde at planting time. The planter is equipped with a reservoir for the formaldehyde, which is

Figure 35. O n i o n smut. (*Courtesy of J. C. Walker, Wisconsin Agr. Exp. Sta.*)

used at a 1:125 dilution applied at the rate of 200 gallons per acre. As the seed are planted, the formaldehyde drips into the furrow, where it disinfests a small mass of soil about the seed and thus protects the seedling during its susceptible early growth period.

LOCAL INFECTION SMUTS: WHITE SMUTS (*Entyloma species*).

White smuts, caused by species of *Entyloma*, occur on numerous kinds of plants including dahlia, water lily, spinach, poppy, buttercup, larkspur, calendula, meadow rue, beet seed capsules, sunflower, and members of the grass and nightshade families. They are rarely if ever important enough to warrant attempts at control.

The white smuts occur mainly on leaves where they cause leaf spots of various types, usually chlorotic, then necrotic. The yellowish chlamydospores are buried in the leaf tissue and germinate there, protruding their promycelia in clusters through the stomata where white masses of rod-like basidiospores are liberated, much resembling conidia of some of the imperfect fungi.

REFERENCES

1. Anderson, P. J. and A. V. Osmun. The smut disease of onions. Mass. Agr. Exp. Sta. Bull. 221. 1924.
2. Christensen, J. J. and H. A. Rodenhiser. Physiologic specialization and genetics of the smut fungi. Bot. Rev. 6: 389–425. 1940.
3. Clinton, G. L. Ustilaginales. No. Amer. Flora 7: 1–82. 1906.
4. Heald, F. D. Diseases due to smut fungi. In Manual of plant diseases: 712–761. McGraw Hill Book Co., New York. 1933. (Includes extensive bibliographies.)
5. Holton, C. S. and F. D. Heald. Stinking bunt of wheat—a world problem. Burgess Publ. Co., Minneapolis, Minn. 1941.
6. Leukel, R. W. Studies on bunt, or stinking smut, of wheat and its control. U. S. Dept. Agr., Tech. Bull. 582. 1937.
7. Leukel, R. W. et al. Wheat smuts and their control. U. S. Dept. Agr., Farm. Bull. 1711 rev. 1938.
8. Walter, J. M. Factors affecting the development of corn smut, *Ustilago Zeae* (Beckm.) Unger. Minn. Agr. Exp. Sta. Tech. Bull. 111. 1935.

Chapter 5

DISEASES CAUSED BY BASIDIOMYCETES:
FLESHY FUNGI; MYCORRHIZAE

The remaining basidiomycetes, apart from the rusts and smuts, for the most part are distinguished by conspicuous fleshy or woody reproductive bodies, mushrooms, crusts, or "conks," clothed with a spore-bearing layer (*hymenium*) of club-shaped *basidia* each bearing at its tip 4 *basidiospores*. (See page 25 for figures of these.) Ordinarily no other spore stage is involved in the life histories of the higher basidiomycetes. The mycelium frequently shows little bridges (*clamp-connections*) connecting adjacent cells (figured on page 24).

In plant pathology the fleshy fungi or *hymenomycetes* are of particular interest in connection with wood and root decays, *Rhizoctonia* damping off of seedlings and potato black scurf, and symbiotic (mycorrhizal) relationships between tree roots and fleshy fungi without which normal tree growth is impossible.

Wood Decay

The wood rots of standing trees and fallen timber in forest and woodlot, and the decay of fence posts and construction timbers are familiar to everyone. Nearly all of this decay is due to the action of hymenomycetes, the bracket-, crust-, or mushroom-like fruiting bodies of which are commonly found on the surfaces of decaying wood. These fungi are largely saprophytic in their habits. Even in destroying the heartwood of living trees, saprophytic nutrition is involved, since the heartwood of a normal tree is largely composed of dead cells. Few of the wood decay fungi can attack and penetrate through living wood, but must enter trees through wounds or branch stubs which expose an infection court of dead heartwood. Once a tree is dead this saprophytic feeding continues until the wood is entirely disintegrated and its components are returned to the soil. The lack of aggressiveness of the wood decay fungi is more than compensated for by their enzymatic activity. Through the production of a variety of enzymes they are able to digest the chemically resistant elements of wood into simpler, chemically active and nutritive substances. The types of enzymes produced determine the type of ensuing decay, resulting in firm, white rots, dark friable rots, pocket rots, and many other types. Each fungus on each kind of wood produces a characteristic type of decay.

In addition to complete or partial rotting, the hymenomycetes and certain of the other fungi produce staining or discoloration in timber. Bluestain, redstain and related troubles may not impair the strength of the wood but reduce its market grade, as stained wood cannot be used for certain purposes because of market prejudices. Redstain pine was not acceptable for railroad ties for many years until the Canadian Forest Products Laboratory showed that it was as strong and durable as unstained wood.

Wood decay is often associated with injury by borers or termites, the insects and hymenomycetes cooperating in the destruction of of the wood. Insects may provide points of entry for the wood decay fungi, or aid in spreading them from one tree to another.

From the fruiting bodies which are abundant on fallen, decaying wood, are produced countless basidiospores, providing an abundance of inoculum, particularly where such wood is allowed to accumulate and is not cleared away. J. H. White has calculated that a single conk of one of the wood decay fungi (*Fomes applanatus*), with an area of one square foot, produces 30,000,000,000 spores in a single day and that this may continue day after day for six months or more.

Melhus and Kent cite some significant figures regarding the losses from wood decay. For example, 900,000,000 new fence posts are set each year, the majority of which are replacement of decayed posts. The Santa Fé Railroad in a single year saved 125,000,000 ties through the use of decay-control measures and this corresponds to a saving of over two million acres of woodland. Furthermore we cannot disregard the prodigious losses from wood decay in standing timber. Already three-fifths of the virgin forest has been cut; we are cutting or burning twelve million acres of forest each year and only deliberately reforesting thirty-six thousand acres. Natural reforestation helps to repair the loss, but conservation of the remaining timber is imperative, and in the conservation program, the reduction of wood decay constitutes a major item.

Hardly a species of tree is immune from the attack of one or more species of wood decay fungi. The fungi themselves may be restricted in host range to one or a few species of trees, or may be capable of attacking many species. The majority of the wood decay fungi can be distinguished as attacking only hardwoods (deciduous trees) or only softwoods (conifers); however, there are a number that attack trees of both categories. Out of the many wood decays which occur, that caused by the fungus *Fomes igniarius* is selected for detailed treatment because of its prevalence and importance and because it has been studied more intensively than many of the other decays.

WHITE TRUNK ROT (*Fomes igniarius*).

Distribution and importance. *Fomes igniarius* has been known for 200 years or more. It occurs throughout the entire north temperate zone, in the United States from Alaska to the Bahamas, and in South America as well. This unusual distribution is doubtless related both to its ability to tolerate a wide range of temperatures, and to its extensive host range. According to Boyce, *Fomes igniarius* causes more loss than any other wood destroyer of hardwoods. In aspen, one of the more important hosts, up to 30 per cent loss may be experienced during the first 70 years of forest growth, and even trees but 30 years old may suffer as much as 15 per cent destruction of their heartwood. It is also the commonest enemy of oak trees, and has been called the most dangerous wood decay organism of fruit trees. In some affected forests, susceptible species may be so severely attacked that hardly a single healthy, sound tree may be found.

Host plants. The attack of *Fomes igniarius* is limited to broad-leaved trees. Of the long list of susceptible species, among the important hosts are aspen, birch, beech, oak, butternut, apple, pear, maple, hickory, black walnut, and alder.

Symptoms and signs. In the earlier stages of infection no external symptoms or signs are observable, because the fungus

attacks the vital sapwood last of all.   Ordinarily the first indications
of trouble are either the breaking over of the tree, or the appearance of fruiting bodies especially at wounds or branch stubs.   These

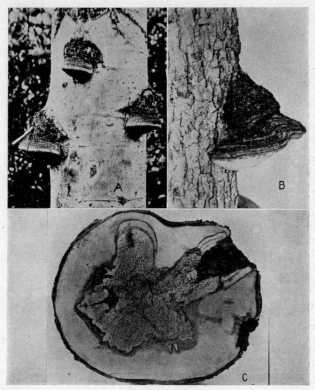

Figure 36.   A: *Fomes igniarius* fruiting bodies at old knotholes on living aspen.
(Photo by G. G. Hedgcock); B: *Fomes igniarius* on living black ash.   A single large fruit
usually forms on an infected tree of most of the hardwoods except the aspens.   (Photo
by H. G. Eno); C: Rot of *Fomes igniarius* in living maple trunk.   Note the broad dark
zone between the healthy wood and the decay; an old knothole at the right is the point
at which the fungus first entered, and the black mass at the right is a developing fruiting
body.   (*From Leaflet 20 published for the New England Section of the Society of American
Foresters*).

are hard, woody, hoof-shaped or less often shelf-like conks from 2
to 3 inches up to 8 inches or more in width (Fig. 36).   The upper
surface is dull gray to black becoming cracked and rough with a
smoother brownish margin.   The lower, or pore bearing surface
is brown, with many tiny pore openings.   The conks are perennial,

i.e. add a new layer of spore-bearing tubes each season. They may attain an age of 40 to 50 years or more. The interior of the conk is rusty brown, showing the old layers of tubes with white-stuffed pores, above the present spore-bearing layer. Presence of a conk usually indicates very extensive decay within the tree.

The rot caused by *Fomes igniarius* is a firm, white decay, that may extend many feet up and down the heartwood. The tree does not become hollow from this decay alone. A cross section of well-advanced decay shows in the center, a white, soft, crumbly core, surrounded by one or more black lines enclosing less advanced stages of decay, which in turn are surrounded by a margin of dis-colored but firm wood, marking the region of advance of the fungus. Wood in the advanced stages of decay is quite useless for con-struction purposes, although it may still have value for manu-facture of paper pulp.

Etiology. The walls of the tiny pores (.15 mm. in diameter) are lined with countless basidia, interspersed with bristles or setae; each basidium bearing 4 very small (6–7 μ) globose, colorless basidiospores. These are shot out from the sterigmata (their points of attachment to the basidium) to the center of the pore, where they drift down and on leaving the conk are picked up by the wind and widely dispersed. On coming to rest on a suitable infection court (branch stub or wound in a susceptible tree), they germinate, the infection thread enters the wood, and begins mycelial development. The mycelium advances rapidly up and down, less rapidly in a horizontal direction, digesting and feeding on the wood elements and thus inducing decay. After a prolonged period of feeding, masses of hyphae grow to the surface where there is exposed dead wood, and combine to form a solid mass of fungus tissue, which develops on its under surface the first layer of pores. Each season a new pore layer is added to the underside of this conk.

Fomes igniarius shows a primitive type of physiologic specializa-tion in that it contains three or more subtypes each of which shows differences from the others in appearance and behavior in culture, which are correlated with species of host trees. Cultures from single basidiospores are haploid. When two haploid cultures of different sources are grown on the same Petri dish, at the line of meeting of the mycelia there is an exchange of nuclei to produce diploid mycelium, indicating sexual mating, although clamp connections are not formed.   Diploid cultures appear to be somewhat more aggressive in causing decay than haploid cultures.

Fomes igniarius does not develop extensively as a free living saprophyte.   Once a tree is infected and killed, the fungus will persist on the dead wood for considerable period, but it does not appear to be well adapted to perpetuation on dead fallen timber alone.

Epiphytology.   The very extensive geographic range of this fungus indicates that it is tolerant of a wide variation in environmental conditions.   In culture the fungus grows between temperatures of 39° and 102°F. with most vigorous development between 74° and 86°.   Likewise it flourishes under both humid and dry conditions.   The most important factors favoring its development have to do with the host tree, its advancing age, thinness of its sapwood, its proximity to other infected trees, its lack of vigor or supression, and particularly the presence of wounds.   Any factor that promotes wounds, scars, or broken branches favors infection. By the nature of the disease it is not of a type that fluctuates in severity from one year to another, but each year advances steadily and evenly in its destruction.

Control.   1. *In individual ornamental or fruit trees.*   Diseased trees should be removed and burned, and replaced with young, vigorous trees of the longer-lived species.   Broken branches and pruning and other wounds should be promptly smoothed off and protected with shellac or tree paint.   The surroundings should be kept in a sanitary condition, free from dead or decaying wood.

2. *In woodlots or other small, managed plantings.*   Here the removal of diseased trees and their prompt use for firewood is practical.   It is not sufficient to remove the conks, as new ones will soon form. Thorough inspection is necessary to eradicate all conk-bearing trees. Fallen decaying lumber and slash from logged-off trees should be destroyed.

3. *In forests.*   Here, because of the acreages involved, the preceding methods of control may be impractical.   Most important is to follow a cutting practice which allows harvesting timber at an age when substantial growth has been obtained and decay has not yet become important.   Decay is a sign of overmaturity.

The studies of Meinecke dealing largely with *Fomes igniarius* decay of aspen illustrate a method of determining the most profitable cutting practice:

By use of an increment borer on many trees of all age classes, it is possible to determine the ages of the trees and the condition of each with regard to decay. Simple formulas indicate the amount of decayed wood and the amount of merchantable wood in board feet. Meinecke's work shows that in the type of forest studied, the total amount of timber in the forest steadily increases, until the trees are about 120 years old (Fig. 37). Decay is hardly a serious factor until the age of 75 to 80 years, after which the volume of

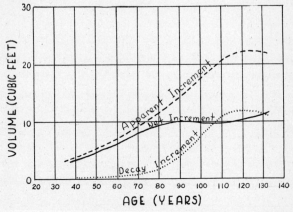

Figure 37. Apparent, decay, and net increments of timber in an aspen stand affected principally by *Fomes igniarius.* (*After Meinecke in U. S. Dept. Agr. Tech. Bull. 155.*)

decay increases as rapidly as the volume of new wood, i.e. the net amount of merchantable wood in the forest (total wood less decayed wood) becomes constant, and there is no increase from year to year. The figure shows that at approximately 80 years, there is no further annual increase in merchantable wood, because the increase in decay volume (decay increment) equals the apparent increment so that there is no net increment (increase in useable timber).

From the pathological standpoint, the desirable practice for this type of forest is, then, to cut when the trees are 80 years old or less, in order to escape serious losses from decay and get a maximum return from the investment. In a similar way the most profitable cutting cycle can be determined for each species of tree and each type of forest.

In addition to escaping decay by following an optimal pathological cutting practice, other means that aid in reducing decay losses include: an effective fire-control program to minimize fire wounds through which decay fungi gain access to trees; encouraging the growth of the more decay-resistant species of trees; logging contracts that require the removal of decayed trees and slash at the time the sound wood is logged off; "hot logging" or avoiding delay between cutting and utilization; sanitation of storage yards; stacking in such a way as to provide adequate ventilation of boards; proper seasoning of lumber; treatment with creosote, zinc chloride, paint or other preservatives of wood that is to be exposed to weather and soil; and development of ways for utilizing partially decayed wood.

SHOESTRING ROOT ROT (*Armillaria mellea*).

History and distribution. Shoestring root rot of many species of woody and herbaceous plants, also known as honey root rot or *Armillaria* root rot, is worldwide in distribution and important wherever it occurs. It is a constant feature of wooded areas. The causal fungus had been known, as a mushroom, for many years before Robert Hartig, in 1873 and 1874 proved that the underground mycelium of the mushroom, *Armillaria mellea*, is the cause of the root rot disease. An extensive bibliography of the disease has accumulated, the studies dealing primarily with the mode of infection of *A. mellea* and its control.

Importance. Shoestring root rot is a major disease of woody plants because of its destructiveness to trees, its wide host range, and its prevalence. It has been regarded as causing the death of more trees in Europe than any other parasitic agency. Piper and Fletcher give figures showing the killing by this organism of half the trees in a 1000-tree prune orchard within 6 years and in another orchard, one fourth of the trees in 3 years. In the great forests of the Pacific Northwest shoestring root rot is a principal factor in the destruction of valuable timber, and in the Ozark region it has been regarded as one of the most serious fruit diseases, capable of destroying entire apple and peach orchards in two years. While the fungus primarily affects woody plants, its attack on potatoes has received attention in Australia and in the more northern potato-growing states.   As it is a very common organism in oak, the most serious effects on orchards usually follow the planting of fruit trees on recently cleared oak land.

Host plants.   The list of species attacked by *Armillaria mellea* is a long one and includes conifers and deciduous forest, fruit, and shade trees, woody and herbacous ornamentals, and vegetables. It has been called practically omnivorous on woody plants.   The most important hosts include apples, apricots, citrus fruits, olives, peaches, plums, prunes, cherries, alder, beech, birch, walnut, almond, chestnut, locust, maple, mulberry, oak, sycamore, and poplar, and of the conifers, cedars, firs, hemlocks, larch, pine, and redwood.   The bush fruits, such as blackberries and raspberries, are very susceptible, as are certain ornamentals such as rhododendrons, azaleas, and boxwood.   Other herbaceous hosts beside the potato include carrots, parsnips, rhubarb, dahlias, cannas, and strawberries.   There is some evidence that two strains of the pathogen exist in America, one on conifers, the other important on oak and fruit trees.   Of the few resistant or immune species, the pear, California black walnut, and fig may be mentioned. Myrobalan plums are resistant giving them value as root stocks for the more susceptible stone fruits.

Symptoms and signs.   The first indication of trouble is usually a decline in vigor of the tree, with cessation of growth, yellowing of foliage, abnormally small leaves, and short twig growth.   Trees often die quite suddenly after displaying these symptoms.   In conifers and stone and citrus fruit trees, there is an exudation, often very copious, of resin or gum, especially at the tree bases.   These symptoms are not always the result of shoestring root rot; similar decline may be due to drought.   Positive determination of the cause of the trouble is based on the signs: rhizomorphs, mycelial fans, and fruiting bodies of the fungus (Fig. 38).   The rhizomorphs are black, shiny or dull mycelial cables, $\frac{1}{25}$ inch to $\frac{1}{12}$ inch in diameter, that ramify in the soil, over the surface of roots and through the decaying wood, or spread out in a branched system, often branching at right angles, under dead bark.   If dead bark is chipped away, white fans of mycelium can often be seen between bark and wood.   The mycelium in infected wood is phosphorescent causing the wood to glow in the darkness.

Figure 38. A: Base of large, dead yellow birch with many fruits of *Armillaria mellea*, showing the collar around the stem under the cap and characteristic manner of growth near the surface of the soil.   B: Shoestrings between the bark and wood of a dead tree.   (*Photos by J. Franklin Collins, originally published in Tree Pest Leaflets for the New England Section of the Society of American Foresters*).

In fall, under wet conditions, the fruiting bodies or mushrooms appear about the bases or on the trunks of affected trees. These are usually produced in groups or clusters, and disintegrate soon after the spores are produced. The mushroom consists of a thick stipe or stem from 3 to 10 inches long, terminating in a hemispherical, umbrella-shaped cap, 2 to 5 inches wide, honey yellow and covered with scales. Below the gills there is a ring or annulus around the stipe. Careful digging will often show a rhizomorph connecting the mushroom with nearby rotted wood. The mushrooms are relished by connoisseurs as among the best of the edible fungi. The rhizomorphs are most useful in identifying the trouble, as the mushrooms are found only infrequently, and mycelial fans may be produced by other fungi than *A. mellea*.

The decay involves both heart- and sapwood. At first the affected wood appears watersoaked, then discolored yellowish or brownish, and in final stages it is white or light yellow, marked with black zone lines, and very light and crumbly.

Etiology. *Armillaria mellea* is a gill fungus (agaric) related to the common edible mushroom of commerce. It lives very extensively on decaying wood as a saprophyte and is a common inhabitant of the forest floor and the woodpile. Two means serve for its dissemination, the wind-borne basidiospores which are produced on basidia lining the surfaces of the sporophore gills, and the rhizomorphs by which the fungus grows readily through the soil, often for considerable distances. The basidiospores are very small $(6 \times 9 \ \mu)$, clear, elliptical, and produced in enormous numbers. In a related fungus a discharge of 40,000,000 spores per hour from a single mushroom has been recorded. These spores may germinate and invade wood under moist conditions, but the rhizomorphs appear to be the exclusive means of attacking living trees. The rhizomorphs may penetrate living, uninjured bark and wood but most frequently take advantage of wounds of any description in entering the plant. Penetration is partly through mechanical force and partly through a suberin-dissolving enzyme. Wood that is depleted of carbohydrates or wood that is previously invaded by other fungi is not attacked by *A. mellea*. Once a plant is invaded, the mycelium rapidly grows through the wood, killing cells in advance of it, digesting their components, and thus producing decay. As the roots are destroyed the water supply is cut off and the tree succumbs. In invasion of the more resistant species, the fungus enters but is walled off by secondary cork layers formed by the host, and thus prevented from extensive invasion. On the death of the host the fungus continues a saprophytic life until the wood is completely decayed.

Epiphytology. The wide geographic range of the shoestring fungus, from cold to sub-tropical climates and from wet forests to prairie, gives evidence of its ability to flourish under the most varied environmental conditions. While abundant fall moisture is necessary for mushroom production, the omission of their development does not interfere with the success of the pathogen, which is well able to sustain itself in the form of mycelium and rhizomorphs. The condition of the host plant, on the other hand, does appear to affect the development of the disease. Devitalized trees and trees with wounds are much more severely attacked than vigorous, sound trees.

The disease is not one that occurs in epiphytotic proportions in certain years and becomes unimportant in others, but instead it produces uniformly serious losses each year. This is characteristic of a disease that is primarily soil borne and exhibits a wide tolerance of environments.

Control. 1. *Shade and ornamental trees.* It is not ordinarily practical to attempt to save a tree once it is obviously infected. With particularly valuable trees where the decay has not progressed to an advanced stage, promising results have been obtained by removing the soil to expose the larger roots, pruning out affected roots, treating cut ends with creosote or Bordeaux paint, and allowing aeration of the root system. One good method of removing the soil without serious root injury is to wash it out with a powerful stream of water.

2. *Orchard trees.* Here the most important concern is to avoid planting an orchard of susceptible fruits on recently cleared oak land, for a period of 3 to 5 years after clearing. In that time the fungus will disappear from the soil especially if the land is used for cultivated farm crops. It has been suggested that when a tree is known to be infected or has been removed, it is practicable to surround the site with a trench, 1 ft. wide and 2 ft. deep, to prevent the

rhizomorphs from growing across to nearby healthy trees.   Infected trees should either be removed and burned or possibly treated as described above.   Susceptible species should not be planted for at least 3 years on the site where a diseased tree has stood.   Measures aimed at increasing the vigor and general health of the tree and at reducing wounding of the root system will also aid in preventing losses from this disease.

3. *Forest trees.*   *Armillaria mellea* is widespread in forest soils and here the treatment of individual trees is impractical.   It is advisable to avoid logging injuries to tree roots.   Drastic opening of a stand will injure the remaining trees from exposure and thus render them more liable to root rot damage.   Thinning lightly and maintaining conditions for vigorous growth are indicated.   In establishing new forest plantations, the trees, particularly conifers, should not be planted on recently cleared oak land.

4. *Biological control.*   *Armillaria mellea* is a serious pest in tropical plantations and various methods of clearing and trenching have been used in attempted control.   In tea culture in Africa it is customary to find stumps of old trees among the young tea trees and these become infested after dying, and serve as reservoirs of inoculum.   Wood depleted of carbohydrates is not invaded by *A. mellea*, and use is made of this fact by removing a ring of bark about the trunk a year before cutting the tree.   Another source of inoculum is *Armillaria*-attacked woody prunings.   By leaving these on the soil surface a month or more they become invaded by other fungi and then cannot serve as a substrate for *A. mellea*.   This also explains why quickly-rotting woods are not usually reservoirs of *A. mellea*, since other wood decay fungi are able to invade them more rapidly than the shoestring fungus.

Mycorrhizae

Many trees require the presence of symbiotic fungi in or on the roots in order to grow normally.   The relationship of tree root and symbiotic fungus is known as mycorrhizal.   Recent extensive tree plantings in the Great Plains for wind and water erosion control are bringing out the necessity of supplying appropriate mycorrhizal fungi in new plantings on prairie soils that normally lack these organisms.   No less than 16 extensive nursery failures in various parts of the world have resulted from ignorance or disregard of the need for this symbiotic relationship.

Occurrence of mycorrhizae. Although mycorrhizal relationships have been studied most extensively in trees, they are found in many other groups of plants. In the *Apetalae* 175 cases of mycorrhiza have been described, the majority of these being in families of trees. In the *Apopetalae* there are 444 cases, outstanding families being the *Ranunculacaeae, Cruciferae, Rosaceae, Leguminosae*, and *Umbelliferae*. There are 267 cases in the *Gamopetalae* particularly in the *Ericaceae, Loganiaceae, Scrophulariaceae* and *Compositae*. Among the monocotyledons, 215 cases have been reported, especially in the grass, sedge, and lily families. Mycorrhizae are numerous in the gymnosperms (135 cases), with 106 cases reported from the pine family alone, and even among the ferns and fern allies some 80 cases of mycorrhiza have been found. Undoubtedly a more thorough search would reveal many more cases than those now on record. We are dealing, then, with a widespread biological relationship.

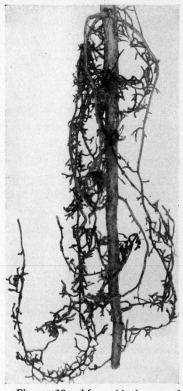

Figure 39. Mycorrhizal roots of pine seedling, showing the short, stubby, sometimes branched fungus-covered side roots.

Types of mycorrhizae. Mycorrhizae are of 4 sorts: *ectotrophic mycorrhizae*, in which symbiotic side roots are very short and are surrounded and cortically invaded by a mantle and net of fungus hyphae which serve to replace the wanting root hairs (Fig. 39); *endotrophic mycorrhizae*, in which the roots are outwardly normal but contain tangles of mycelium within the cortical cells; *ectendotrophic mycorrhizae*, in which the features of the first two types are combined, and *pseudomycorrhizae*, which in contrast to the other types are nonbeneficial or injurious invasions of roots by pathogenic soil fungi. Ectotrophic mycorrhizae are found associated with trees, while in herbaceous plants the predominating type is endotrophic.

Mycorrhizal fungi.   The fungi that participate in mycorrhizal relationships for the most part are members of the hymenomycete group of basidiomycetes although certain lower phycomycetes are sometimes involved.   Many of the mushrooms and puffballs to be found in woodlands are fruiting bodies of mycorrhizal fungi, as is seen in the fact that certain species of fleshy fungi are found chiefly or only about the roots of given species of trees.   Many of these relationships are quite specific, i.e. a single species or strain of fungus may be required for a given species of tree.   In a few cases the mycorrhizal fungus may be a species that under some conditions is capable of severe parasitism as with *Armillaria mellea* and species of *Rhizoctonia*.   Indeed, there is some evidence that the mycorrhizal relationship is the end-product of an evolutionary trend in which an earlier active parasitism has stabilized into a non-injurious and finally a beneficial relationship.

Function of mycorrhizae.   The significance of mycorrhizae has been disputed in the past, some believing them to be harmful, others beneficial, but recent experimental evidence indicates clearly that mycorrhizae are not only an aid but sometimes an indispensable aid to normal plant growth.   This has been shown particularly in experiments with mycorrhizal and nonmycorrhizal trees in prairie soils, where the trees without the mycorrhizae make very poor growth and exhibit symptoms of starvation.   The best evidence at present indicates that the ectotrophic mycorrhizae increase the absorbing areas of roots permitting the plant to absorb far more phosphorus, potassium, nitrogen, and doubtless other substances, than is possible without the fungus.   In addition they offer protection against the collapse of rootlets during drought.

Control of mycorrhizal deficiency.   Whenever trees are introduced on soil that has not supported the same species of trees in recent years, it is advisable to infest the soil with the proper mycorrhizal fungi.   This may be done by interspersing the new planting with inoculated trees or soil from other localities where the mycorrhizal relationship is already established.   Small amounts of soil sprinkled in the new planting will suffice.   This, of course, involves the danger of bringing in harmful pathogens at the same time, but the benefits of adding the mycorrhizal fungus will ordinarily outweigh the hazards involved, especially if the inoculum comes from a nearby natural, vigorous stand or a thrifty, reasonably old plantation.   Once the species of fungus required is known, the possibility of using pure cultures for inoculation becomes apparent, and this would furnish an entirely safe means of artificially producing the desired mycorrhizal relationship.

RHIZOCTONIA DISEASE (BLACK SCURF) OF POTATOES
(*Corticium vagum* = *Rhizoctonia solani*).

History and distribution.   The fungus *Corticium vagum* is one of the most widespread of all pathogenic soil fungi.   In nature it is most frequently found in the imperfect stage, in which it has long been recognized under the name *Rhizoctonia solani*.   In 1903, Rolfs discovered that the perfect stage was a previously known crust-like hymenomycete, *Corticium vagum*, but contrary to the best usage the name *Rhizoctonia*, referring to the stage ordinarily found, is the name most commonly used today in referring to this fungus or to the disease it causes in potatoes.

Pathologically, *R. solani* has a double interest, first as the cause of a root and stem disease of potatoes, beets, and other root crops, and second as one of the most important organisms producing dampingoff of seedlings of many species of plants.   At this point discussion is largely limited to the former, the subject of damping-off, as produced by numerous soil fungi, being reserved for later consideration.   *Rhizoctonia solani*, on various hosts, occurs in all parts of the world, and is a factor in production wherever potatoes are grown. This is due both to its ready transmission to new areas on tubers, and to the fact that it is a normal inhabitant of many virgin soils. It was first recognized in Europe in 1858 and in America about 1900, although it doubtless had been common in both areas long before these dates.   The early reports frequently confused *R. solani* with a closely related form, *R. crocorum*, the cause of violet root rot of alfalfa, beets and other crops.   The *Rhizoctonia* disease is now general throughout all potato growing sections of North America, being evident everywhere, but particularly under the cooler conditions of potato culture.

Importance.   The average national loss from *Rhizoctonia* is quite regularly from 2 to 3 per cent of the potato crop or about 10,000,000 bushels.   Losses in the individual States range up to 15 per cent, with such important producing states as Maine, Washington, Oregon, and California occasionally reporting 8 to 10 per cent annual loss from this disease.   In individual fields, losses as high as 51 per cent have been experienced.   The losses are of several types: (1) destroying the young sprouts before they emerge from the soil, so as to reduce the stand, (2) rotting the roots and girdling the stalks of older plants so as to shut off transport of foodstuffs, resulting in poor yields, (3) predisposing the tubers to decay before harvest, and (4) injuring the quality of the harvested crop by unsightliness, which results in a lower grade and price, or by cankering, cracking, or even rotting of the tubers.   The lowering of grade is particularly costly when the potatoes are intended for certification or ordinary seed use.   In fall crop potatoes, vines affected by *Rhizoctonia* are noticeably more subject to injury by light frosts than are healthy plants.

Host plants.   The list of plants attacked by *R. solani* is far too long to enumerate.   Twenty-five years ago 165 species of plants were listed as susceptible, and doubtless many others could be added today.   While most of these hosts are herbaceous dicotyledons, some of the grains and grasses, onions, and other monocotyledons, as well as several gymnosperms and equisetum are listed as suspects.   Woody seedlings and cuttings are often destroyed by *Rhizoctonia* and occasionally the pathogen may even attack more mature woody tissues.

Symptoms and signs.   A number of striking and characteristic symptoms and signs make this disease easily recognizable.   The first indication of the trouble is missing hills or hills in which the sprouts decay back, to be succeeded by secondary sprouts which in turn may decay.   In later stages the plants show symptoms similar to those of drought injury, with curling of the leaves and stunting or rosetting.   The stems are often decayed at or just below the soil line.   This interrupts the downward flow of carbohydrates, with the result that clusters of little green or reddish aerial tubers are formed (Fig. 40A).   Underground the secondary, feeding roots may be extensively killed back, to be replaced by successions of

adventitious rootlets.   Affected vines show a high percentage of
small tubers.   The best known sign is the presence on the tubers of
crust-like black sclerotia, the "dirt that won't wash off," few or so
numerous that the surface of the tuber may be largely covered by
them (Fig. 40C).   Other tuber symptoms sometimes encountered
are a brown, deep stem-end rot, jelly-rot of the stem end, and dry

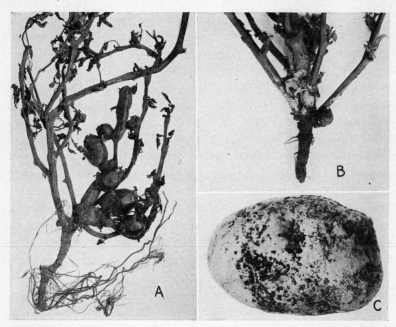

Figure 40.   Rhizoctonia disease (black scurf) of potato.   A, aerial tubers are
often seen on affected plants; B, occasionally the fruiting stage of *Corticium vagum* is seen
as a white, powdery film on the lower branches; and C, the familiar "dirt that won't
wash off,"—black, crust-like sclerotia by means of which the fungus may persist from
harvest until planting time.   (*Courtesy of P. E. Tilford, Ohio Agr. Exp. Sta.*).

lesions at the lenticels.   In advanced stages of the disease, where
moisture is suitable, the perfect stage of reproduction may be seen
as a white, powdery crust partly or entirely girdling the base of the
potato stem, the powder consisting of large numbers of basidiospores
(Fig. 40B).

   Etiology.   The primary inoculum may come from either of
two sources, the soil, or sclerotia on the seed tubers.   Judging by
the effectiveness of seed selection, seed treatment, and rotations in

control, the tubers are most important in this regard.   Under favorable conditions the sclerotia of the soil or tubers germinate by producing mycelium which is able to attack the roots and stems of the potato, initiating decay.   The mycelium continues to invade the tissues, killing the cells until the characteristic root and stem rot symptoms are produced.

During this period of active parasitism, no spores are produced. Secondary sclerotia may form in the soil and these may in turn germinate to produce secondary cycles of infection, but the principal mechanism of progressive invasion is the mycelium itself.   The mycelium of *Rhizoctonia solani* is easily recognizable.   The hyphae are large and coarse, at first pale, later brownish, with coarse side branches that often depart from the main hypha at right angles. At the point of departure there is a slight constriction of the side branch and just out from this a cross-wall.   (Fig. 119).

In the later stages of the disease, mycelium aggregates about the stem bases in the form of a mantle or crust covered with club-shaped basidia, each bearing at its tip 4 basidiospores.   The function of the basidiospores is obscure.   They evidently play little part in dissemination of the disease during the growing season, but they may be important sources of soil infestation, returning to the soil where they germinate to form saprophytic mycelium which in turn may produce resting sclerotia.

Between crops the fungus persists either as sclerotia on tubers or in the soil, or as saprophytic mycelium in the soil.   Here the mycelium can grow for long distances and produce sclerotia, independently of any living host.   The pathogen appears to be well adapted to this soil existence.

Epiphytology.   *Rhizoctonia* infection is favored by cool temperatures, between 70° and 48°F. with optimum infection at 64°F. Little infection results between 70°F. and 75°F., possibly because the potato sprouts develop very rapidly at these temperatures and may be able to outgrow the danger.

Ample moisture appears to favor the disease, which is ordinarily most serious in wet seasons and low wet soils.

There is some difference of opinion regarding soil reaction in its effect on *Rhizoctonia*.   Textbooks commonly state that the disease is most severe on acid to neutral soils, least on alkaline soils, and partially controllable by liming. Critical experiments on the effect of soil pH in influencing the *Rhizoctonia* disease are needed.

High soil fertility favors the disease, perhaps by its influence on the saprophytic development of the fungus. The disease is more severe on heavy than on light soils, this perhaps being indirectly due to soil moisture in the two cases. Vigor of the plants is said to reduce their injury from *Rhizoctonia* which may relate to the ability of rapidly growing plants to grow away from the fungus.

With favorable environmental conditions the amount of damage will vary with the amount of inoculum in the soil and on the tubers, particularly the latter. As is generally true of seed- and soil-borne diseases, in contrast to primarily air-borne diseases, the *Rhizoctonia* disease does not appear in severe epiphytotics certain years, and disappear during others, but produces rather constant losses each year, the only significant variation being a slow steady decrease during the past decade or two, thanks to the extended adoption of preventative seed treatments.

Control. 1. *Use of non-infested seed tubers.* As infested tubers are the most important source of infection, the use of non-infested tubers affords a first line of defence against *Rhizoctonia*. In securing such tubers the grower is aided both by state seed inspection service and by seed certification. Three main categories of seed are available for planting.

Certified seed. The Nebraska certification rules (1938) illustrate the treatment of the *Rhizoctonia* problem in potato certification. These rules define "Slight *Rhizoctonia*" as that in which not more than 5 per cent of the tuber surface is covered with sclerotia, while if more is present the condition is termed "Severe *Rhizoctonia*." In the three grades of certified seed available from Nebraska, the blue and red tag grades allow a total of not over 15 per cent of *Rhizoctonia*, not more than 5 per cent of which can be severe. The white tag grade meets the requirements of the other two grades except for *Rhizoctonia* and scab, and as these are often seconds or sortouts from the other grades, they may be expected to carry a rather heavy *Rhizoctonia* infestation. The reason for issuing them as certified is that they are as free from virus diseases as the better grades and they can be seed-treated for *Rhizoctonia* and scab.

State inspected seed. Tubers for seed purposes are usually subject to inspection on entry into the state. The Oklahoma law, for example, permits up to 20 per cent of slight *Rhizoctonia* on seed potatoes, this being defined as "scattering *Rhizoctonia* sclerotia, ½ inch in diameter or less in the aggregate." The Louisiana law allows up to 6 per cent of the tubers to have 5 per cent or more of their surfaces covered by *Rhizoctonia* or scab. Laws of other states are similar.

Market potatoes. These are graded by United States standards, which affect *Rhizoctonia* as follows:

1. U. S. Fancy
2. U. S. Extra No. 1 } 94 per cent of the tubers free from *Rhizoc-*
3. U. S. No. 1   *tonia*
4. U. S. Commercial: 80 per cent of the tubers free from "foreign matter affecting the appearance" and 74 per cent free from serious "foreign matter, etc."

While these standards all seem rather tolerant of *Rhizoctonia*, it must be borne in mind that lower tolerances of *Rhizoctonia* would materially reduce the supply and raise the price of the better grades, and that other diseases, particularly virus diseases, are much more dangerous in tubers, while *Rhizoctonia* infestations can be easily removed from tubers by seed treatment.

2. *Seed-tuber treatments.* While it is better to select *Rhizoctonia-*free potatoes for planting, moderately infested potatoes can be satisfactorily disinfested by tuber treatments. Several types of treatment are available:

1. Soak tubers 1½ to 2 hours in loose sacks in a solution of 1 pint formaldehyde in 30 gal. water.

2. Soak tubers 4 minutes in a solution of 1 pint formaldehyde in 75 gal. water at 125°F. This treatment now largely replaces the cold formaldehyde method but is less effective against *Rhizoctonia* than against potato scab.

3. Soak tubers 1½ hours in a solution of 4 oz. of corrosive sublimate (dissolved in 2 qts. hot water) in 30 gal. water.

4. Soak tubers 5 minutes in a solution of 6 oz. corrosive sublimate plus 1 qt. hydrochloric acid plus 25 gal. water. Acidified mercury is available commercially (e.g. Mercurnol).

5. Soak tubers 2 minutes in a solution of 4 oz. corrosive sublimate in 30 gal. water at 126°F.

6. Dip tubers momentarily in solutions of organic mercury compounds such as Semesan Bel, according to directions of the manufacturer. Mercuric oxide (e.g. Cinnex-20) is used similarly.

In using the mercury treatments it must be remembered that the chemicals are poisonous, and that corrosive sublimate will erode metal, and proper precautions must be taken to avoid these hazards. In using corrosive sublimate the strength of the solution must be frequently fortified as treatment progresses. Any of the treatments should be carried out strictly according to directions as there is danger of serious tuber injury from careless or improper treatments. Insofar as *Rhizoctonia* is concerned, any of the treatments may be used, although there is some preference for the mercuries as compared with formaldehyde. No treatment will be wholly effective if large sclerotia are numerous on the tubers, and such tubers should not be used for planting, even with treatment. Moreover, if the soil is heavily infested with *Rhizoctonia*, seed-tuber treatment by itself may not give effective control.

3. *Cultural practices.* A three year rotation is advised once the soil is heavily infested with *Rhizoctonia*. Crops of the grain and grass family are suitable for the intervening years. While this will not completely eradicate the fungus from the soil, in combination with seed-tuber treatments it will give a profitable degree of *Rhizoctonia* control. Other cultural practices such as liming, late planting, and early harvesting either are of doubtful value or may be antagonistic to more important principles having to do with the optimal growing of the crop.

REFERENCES

1. Boyce, J. S. Forest pathology. McGraw-Hill Book Co., New York. 1938.
2. Dana, B. F. The *Rhizoctonia* disease of potatoes. Wash. Agr. Exp. Sta. Bull. 191. 1925.
3. Hatch, A. B. The rôle of mycorrhizae in afforestation. Jour. For. **34:** 22–29. 1936.
4. Hubert, E. E. An outline of forest pathology. John Wiley and Sons, Inc., New York. 1931.
5. Meinecke, E. P. Quaking aspen: a study in applied forest pathology. U. S. Dept. Agr., Tech. Bull. 155. 1929.
6. Sanford, G. B. Studies on *Rhizoctonia solani* Kühn. I–V. Can. Jour. Res. (C) *and* Scient. Agr. 1936–1941.
7. Thomas, H. E. Studies on *Armillaria mellea* (Vahl.) Quel., infection, parasitism, and host resistance. Jour. Agr. Res. **48:** 187–218. 1934.

Chapter 6

DISEASES CAUSED BY ASCOMYCETES

The ascomycetes are fungi that ordinarily reproduce in two ways.   In the *imperfect* stage, which is usually the stage involved in active parasitism and the production of disease, *non-sexual* spores or *conidia* are produced, often in great abundance.   The conidia, sometimes called summer-spores, serve for the widespread propagation of the disease during the growing season of the host.   With the advent of unfavorable growing conditions, as onset of winter or hot, dry summers, when the host plant matures or goes into a state of dormancy, the fungus usually becomes saprophytic, and during this saprophytic stage there appears the reproductive mechanism of the *perfect* stage, typified by *sexually-produced ascospores*, borne in sack-like *asci* (plural) usually 8 ascospores to an *ascus* (singular).   The ascospores are matured and discharged into the air at the onset of more favorable growing conditions; on reaching a suitable infection court they germinate, and initiate primary infections, which soon result in the production of mycelium bearing *conidia*, responsible for secondary infections and the general spread of the disease.

Although many of the ascomycetes are harmless or useful saprophytes, the group includes a large number of species that are important pathogens.   The principal ascomycetous pathogens are in several sub-groups, the *Sphaeriales* and kin in which the asci are contained within a flask-like *perithecium* opening by a pore, the *Perisporiales*, the perithecia of which have no opening and are called *cleistothecia*, the *Pezizales* and kin with the asci lining the inner surface of a cup-like *apothecium*, and the *Taphrinales*, in which there is no fruiting body but the asci are borne in exposed layers on the surfaces of host tissues.   These various fruiting structures are illustrated in Fig. 8.

SCAB OF CEREALS (*Gibberella zeae*).

History and distribution.   Scab, or *Fusarium* blight of cereals occurs in all parts of the world.   In the United States it is most prevalent and destructive in the corn belt, although it is found from New York to North Dakota and California and southward to Florida and Oklahoma. The disease is one of long standing. As early as 1891 its importance in America was recognized, and since that time, beside significant losses in numerous years, there have been occasional very destructive epiphytotics, as in 1919 and 1928.

Importance. The scab epiphytotic of 1919 cost American growers 80,000,000 bushels of wheat, the greatest loss occurring in Iowa, one-fourth of the crop. In other years the national losses

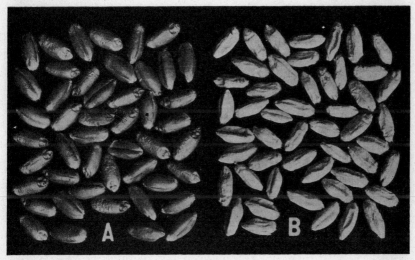

Figure 41. Scab in wheat. A, healthy kernels; B, scab-infected kernels, shrivelled, light in weight, bleached, and sometimes showing a pink discoloration or orange, waxy scale of scab spores. (*Courtesy of Benjamin Koehler, Ill. Agr. Exp. Sta.*)

in wheat range from 500,000 to 8,000,000 bushels annually, and in addition the disease causes significant losses in barley, corn, and rye. The bulk of these losses are in the central states where wheat is seriously affected; in the South the disease is less prevalent, except on corn. The losses are of various types: poor stands, lowered yields through root and stalk rot, and inferior quality of the harvested grain. Scabby barley contains a poison with an emetic effect that can be tolerated by hogs only in very small amounts, and bread made from scabby rye is also poisonous.

Host plants. Beside the cereals, wheat, barley, corn, rye, oats, spelt, and emmer, the fungus also causes a disease of clover and alfalfa, and has been recorded as a parasite of sweet potato, poke-weed, and umbelliferous plants, but wheat, barley, and corn are the principal suscepts.

Symptoms and signs.   Cereal plants are attacked at all stages of development and the various manifestations of the disease are referred to as seedling blight, foot rot, stalk rot, and head blight or ear rot.   In seedling blight, young seedlings are invaded by the fungus and sometimes totally destroyed before or soon after emergence, or so badly injured that the plants remain crippled for life.   The roots of the developing plant may be progressively destroyed in the foot-rot or root-rot stage, producing inferior or worthless plants.   In corn the stems may be invaded, causing lodging or barrenness. Via the stem, the fungus may pass out through the shank, infecting the ear.   In the southern states the corn root and stalk rot stages are common; head blight is rarely seen. In head blight or ear rot, the glumes, husks, and grains become overrun with white, cottony myce-lium on which, in moist weather, are produced abundant salmon-colored masses of conidia.   In dry weather these may dry down to form orange, waxy scales or crusts

Figure 42.   Scab in wheat.   A, healthy head; B, head with central part affected; C, head with upper half affected; and D, entire head affected. At harvest, the kernels of affected parts will appear as in Figure 41.   (*Courtesy of Benjamin Koehler, Ill. Agr. Exp. Sta.*)

on the infected parts.   The grains become invaded by the fungus in which case they are shrivelled, molded, discolored, or partly rotted, often with scabby, tufted mycelium over the seed surface (Fig. 41). In small-grains the affected heads are partly or entirely straw colored (Fig. 42).   Late in the season, or, in the South, during the following season, numerous small black bodies may be seen over the surface of affected parts, especially the glumes of small grains and corn stalks; these are the perithecia, containing the ascospores.

Etiology.   The fungus causing scab is an ascomycete, *Gibberella saubinetii* or more properly, *G. zeae,* * the imperfect or conidial stage of which is *Fusarium graminearum.*   Two other closely related *Fusaria, F. culmorum* and *F. culmorum var. cereale* are associated with such similar symptoms, especially in the northern regions, that they are considered together with *G. zeae* in the etiology of scab.

Gibberella zeae overwinters in several ways: in the perithecial stage on blighted grain heads, straw, and corn stalks, as saprophytic mycelium in crop residue, as conida on seed or in the soil, and in the case of *F. culmorum* as vegetative resting spores (*chlamydospores*).

The initial infections may be brought about in several ways.   If infested seed or soil are concerned, the first evidence of disease may be the blighting of seedlings.   As the fungus grows through the seedling tissues, destroying them, there are produced on the tissue surfaces large numbers of conidia.   These are pink in mass, colorless under the microscope, sickle-shaped, generally 6-celled.   They are easily detached, and blown about by the wind.   They may be responsible for head infections, or these may result from ascospores that are shot out of the overwintered perithecia.   The ascospores somewhat resemble the conidia.   They are spindle-shaped, slightly curved, largely 3-celled, colorless, borne 8 in an ascus.   During the growing season there will be successive crops of conidia, producing secondary cycles of infection, until entire fields are destroyed.   At harvest the fungus passes into a dormant stage or continues in saprophytic activity, feeding on the residue from the affected crop.

True physiologic specialization probably does not occur in this fungus but various isolations differ markedly in their pathogenicity; some are capable of destroying nearly all inoculated plants, while others are practically non-pathogenic.

Epiphytology.   Seedling blight from the scab fungus is favored by relatively dry soil, low temperatures (46°–65°F.) in the case of corn, and higher temperatures (68°–86°F.) in wheat.   The best corn growth occurs in warm soil, and that of wheat in cool soil,

---

* The latter name is now considered correct; the former, however, is the name by which the fungus is commonly referred to in the literature on this disease.

hence in both cases the least seedling blight is under temperatures that are most favorable for the culture of the crop (Fig. 190).

The head phase develops most extensively at temperatures of 70°–80°F., and under moist conditions that favor germination of the conidia. Epiphytotics occur when there is an extended succession of humid, dewy, or muggy days from heading time onward. Local variations in infestation are also in large part due to methods of handling the crop, use of rotations, and planting of infested seed. Shading by weeds, high seeding rates, and lodging all may increase the amount of infection.

Control. 1. *Sanitation and rotation.* The residue from infested crops, stalks, straw, and chaff that harbor mycelium, conidia, and ascospores of the fungus, is the chief source of infection. Clean plowing soon after harvest, turning this material thoroughly under, goes a long way toward controlling scab. Where scab is a problem, a rotation should be practiced in which cereal crops do not directly follow one another.

2. *Disease-free seed.* A second important safeguard is to use non-infested seed. Seed corn should be field-selected for healthy appearance, quickly cured, tested for freedom from germination trouble before planting, and treated with an organic mercurial dust such as "New Improved Semesan Jr." Small-grain seed should be selected from disease-free fields, lots with numerous discolored, scabby or light-weight grains should be rejected, and the seed should be thoroughly cleaned by fanning to remove light-weight, internally infected kernels, and then dust-treated as for surface-borne smuts.

3. *Resistant varieties.* Cereal varieties differ in their susceptibility to scab but the work in breeding for scab resistance is still in an early stage. Scab-resistant inbred corns exist, but as yet have not been satisfactorily combined in hybrids for general use. In barley the smooth-awned varieties are more susceptible than Manchuria types. Hooded varieties are very susceptible to scab. In wheat some Turkey selections are rather scab resistant, and in the corn belt, Illinois No. 1 and Progress wheats have largely replaced Marquis because of resistance to scab and other diseases.

APPLE SCAB (*Venturia inaequalis*).

History and distribution. Scab is the first ranking apple tree disease in nearly every part of the world where the crop is grown. It has attracted attention of growers and pathologists alike particularly in North America, Europe, Australia, and South Africa. In the United States it occurs in every state, although its greatest severity is seen in the cooler sections. Scab is also a disease of long standing. It was recognized in the United States more than a hundred years ago, and had been recorded in Sweden and Germany prior to that time. There is some evidence that the disease is native to some other part of the world than America, and that it was brought to this country on imported stock. The early work on scab was devoted largely to study of the life history of the causal fungus and its control by spraying. The interest in spraying and dusting has lasted to the present as one improvement has followed another in scab control. Among the most recent developments are the use of wettable sulphur sprays, ground sprays for eradicating the overwintering stage, and forecasting scab outbreaks, by following the overwintering stage, in time for spray warnings as a service to orchardists.

Importance. Scab is by all odds the most damaging apple disease in the nation as a whole. In the 10-year period, 1928–1937, the average national loss from apple scab was 8 per cent of the crop or over 10 million bushels of apples per year. In important apple growing states the scab losses reach very high levels during favorable years as instanced by the following estimated loss percentages (Pl. Dis. Rep.): 1928, New York, 30%; 1933, Virginia 25%, Illinois 40%, Indiana 50%; and 1935, Maine and Pennsylvania 30%, Arkansas 25%. This is all the more striking when we consider that scab can be completely prevented by a suitable spray program and it indicates the profit that lies within reach of progressive growers.

The losses from scab are of several sorts. The leaves are affected reducing the vitality of the tree, and the fruit is rendered unmarketable or of poor grade because of the unsightliness of the scab lesions and because these often serve as entering points for decay organisms. Even with scab freedom the cost of spraying to secure this must be entered on the debit side of our account with *Venturia inaequalis*.

Host plants.   The apple scab fungus attacks only the apple and a few closely related species.   The scab disease of pears is due to a similar but distinct species of *Venturia*, while scab of stone fruits is caused by a wholly unrelated fungus.   Commercial apples differ considerably in their resistance or susceptibility to scab.   It is not possible to give a dogmatic list of susceptible and resistant varieties, because apple varieties often differ in their degree of susceptibility from one locality or year to another, possibly due to strain differences in the fungus.   Varieties that have been reported as particularly

susceptible include Winesap, Rome, Virginia Beauty, Lowry, Black Twig, Ben Davis, Gano, Delicious, Stayman, King David, and Early Harvest, and as less susceptible, Baldwin, (sometimes badly attacked), Jonathan, Duchess, Transparent, York Imperial, and Grimes.

Figure 43.   Apple scab.   Left, scab spots on under side of an apple leaf.   Right, scab on a mature apple; note the cracks.   (*Photo by Bureau of Plant Industry, U. S. Dept. of Agriculture.*)

Symptoms and signs.   *On the leaves* scab takes the form of olive drab, moldy spots, especially on the underside of the leaf, ¼ inch or more in diameter, without a sharp outline.   Some leaf distortion may occur as the leaf puckers about the lesions.   With many leaf lesions the leaf usually turns brown and drops somewhat prematurely (Fig. 43).

On the blossoms similar olive-colored spots are sometimes seen on pedicel, calyx, and petals.   Blossom infection is usually followed by the dropping of the blossoms of young fruit.

On the twigs scab lesions are uncommon but are occasionally found on 1-year old wood. They much resemble those on the fruits.

On the fruits the lesions are first seen at the blossom end, later all over the fruits. At first they are small, rounded, sharply-outlined, dark, moldy spots with a white rim (Fig. 43). Later the inner dark area becomes corky, and often ruptures to form a star-shaped crack. If many lesions are present, they coalesce and large areas of the fruit are cracked and split, the fruit becoming lopsided about the scabby area. Later secondary organisms, as pink and green molds, may enter through the scab lesions, causing more or less extensive decay. The scab fungus alone does not produce such decay.

Etiology. The fungus, *Venturia inaequalis* is an ascomycete, the ascospores and asci being produced in small, dark, flask-shaped perithecia, buried in the tissues of dead, overwintered infected leaves. The ascospores are brown, 2-celled with one cell smaller than the other (unequal = *inaequalis*), and are borne 8 in an ascus. The spores mature at about the time the apple tree is blossoming. At this time the asci stretch out until they protrude through the opening (ostiole) of the perithecium and the spores are shot out violently. They are picked up by wind currents, and if carried to susceptible apple tissues they inaugurate primary infections. The ascospore germinates sending out a hypha that penetrates the cuticle of the host tissue, and a layer of mycelium develops just under the cuticle. The hyphae of this mycelium branch and extend, killing the tissues ahead by a secreted poison, and feeding on them. In about 10 days the lesion becomes evident, the hyphae mass under the point of infection, and brown conidiophores appear on the surface, bearing at their tips one-celled, slipper-shaped brown conidia. These in turn may be carried by the wind to new infection courts where they germinate and produce new infections on leaves and fruit. At the end of the growing season the infected leaves die and fall, and the fungus remains throughout the winter as a saprophytic mycelium, feeding on the dead leaf tissues until spring, at which time new perithecia and ascospores are formed.

In the past, it has generally been considered that this is the only method of overwintering. However, recent studies in England have shown that the fungus may also overwinter in the fruit bud scales and in the wood at the base of the scales. This serves to explain the formerly unaccountable value of dormant and delayed dormant sprays in contributing toward scab control.

Prior to 1901, when Clinton proved that the saprophytic perithecial stage and the parasitic conidial stage are two phases in the life history of *Venturia inaequalis*, only the conidial stage was associated with the scab disease. As the perfect or ascosporic stage was unknown, the fungus was placed in the appropriate genus of the imperfect fungi, and named *Fusicladium dendriticum*. With the discovery of the sexual stage the imperfect name becomes obsolete, but it may still be found in the older literature on apple scab.

Storage scab. In commercial storage at low temperatures, established lesions do not enlarge to a great extent, but new lesions may appear, due to infections that occurred in the orchard but were not apparent at picking time. Storage scab is favored by humidity, by the higher storage temperatures, and by delay in harvesting and storing. The incubation period in storage may vary between 23 days and $6\frac{1}{2}$ months. Storage scab lesions may differ considerably from field lesions, being in the form of black specks or spots, up to $\frac{1}{8}$ inch in diameter, round or irregular or star-shaped. Storage of scabbed apples also is a hazard in view of the fact that the broken cuticle allows excessive transpiration, producing shrivelled fruits.

Epiphytology. A study of the scab loss estimates over a series of years brings out clearly the dependence of this disease on environment and its ability to become epiphytotic under suitable weather conditions. The discharge of ascospores is most favored by temperatures from 50–54°F. accompanied by rains, although they can be discharged between 33° and 86°F. The release of ascospores may continue over a period of 2 to 3 months. The ascospores germinate and infect at temperatures from 41°–79°F. Infection, primary or secondary, can only occur when there is a film of moisture on the tree. Cool rains at any time after primary infection favor secondary spread of the disease, thus it will be most prevalent during cool moist seasons and is inhibited by either dryness or temperatures above 80°F. These facts explain both its greater severity in northern regions or at high altitudes in southern regions, and its annual variations in destructiveness.

Other factors influencing the disease are prevalence of infected leaves from previous crops, susceptibility of apple varieties, rank growth in poorly pruned trees, low, moist locations, excessive nitrogenous fertilization, and the efficiency of the spray program.

Control. 1. *Spray schedule.* A suitable spray schedule has long been recognized as the main essential for scab control. Dusting is also useful, in some instances supplanting spraying. The spray materials, number of applications, time of applications, and equipment all vary according to scab severity, size and location of the orchard, and personal preferences.

Time and number of applications. A complete spray schedule, under conditions of severe scab hazard consists of the following applications.

a. *Dormant spray* of lime-sulphur. This is not usually included in the scab control program, although the recent discovery that the scab organism can overwinter in buds, indicates that it may possess value in scab control.

b. *Delayed dormant spray,* at the time the leaf buds are bursting.

c. *Pre-pink spray,* when the pink of the blossom buds can first be seen.

d. *Pink spray,* when the blossom buds are enlarged and beginning to open, but before full bloom.

e. *Calyx, petal-fall, or shuck spray,* just after the majority of blossoms have fallen but before the shucks have closed over the fruits.

f. *Ten-day spray,* ten days after the calyx spray.

g. *Thirty-day spray,* thirty days after the calyx spray.

In few cases would it be necessary to resort to all of these applications; unless the scab hazard is great, two or three applications will give practical control. Heald considers the calyx spray as most important, accounting for 40 per cent control, the three sprays preceding it giving another 40 per cent control, while the last two sprays have each 10 per cent value.

Spray materials. Bordeaux mixture (4–4–50 or weaker) and lime sulphur (1–40 or 1–50) have both been used very extensively for scab. Bordeaux mixture has a tendency to burn or russet during cool weather and lime sulphur is likely to burn during hot weather, hence the practice of using lime sulphur for the early applications and Bordeaux for the later ones is often followed. Flotation sulphur (8 to 10 lb. per 100 gal. water) is nearly as effective in scab control as lime sulphur, and is non-injurious to foliage or fruit, but is somewhat more expensive. Numerous wettable sulphurs are used for apples, and good results have been obtained from dusting with sulphur in some such combination as: sulphur 90 parts + lead arsenate 10 parts, or sulphur 40 + lead arsenate 20 + lime 40, or lime 86 + dehydrated copper sulphate 10 + calcium arsenate 4 parts.

Efficiency of spraying. To be effective spraying must be thorough, covering (but not drenching) all foliage and fruit (Fig. 205). To facilitate efficient spraying, large orchards should be so arranged that trees blooming at the same time will be together in blocks. Unless the spraying is properly timed, and an appropriate material thoroughly applied at the right concentration, unsatisfactory results or injury will follow.

Eradicant spraying. A recent development in scab control that has given spectacular results in preliminary trials is to spray the ground around the trees at the time the fruit buds are bursting, to kill the ascospores. The materials used with success are Elgetol (the sodium salt of di- nitro- ortho cresol plus a spreading and penetrating agent), 8 per cent fruit tree carbolineum, 1 per cent helion, or 4 per cent calcium arsenate, applied at the rate of 500 gal. per acre at a cost of $5.00 per acre or about 10 to 15 cents per tree. The ground sprays are not a control program in themselves. They are chiefly regarded as a means of lightening the tree spray program. As yet, they are not fully understood with regard to such problems as the most suitable and economical ground spray material, possible detrimental effect on the soil, danger of nearby orchards, and the cost-value factor in relation to the entire scab-control program.

Spray warnings. By examining, in the spring, the fallen leaves on which the scab organism has overwintered, it is possible to determine the most effective time for spraying, and the results are broadcast to growers in the form of spray warnings.

Combined-purpose sprays. Scab is rarely if ever the only reason for an apple spray program. Other apple diseases, such as blotch, bitter rot, and black rot, and insect pests as the San José and other

scales, the curculio, codling worm, canker worms, aphids, and leafhoppers, call for regular control each year by spraying with fungicides, arsenicals, contact insecticides, or oil sprays.   In this regard
each locality, each orchard, and each season presents its own particular problems to be solved by the grower with the help of agricultural advisors, making use of compatible spray mixtures designed
to accomplish the most in yield improvement at the least expense.

   Hazards of spraying.   Spraying and dusting are accompanied by
certain dangers, such as injury to the tree, poisoning of fruit, injury
to the soil, and poisoning of beneficial insects.   These will be considered later.

   2. *Supplementary control practices.*   Although spraying is the major
factor in scab control it is not the only one to consider.   Spraying
will be least risky and most effective if it is combined with other
precautionary measures, such as diminishing the source of inoculum
by disking under or burning fallen leaves, good pruning to produce
a well-aerated tree, and, other things being equal, showing a
preference for the less susceptible apple varieties.

APPLE BLACK ROT (*Physalospora obtusa = Sphaeropsis malorum*).
   Black rot is another of the leading apple diseases east of the
Rocky Mountains.   It attacks leaves, twigs, and fruits.   On the
leaves, where the disease is sometimes called frog-eye leaf spot,
the mature lesions have a concentric ringed appearance.   On the
twigs ("New York apple tree canker") the canker either takes the
form of a considerable expanse of roughened bark, or the wood will
be killed, the bark cracked, and the limb girdled.   The fruit rot is
primarily one of mature fruit, a rounded, very dark, often zonate
lesion that extends into the flesh producing a dark decay, that
eventually consumes the entire fruit, converting it into a shriveled,
black, shiny mummy (Fig. 44).   Black, dome-like fungus fruiting
bodies (pycnidia) are found on stem and fruit lesions (Fig. 44).
The black rot fungus makes little use of the ascosporic stage in its
life history, although perithecia with ascospores are regularly found
in the wood cankers.   It normally overwinters as a saprophyte in
the form of mycelium or as conidia in the mummified fallen fruit
and in cankers.   Dead trees and limbs killed by fire blight or other
causes are particularly dangerous sources of spring infection.   In

the spring the conidia are released from their flask-like pycnidia in tiny tendrils.   They are borne to infection courts by wind, splashing rains, or insects, and finding an injury, such as a mechanical bruise

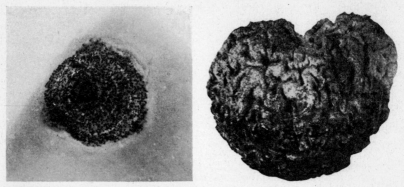

Figure 44.   Black rot of apple.   Left, black rot lesion on fruit, enlarged to show the individual pycnidia; right, mummified apple, the overwintering stage of the black rot fungus.

Figure 45.   Apple fruit showing lesions of bitter rot with rings of fruiting pustules (acervuli).   This is another of the common apple diseases, controllable by spraying. (*Photo by Bureau of Plant Industry, U. S. Dept. of Agriculture.*)

or insect wound, the germ tubes penetrate and begin a series of infection cycles.   The fungus cannot infect uninjured tissues. Control of black rot involves late-season spraying with Bordeaux mixture, avoidance of bruising in handling fruit, storage between

31° and 34°F., pruning or tree surgery to remove the cankers, and orchard sanitation, disposing of mummies by plowing under or burning, and burning of pruned wood.

APPLE BLISTER CANKER (*Nummularia discreta*).

In Kansas, Missouri, Oklahoma, and Nebraska millions of apple trees have been killed by blister canker, which is also a major apple tree disease in the corn belt and east to New York and Virginia. The disease attacks only the wood, affecting both large and small limbs. In later stages the cankers are easily recognized as dead areas, mottled with living wood, 3 feet or less in length, shedding the bark, and exposing numerous round, nailhead-like fungous cushions (stromata), giving the wood a blistered appearance (Fig. 46). The causal fungus, *Nummularia discreta* is an ascomycetous wound parasite, entering through branch stubs or bark injuries, destroying the wood, and producing honey-colored conidia and later ascospores from flask-shaped perithecia imbedded in the stromata. Both conidia and ascospores appear to be involved in dissemination of the disease. Control depends almost entirely on the early detection, pruning out, and burning of cankered wood.

Figure 46.   Blister canker on apple branch.

GRAPE BLACK ROT (*Guignardia bidwellii*).

Black rot is the most important disease of grapes east of the Rocky Mountains, causing regular losses that at times involve 30 per cent or more of grape crops in individual states. It involves all green parts of the vine. On the leaves, it produces reddish-brown dead spots sprinkled with tiny fungus fruiting bodies (pycnidia). When fruits are about half grown the disease appears as a pale spot, soon turning brown, involving the entire berry, which shrivels, becoming a black, dry mummy that will shatter off or remain in the cluster.   Half to all of the grapes in a cluster will be so affected.

Guignardia bidwellii is an ascomycete, reproducing by ovoid conidia and threadlike microconidia formed within flask-shaped pycnidia on the leaves and mummies in summer and fall and in the following spring, and by ascospores produced from stromata on the mummies that in the spring become converted into spore-bearing perithecia.   Control by spraying with Bordeaux mixture, 5–5–50, at the blooming period and sometimes thereafter, is required in nearly every vineyard.   In addition the mummies should be destroyed at picking time, or at least plowed under in the spring.   A number of grape varieties are quite highly resistant to black rot.

Figure 47.   Black knot of plum.

BLACK KNOT OF PLUMS AND CHERRIES (*Dibotryon morbosa*).

Black knot is a native disease of plum and cherry twigs occurring wherever these crops are grown in America, and sometimes producing disastrous losses.   It is easily recognized as black, rough, cylindrical, or spindle-shaped enlargements of the twigs usually 2 to 4 times the thickness of the normal twig and several inches long (Fig. 47).   The twigs commonly die back to the knots.   In the summer the knots become velvety with a layer of conidia, and later turn black and are covered with innumerable flask-like perithecia that liberate ascospores in the spring. Both types of spores are involved in spread of the disease. Control depends mainly on pruning out of the knots 3 to 4 inches below the swelling, best done in winter or very early spring when the knots are most obvious and before ascospores are liberated. Wild affected plums near the

Figure 48. Elm leaf spot. A severe attack on young shoots of Chinese elm, showing the appearance of the leaf lesions and killing back of the growing shoot.

orchard should also be pruned or eradicated. It is held that Bordeaux applications in the spring are a minor aid in black knot control, and in Canada a dormant spray of lime-sulphur or Bordeaux-oil emulsion is advised.

ELM LEAF SPOT (*Gnomonia ulmea*).

Our commonest leaf disease of American and some of the Asiatic elms is the black leaf-spot caused by the ascomycete, *Gnomonia ulmea*. The spots are in the form of black raised fungus masses, partly covered or surrounded by white epidermis (Fig. 48).   They may be very numerous on the leaves, in which case early defoliation results.   Also in severe cases the twig terminals may be attacked and killed producing a condition resembling fire blight of apple and pear.   Conidia are produced on the lesions during the summer, and ascospores in perithecia are formed on the fallen, dead leaves in the spring.   Few data on control are available.   Control is only

required during very wet seasons. It is suggested that the fallen leaves be raked up and burned and that the tree be protected with applications of Bordeaux mixture at the time the leaves are unfolding and again when they are fully expanded.   A stomach insecticide for chewing insects is often desired in the same spray, reducing the cost factor for leaf-spot alone.

SYCAMORE ANTHRACNOSE
(*Gnomonia veneta* = *Gloeosporium nervisequum*).

This disease is universally present on the sycamore and also occurs on oak.   It is the most common and destructive disease of the sycamore.   The causal fungus, an ascomycete, *Gnomonia veneta*, which is closely related to the elm leaf-

Figure 49. Sycamore anthracnose, showing blighting of leaves and twigs.

spot organism, attacks leaves causing extensive dead blotches, finally involving the entire leaf, and easily confused with drought or frost injury (Fig. 49).   In moist seasons all the terminal shoots of large trees may be blighted and killed back.   Cream-colored masses of conidia are exuded along the veins during wet weather.   Cankers are also formed on the smaller branches and twigs, often killing back the branchlets.   These also bear conspicuous pimple-like spore masses in moist weather.   Perithecia, containing ascospores, are produced in the spring on overwintered infected leaves.   The spring infections arise either from conidia emerging from infected twigs, or from ascospores. These initiate numerous secondary cycles of infection under damp conditions.

The disease can be controlled by a dormant application of lime-sulphur (1–9), followed by thorough applications of Bordeaux mixture (4–4–50 or 5–5–50) beginning just after the buds burst and before the first leaves are half grown, coupled with burning of fallen leaves, and pruning of dead twigs, insofar as this is practicable. Sycamores suffer severely only during occasional years, and even when badly blighted they will usually replace the damaged leaves with new foliage as soon as the period of excessive rains is past. For this reason annual spraying is not ordinarily recommended except for unusually valuable trees, or in cases where the combined value of spraying with a fungicide-insecticide mixture justifies the cost of the applications.

IRIS LEAF SPOT (*Didymellina macrospora* = *Heterosporium gracile*).

This is the most common disease of varieties of the German iris group, rivalled in importance only by the bacterial rhizome rot of iris. It devitalizes the plants and impairs their appearance. The disease occurs on the leaves, especially the upper portions. The spots at first are minute, brown, with watersoaked margins, later slowly enlarging, becoming yellow, then brown and dry (Fig. 50). The leaves die prematurely, and in severe cases the entire plant is killed. Iris leaf spot is due to an ascomycete, *Didymellina macrospora*, that forms dark tufts of conidiophores and conidia on the surfaces of the lesions during

Figure 50. Iris leaf spot, showing an early stage in the development of the necrotic spots with pale halos. In later stages the leaf dies back from the tip. (*Courtesy of P. P. Pirone, N. J. Agr. Exp. Sta.*)

the summer, and perithecia containing ascospores in overwintered leaves. The conidia are the means of rapid summer spread. The ascospores are responsible for primary infections in the spring. A practical control is usually obtained by gathering and burning the diseased leaves in the fall.   Good results also follow applications of Bordeaux mixture 4–4–50 or flotation sulphur 4–50 with a good spreader and sticker.   A long list of iris varieties classified according to susceptibility is given in the Florists Review, 80 (2072): 24–25, 1937.

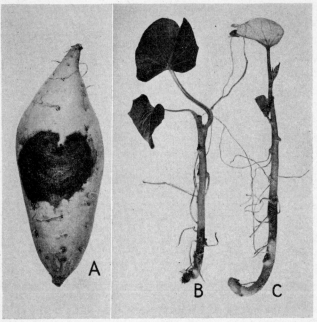

Figure 51.   Black rot of sweet potato.   A, a potato from the field at digging time, showing the slightly sunken spot with a somewhat circular outline, characteristic of the disease.   B and C, two sweet potato plants pulled from a commercial seed bed, B showing that infection had taken place from the growth of the parasite from the potato to the stem, C from soil at a point some distance from the potato.   (*Photo by the Bureau of Plant Industry, U. S. Dept. of Agriculture.*)

SWEET POTATO BLACK ROT (*Ceratostomella fimbriata*).

Black rot causes greater sweet potato losses than any other sweet potato disease with the possible exception of stem-rot or wilt, and is coextensive with the crop.   Although most destructive in storage, it is also a seedbed and field disease.   On the potatoes it appears as rounded, blackish spots extending into the vascular ring or sometimes deeper.   If such roots are bedded the sprouts are often sickly, with black cankers below ground, or killed entirely (Fig. 51).

When affected sprouts are set in the field there is more or less root decay although the plants may survive and produce a fair to good yield.   Three types of spores are produced freely on infected tissues, rod-like hyaline conidia, thick-walled, ovoid, brown conidia, and ascospores, the latter borne in perithecia with extremely long necks. All are instrumental in spread both in the field and in storage, while the brown conidia appear most resistant.   Control of black rot requires selection for propagation, preferably in the field, of sound roots from healthy vines, disinfestation of the roots in corrosive sublimate (1 oz. to 8 gal. water) or organic mercury compounds (e.g. Semesan Bel) before bedding, use of new or sterilized soil in the hotbed, and a 3 or 4 year rotation of sweet potatoes with any other crops.   There are no sweet potato varieties highly resistant to black rot.

DUTCH ELM DISEASE (*Ceratostomella ulmi* = *Graphium ulmi*).

The Dutch elm disease was first observed in northern Europe in 1918, and by 1921 had become epiphytotic and disastrous to European elms.   It was brought to America on elm wood from Europe, and found in 1930 in Ohio, where it was eradicated, but it reappeared in New Jersey and nearby states in 1933, since when it has destroyed many thousands of trees in that area.   The causal fungus, *Ceratostomella ulmi*, is a wound parasite that invades the water conducting tissues producing prompt or delayed wilting and death of trees of all ages (Fig. 52).   Wood of affected trunks and branches shows a dark xylem ring (Fig. 53), although other diseases have a similar symptom and culturing is necessary for diagnosis.   Conidia are produced in sheaf-like fascicles (coremia) especially in insect tunnels, and the spores often bud in the fashion of yeasts.   Although rare or absent in nature, an ascosporic stage has been produced experimentally by crossing + and − strains of the fungus on sterilized elm twigs.   The perithecia are long necked as in the sweet potato *Ceratostomella*.   The fungus is transmitted principally by bark beetles (*Scolytus* species).

Control is largely a problem of quarantine and eradication. This has been done on a very extensive scale by the Federal Department of Agriculture, making use largely of W.P.A. labor, and at the present time the disease appears to be under control although much work remains.   The eradication program is hampered by a virus disease of elm trees that has recently appeared in the East.   This last disease owes its importance, in relation to the Dutch elm dis-

Figure 52.   An American elm dying from the Dutch elm disease and showing extreme wilting and partial defoliation.   Such trees are a menace to nearby healthy trees, and should be promptly felled and burned.   (*Photo by N. Y. Agricultural Extension Service.*)

ease, to the fact that it kills trees thus providing breeding places for the bark beetles that spread the Dutch elm disease. Prompt burning of affected wood is a necessary accompaniment of the program.   Miss Buisman, a Dutch pathologist, who has given us much of our present information on the disease, after breeding and selection of elms for a number of years, finally produced, just before her untimely death, a variety of elms, now named in her remembrance "Christine Buisman," which has withstood much natural and artificial exposure to the Dutch elm disease, and promises to be a solution to the problem whenever it is adapted.

CHESTNUT BLIGHT (*Endothia parasitica*).

Chestnut blight, an introduced disease from Asia, first found in New York in 1904, and epiphytotic from Massachusetts to Virginia by 1908, has in succeeding years practically eliminated this valuable tree from American forests. The causal fungus, an ascomycete, *Endothia parasitica*, is a wound parasite that produces large, sunken cankers on branches and limbs, killing both individual limbs and ultimately the entire tree.

Figure 53. Cross section of an elm branch affected with the Dutch elm disease, showing brownish discolorations in the sapwood. (*Photo by Dept. of Plant Pathology, N. Y. Agr. Exp. Sta.*)

The fungus fruits early and abundantly in crevices of the broken bark over the cankers, first producing conidia which exude in tendrils from numerous reddish pycnidia, and later ascospores from perithecia imbedded in orange masses of fungus tissue (stromata). The ascospores are readily spread by wind, their main agency of dissemination, while the sticky conidia are carried largely by insects and birds. Tawny fans of mycelium are seen under the affected bark. Insect injuries commonly serve as infection courts. After the tree is killed the fungus continues for about one year as a saprophyte, still sporulating. Although many control measures were tried, all failed, and the disease has run its course until the host species has been practically wiped out. It gives us a tragic lesson in the effect of an introduced pest on a susceptible native crop.

ERGOT OF GRAINS AND GRASSES (*Claviceps purpurea*).

History and distribution. Since the time of the Caesars, long before its recognition as a fungous disease, ergot has been known as the cause of human pestilence, the "holy fire" of the Middle Ages.

As the disease is most prevalent in rye, the universal bread grain of Europe, we read in European literature of many epidemics of human suffering and terrible death from the gangrenous poisoning produced by mixtures of the ergot sclerotia in bread grain. It was not until 1842 that Léveillé in France first discovered that the black ergot horns are the product of fungous disease, and a few years later the scientific farmer Julius Kühn completed the story of the life history of the ergot fungus.

Ergot occurs in most places where its hosts, numerous grains and grasses, are found, although it is rare in the southeastern United States. It is prevalent in every continent, throughout Europe, and in nearly all parts of the United States. It is particularly abundant in Siberia, the main source of the supply for the drug trade.

Importance. Ergot is primarily important on rye and certain pasture grasses because it lowers the yield, impairs the crop for seed purposes, and produces poisoning of man or animals eating infected crops or their products. Although yield decreases from ergot are relatively unimportant as a rule, losses as high as 20 per cent have been suffered in Russia. The annual losses for the United States in rye range between 50,000 and 350,000 bushels, mainly in the Lake States area. In the 1938 crop, for example, 382 carloads of rye were found to be ergoty, all but 22 of which were marketed at Minneapolis and Duluth. In grasses the yield may be affected to a serious extent, as in instances in Ireland and the United States where hay has been found to contain one eighth of its weight of ergot.

Ergot poisoning of humans is relatively rare today except in the more backward sections of rye-eating countries. The loss to livestock is considerable but difficult to estimate. There are frequent reports of ergotism in small numbers of cattle, horses, and sheep, and occasionally serious local losses, largely due to feeding ergoty hay, as the feeding habits of animals would normally lead them to avoid ergot in the pasture.

In discussing the importance of the disease, mention should be made of the drug prepared from ergot which is an important constrictor of smooth muscle, indicated in cases of excessive bleeding and to aid childbirth.

Host plants.   There are about 20 species of _Claviceps_ affecting various _Gramineae_, but ergot, in ordinary understanding, refers to _Claviceps purpurea_.   This common species attacks over 100 species of grains and grasses and a few of the sedges.   Of its cultivated hosts, rye is more commonly attacked than wheat, oats, and barley, although occasionally wheat, especially that designed for macaroni, may be appreciably injured.   Among the pasture grasses in the Great Plains, western wheat grass (_Agropyron Smithii_), quackgrass

A   B   C

Figure 54.   Ergot.   B, in rye; A and C, in pasture grasses, (A) Canada wild rye (_Elymus canadensis_) and (C) western wheat grass (_Agropyron Smithii_).

(_A. repens_) and wild rye (_Elymus canadensis_ and _E. Virginicus_) are commonly affected.   The fungus _Claviceps purpurea_ consists of a number of physiologic races, specialized to attack particular hosts and not others.

Symptoms and signs.   The disease is recognized primarily by black, hard, banana- or horn-shaped sclerotia which protrude from the head in the place of normal grains (Fig. 54).   They usually occur here and there in individual spikelets of the head.   Earlier in the development of the head, before the sclerotia appear, a careful examination will reveal a sticky secretion oozing out from between the glumes, the "honey-dew." In harvested rye grain the sclerotia are easily recognized as a contamination and important grading factor.

Etiology. The sclerotia of the ascomycete, *Claviceps purpurea*, are compact masses of fungus tissue that serve as resting or over-wintering bodies. In harvesting grain or in nature these fall to the

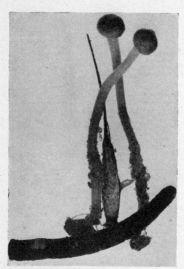

ground, where they overwinter, or they are introduced into a field by planting contaminated seed. In the spring they germinate, producing a globular, purplish stroma, at the tip of a long, often twisted stalk that may grow up through the soil for an inch or more. This stroma has the outward appearance of a golf ball, the irregularities representing mouths of many flask-like perithecia that are buried in the stroma (Fig. 55). The perithecia contain numbers of long asci, each in turn containing 8 thread-like ascospores (Fig. 56). The ascospores are wind-borne to the host heads at the time of blossoming. On coming to rest on a stigma, the ascospore germinates, sending out an infection hypha which grows down the style and into the ovary much in the fashion of a pollen tube.

Figure 55. Germinated ergot sclerotium, enlarged. The golf-ball-like stromata are mature, ready to eject the ascospores that initiate spring infections.

The embryo is attacked and practically destroyed, being replaced by yellowish-white mycelium. With further development of the fungus there appears on the blossom the shiny, sweetish honey dew, which is cloudy from containing multitudes of conidia that have been produced by the mycelium (Fig. 56). The fluid attracts insects, which visit the heads and carry the conidia from diseased florets to healthy ones where the spores initiate new secondary infections and thus spread the disease. Later on the buried fungus mass grows larger, hard, and dark, and finally protrudes from the mature head as a sclerotium, the only form in which the fungus can overwinter.   The sclerotium will germinate only after a period of cold, and can survive 2 years or longer in storage before germinating.

Epiphytology.   Ergot infestation varies considerably from one year or locality to another, being very dependent on environmental conditions.   Germination of the sclerotia and infection by the spores are believed to be favored by seasons with abundant spring moisture and by damp, low locations.   Since infection takes place

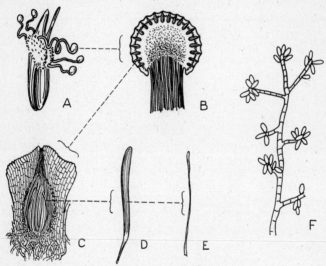

Figure 56.   Reproductive structures of the ergot fungus.   A, germinating sclerotium with 5 perithecial stromata; B, single stroma, enlarged section showing many perithecia; C, single perithecium containing many asci; D, single ascus with 8 ascospores; E, single ascospore such as initiate primary infections; F, conidia which are produced with honey dew in grain or grass blossoms and serve for secondary spread of the fungus.   (*B-F after Tulasne and Gäumann.*)

at blooming time, any factors, such as decreased sunshine, that lengthen the period in which the flowers are open, will have a tendency to increase the amount of infection.   Irregular depth of seeding, such as results from broadcast planting and the use of mixed grains for seed, has a similar effect in lengthening the period during which open flowers are present in the field.

Ergotism.   Ergot poisoning or ergotism is caused by the powerful alkaloid, ergotoxin or ergotinin, which is contained with other poisons in the ergot sclerotia.   This drug in small amounts produces a weakening of livestock without further symptoms.   When larger amounts are consumed, gangrenous ergotism results, in which the blood supply to the extremities is insufficient.   The consequence is a sloughing off of horns, hooves, teeth, ears, and hair, and ultimately a painless dry decay of the feet.   The animal may become emaciated and die from the direct effects of ergot poisoning, or on the range it may more commonly die of thirst or starvation, being unable to move about.   Other symptoms sometimes occur, such as blindness, convulsions, paralysis, and internal disorders.   Poultry are also affected.

Control.   It is important that rye and grass seed be free of ergot sclerotia, as the disease is usually introduced in a planted crop through contaminated seed.   If ergoty seed must be used, the ergot sclerotia can be partially removed from the seed by fanning or screening, and completely by covering the seed with a 20 per cent solution of common salt (40 lb. of salt in 25 gal. of water) or a 32 per cent solution of potassium chloride.   In such a solution the seed sink and the sclerotia float to the top, where they may be skimmed or poured off.   The seed are then washed in water and dried.   Rye should not be planted until the third year in a field in which the preceding crop was ergoty, and efforts should be made to destroy ergoty grasses in furrows and fence rows.

In native pastures ergot can be controlled by cultural or cropping practices, such as burning over the patches of affected grass, by harvesting the grass for hay before the sclerotia form, or by close grazing to accomplish the same purpose.   In cases of heavy infestation the grower might consider the possibility of harvesting the sclerotia for drug manufacture.

POWDERY MILDEW OF CEREALS (*Erysiphe graminis*).

History and distribution.   The powdery mildew of cereals and grasses has been known as a disease since early historical times and as a subject for investigation since 1815.   It apparently occurs wherever cereals are grown, particularly in the north and south temperate zones, and in the United States it has attracted attention especially in fall-sown barley in the southern and eastern Mississippi Valley States and on the Pacific coast.

Importance.   Because of its common occurrence and the infrequency of its epiphytotic development, powdery mildew is often regarded as a benign and harmless disease. Yet, according to Melhus and Kent, "it may produce a great deal of damage when favorable environmental conditions allow widespread infections early in the season." Whetzel also holds that its annual widespread occurrence suggests that it is probably far more important as a factor in reducing the yields of wheat, oats, barley, and rye than plant pathologists or growers generally appreciate. The injury takes the form of yellowing and premature killing of the lower leaves which in turn retards the development of the plant and interferes with the filling of the grain, or in severe cases even prevents heading.

Host plants. More than 50 species of *Gramineae* are attacked by *Erysiphe graminis*, including barley, wheat, oats, rye, and many wild and cultivated grasses. The pathogen exhibits physiologic specialization, with seven varieties each adapted to certain hosts. The principal varieties on barley, wheat, oats, and rye are *E. graminis* varieties *hordei*, *tritici*, *avenae*, and *secalis* respectively. Not all varieties of the cultivated grains are equally susceptible. The more resistant varieties recorded include:

Barley: Arlington Awnless, Chilean, Duplex, Kwan, Bolivia, and Consul.

Winter Wheat: Fulcaster, Fultz, Fultzo-Mediterranean, Hardired, Hungarian, Hussar-Hohenheimer, Illinois No. 2, Mediterranean, Mediterranean-Hope, Michigan Amber selections, Penquite, Redhart, Chiefkan, Hope-Hussar, Hussar, Kharkov, Relief-Ridit, Turkey selection, and Wisconsin Pedigree No. 2.

Rye: Abruzzes selection (also stem-rust and leaf-rust resistant).

Symptoms and signs. Powdery mildew is recognized by white, mealy or fluffy, somewhat circular mycelial coatings, largely on the leaves, sometimes so numerous as practically to cover the leaf (Fig. 57). Later the mycelium becomes brownish and is sometimes studded with tiny brown fruiting bodies, the perithecia. The mealy appearance is due to myriads of conidia over the surface of the mycelium. The fungus does not penetrate deeply, so that the tissue under the lesions is green until advanced stages when the entire leaf becomes yellow and may die. The plants are likely to be stunted, with light grain or even blasting or lack of heading.

Etiology. The fungus, *Erysiphe graminis*, an ascomycete, is an obligate parasite. The perithecia, formed late in the season, constitute the principal overwintering stage, although in mild climates where the hosts are in the vegetative stage throughout the winter, the fungus may pass the winter in the parasitic, conidial stage. The perithecia overwinter in decaying host tissues. In the spring ascospores develop in 8 to 10 asci within each perithecium. There is no opening to the perithecium, and this particular form of perithecium is often termed a cleistothecium (see Fig. 8). Under pressure of the developing asci it bursts, liberating the ascospores by forcible dis-

Figure 57. Powdery mildew of wheat.

charge. These may be wind-borne to new host leaves and there infect. The ascospore germinates forming an infection hypha which, coming into contact with the epidermis, flattens out to form a sucker-like disc (appressorium) attaching the hypha to the epidermis. From the center of the appressorium a fine peg forces its way through the cuticle, then expands to form finger-like feeding organs (haustoria) within the epidermal cells. By progressive growth and branching, more and more epidermal cells are involved but the fungus does not penetrate deeper into the leaf tissues. After a period of feeding, and development of surface mycelium, erect hyphae (conidiophores) are extended upward from the mycelium, each bearing a chain of thin-walled, barrel-shaped conidia. As the terminal conidia mature and blow away, new ones are formed at the base of the chain. The conidia, produced in great numbers, initiate the secondary cycles and thus spread the disease. With the advance of the season, sexual union occurs between specialized cells of the mycelium, and as a consequence the globose, hard, thick-walled, dark perithecia appear. The perithecia are ornamented with characteristically formed appendages, and the various genera of powdery mildews are separated by the character of the appendages and the presence of one or of more than one ascus per perithecium.

The injury to the host tissues is due to exclusion of light, excessive loss of water from infected leaves, and the presence of a toxin, liberated by the fungus, that passes through the leaf tissues, yellowing and killing the cells.

Epiphytology. While the conidia of *Erysiphe graminis* do not require a film of water for germination, they germinate best in a moist atmosphere (above 95 per cent). This is the main limiting factor to the development of the disease in dry locations. As with the rusts, this obligate parasite is most destructive on vigorous and succulent plants. Temperature is a factor principally as it increases or decreases the vigor of the host, rather than through its direct effects on the parasite. Abundant nitrogen fertilization favors powdery mildew; potassium and phosphorus decrease it. Light is essential to infection, evidently because the fungus can only infect those tissues in which photosynthesis is active. Summarizing, the disease is most severe under moist conditions and those favoring a vigorous, luxuriant growth of the host. As these conditions are not realized regularly from year to year and from one location to another, the disease tends to appear in destructive epiphytotics on some occasions, while at other times it is inconsequential.

Control. As indicated above, there are numerous varieties of the small grains that exhibit resistance to all or most of the strains of powdery mildew. In areas of infestation, these resistant varieties, or the newer varieties constantly being produced from mildew-resistant breeding stocks, offer the best means of control. In grain breeding programs, powdery mildew resistance is being considered, along with other characters, for incorporation into newer synthetic varieties.

Powdery mildew may also be effectively controlled on susceptible crops by applications of sulphur dust.   In normal field culture, this would not ordinarily be practicable, but dusting has its use in protecting valuable seed plots or show grain.   Sulphur dust is also effective against other small grain diseases, such as the rusts, and since the rusts and powdery mildew develop under similar conditions, the combination of rust and mildew might at times warrant airplane applications of sulphur, now available at reasonable cost. If leaf-chewing insects are a factor, an arsenical could be economically applied with the sulphur.

Figure 58.   Powdery mildew of cucumber, a common problem in cucumbers under glass, controlled by sulphur dusting.

POWDERY MILDEW OF LEGUMES (*Erysiphe polygoni*).

This powdery mildew is best known on legumes: clover, peas, beans, alfalfa, and others, although it is capable of attacking some 200 species of 90 genera of plants of diverse botanical relationships. It consists of several physiologic races, there being three on red clover alone.   Ordinarily a rather benign trouble, powdery mildew occasionally breaks out on legumes in serious amount, as in the epiphytotic on clover of 1922 which involved the entire eastern two thirds of the United States, and was looked upon as the most note-worthy plant disease outbreak of the year.   In pea growing sections of the Pacific Coast and occasionally in other states, control meas-ures are required every year in order to produce a crop.   With the recent increased use of field legumes for soil conservation in the Great Plains, powdery mildew is frequently found doing consider-able injury to these.

The general features of the disease are much like those of the grain mildew, with the exception that perithecia are sometimes lacking. Likewise the control measures are similar: use of the more resistant varieties, and sulphur dusting, using several applications of fine (325 mesh) dusting sulphur during the growing season.   Crop rotation with non-legumes, and plowing soon after harvest are also recommended.

POWDERY MILDEW OF ROSES
(*Sphaerotheca humuli* and *S. pannosa*).

On some of the ornamentals, powdery mildews may be extremely destructive diseases because of their virulence, and because even light mildew attacks may ruin the orna-mental value of the hosts.   This is

Figure 59.   Powdery mildew of roses; powdery mildews of other hosts are very similar in appearance. (*Courtesy of P. P. Pirone, N. J. Agr. Exp. Sta.*)

particularly true of the powdery mildews of zinnias, phlox, and roses, for example.   The former are two killing diseases, the latter causes serious disfigurement, devitalization, and inhibition of blossoming.   All aerial parts of the rose are affected, especially new growth and bud clusters.   The familiar mealy, white mycelium covers affected parts, and leaves are often much wrinkled, somewhat discolored, distorted, and reduced in size (Fig. 59).   In general features, rose mildew resembles the powdery mildews discussed previously.   The fungus overwinters either by perithecia on fallen leaves, or as conidia, and constant successions of conidia under moist conditions in the spring produce the heavy infestations so commonly seen.   Highly nitrogenous soil, such as often accompanies rose culture, promotes the succulent, vigorous type of growth most favorable to the disease.   Satisfactory control is obtained by periodic use of a fungicide.   Sulphur dust is usually recommended, but Bordeaux mixture, and sulphur or copper oxide sprays are also effective.   Green-colored sulphurs are available to avoid disfiguring the plants.   In greenhouses, sulphur paste is daubed on the steam pipes.   Roses vary in susceptibility to mildew, but desirable susceptible varieties need not be rejected in view of the ease of chemical control.

BROWN ROT OF STONE FRUITS (*Sclerotinia fructicola**).

History and distribution.   Brown rot has been known as the most generally destructive disease of peach, plum, cherry, and related stone fruits in America.   It occurs wherever these fruits are grown in the United States and Canada, and is also a problem in Australia, Tasmania, New Zealand, and possibly South America. A very similar disease, often confused with this, but caused by a distinct species of *Sclerotinia*, is common in Europe and also occurs in the Pacific States and British Columbia.   Brown rot has been troublesome in the United States for at least 150 years.   It was first studied scientifically in 1881 by the mycologist Peck.   The sexual overwintering stage was determined in 1909.   Control by the use of self-boiled lime sulphur was discovered in 1908–1910, and recent studies have been largely concerned with the etiology of the disease and its control by improved spraying practices, sanitation, and the use of varietal resistance.

Importance.   Brown rot is most destructive in the more humid areas although not limited to these.   The average annual loss in the peach crop exceeds $5,000,000 and the loss in Georgia alone has reached $2,000,000, or 40 per cent of the crop, in some years.   At times the losses for individual states are nearly 100 per cent, as in Alabama in 1897, while state losses of one-third to two-thirds of the crop have not been uncommon.   In addition to losses in the

---

* More properly known as *Monilinia fructicola*, but the name *Sclerotinia* has been almost universally used in literature up to the present.

orchard, many carloads of stone fruits in transit show considerable brown rot, sometimes reaching 90 per cent, and similar destruction is encountered in markets.

The losses from brown rot are of several types. The disease affects the blossoms causing barrenness, from which point it may work down into the twigs, killing them, and it occasionally causes large leaf spot lesions. It may affect the green fruits, but the principal damage is on the ripe fruits, which are very quickly rotted, either in the orchard or in storage or transit.

Host plants. The most important hosts of the brown rot fungus are the stone fruits, peaches, plums, cherries, apricots, almonds, and nectarines. Many wild species of *Prunus* are affected and the disease is sometimes found, although not usually serious, on other plants in the *Rosaceae* such as quince, apple, pear, rose, and blackberry.

Considerable variability in attack has been observed among commercial varieties of stone fruits. The reason why a number of the newer varieties have replaced older ones is their lower damage from brown rot as observed by growers. In general it may be said that the early and light-colored peaches, the Japanese, light-colored, and thin-skinned plums, and the sweet and white cherries are most severely attacked. The greater freedom from attack of other varieties is probably not due so much to inherent resistance as to their growth habits that permit them to escape rather than resist the disease, e.g. by maturing when weather conditions are unfavorable for brown rot infection.

Symptoms and signs. *In blossoms*, the disease causes cessation of growth, reduction of size, wilting, pallor of the calyx, and killing of the petals, all of this inhibiting fruit development.

In twigs, the fungus grows from the blossom or fruit pedicel into young twigs, killing them back much as in fire-blight of apple and pear. This phase is rarely found.

In leaves, the entire leaf may wither as a result of twig infection, or it may rarely show large, circular, dead spots that drop out.

In limbs, cankers may result as the fungus passes down the twigs into the larger wood. The bark is killed, cracks open, and exudes gum. This may be followed by callusing only to enlarge the following years, so that ultimately large limbs may be girdled and killed.

In fruit we have the most familiar symptoms (Fig. 60).   Fruits can be attacked at any time after they are half grown but usually infections are noticed after ripening.   Lesions first appear as small, round, well defined, light brown spots which enlarge so rapidly that within a few days the entire fruit is rotted.   Beneath the lesion the decayed flesh is soft, and dark brown.   The surface of the lesion is covered with fruiting tufts (sporodochia) of the fungus, consisting of numerous conidiophores bearing chains of conidia (*Monilia* stage).   These tufts are often arranged in concentric rings, marking

Figure 60.   Brown rot of peach, showing masses of spores (conidia).   *(Photo by Bureau of Plant Industry, U. S. Dept. of Agriculture.)*

diurnal fluctuations in environment.   On plums the lesions are sometimes difficult to detect in early stages because of the dark colored and thick skin.   After fully decaying, the fruit shrivels and becomes a dry, hard, wrinkled mummy, hanging on the tree or falling to the ground.

Etiology.   The ascomycete, *Sclerotinia fructicola*, overwinters as mummies, which in reality are sclerotial masses, and to a less extent in limb cankers.   The primary infections in the spring, which usually occur on the blossoms, are due either to conidia from the limb cankers or mummies hanging on the trees, or to ascospores that are formed in cup-shaped apothecia.   The latter, borne on stalks, are produced by the germination of mummies partly buried in the soil (Fig. 61). Lining the inner surface of the apothecium are many asci, that shoot out clouds of ascospores in visible puffs, which then may be wind borne to infection courts, the stigmas of blossoms. Here the germ tube of the germinating spore, making use of the nectar in the blossom as foodstuff, penetrates and infects the floral parts. Soon conidia are formed over these from the feeding mycelium, and these begin a series of secondary cycles. Meanwhile the mycelium advances into the twigs producing twig blight. As the fruits mature conidia are wind-borne to them, infecting usually

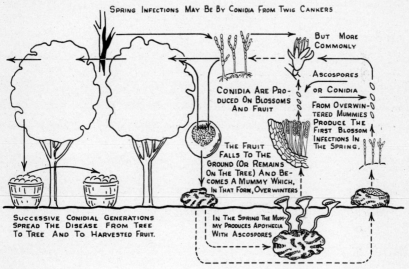

SPRING INFECTIONS MAY BE BY CONIDIA FROM TWIG CANKERS

BUT MORE COMMONLY

ASCOSPORES OR CONIDIA FROM OVERWIN-TERED MUMMIES PRODUCE THE FIRST BLOSSOM INFECTIONS IN THE SPRING.

CONIDIA ARE PRO-DUCED ON BLOSSOMS AND FRUIT

THE FRUIT FALLS TO THE GROUND (OR REMAINS ON THE TREE) AND BE-COMES A MUMMY WHICH, IN THAT FORM, OVER WINTERS

SUCCESSIVE CONIDIAL GENERATIONS SPREAD THE DISEASE FROM TREE TO TREE AND TO HARVESTED FRUIT.

IN THE SPRING THE MUM-MY PRODUCES APOTHECIA WITH ASCOSPORES

Figure 61. The life cycle of brown rot of stone fruits. (*Section of apothecium after Norton et al.*)

through wounds, especially the punctures made by the curculio and oriental fruit moth. Ninety per cent of fruit lesions develop about such wounds. As the fungus sporulates on the fruits countless new conidia are formed, available for secondary cycles in the orchard and in storage. In the act of decay the advancing mycelium gives off a toxin that kills the cells in advance, liberating food materials for its use. The rotted fruit continues to produce conidia until it dries, shrinks, and becomes a mummy, in which the sexual processes preceding apothecia-formation take place.

Epiphytology. *Sclerotinia fructicola* is active at temperatures from 32°F. to 90°F. with a pathogenic optimum at about 75°F.

This temperature relation would rarely limit its activity. Moisture at infection periods is the most important single factor predisposing toward epiphytotics, spring rains promoting apothecial development, conidial spread, and spore germination. The spores will germinate only in a film of water. Low lying orchards suffer most because of slow drying after rains. Well-pruned, open trees suffer less for a corresponding reason. Wounds, caused by other diseases, hail, insects, and birds, play a large part in permitting infection. Apothecial production is most favored in acid soil. Altogether the fungus is capable of developing under a wide range of environments, provided adequate moisture is available, and local or periodic epiphytotics are largely correlated with spring precipitation.

Control. *Spraying or dusting* is the most important part of the control program for brown rot. There is some question of the value of spraying at blossoming time to prevent primary infections and blossom blight. As yet we lack sufficient information to warrant a definite recommendation for such early sprays. The standard fungicidal program for preventing fruit rot consists of 3 applications:

1. When calyces or "shucks" are shedding (about 10 days after petals fall) using as a *spray* lead arsenate, 1 lb. (or 2 lb. of the paste) + the milk of lime from 3 lb. of stone lime or 4 lb. of hydrated lime + water to make 50 gallons; or as a *dust*, (a) hydrated lime 95% + lead arsenate 5%, or (b) sulphur 80% + lead arsenate 5% + hydrated lime 15%.

2. Two weeks after the first application or 1 month after petal fall, using as a *spray* a mixture of a wettable sulphur + 1 lb. powdered lead arsenate or 2 lb. lead arsenate paste per 50 gallons, or as a *dust*, sulphur 80% + lead arsenate 5% + hydrated lime 15%.

3. One month before each variety is expected to ripen, using as a *spray* a suspension of wettable sulphur or as a *dust* sulphur 80% + hydrated lime 20%.

Considering the dependence of brown rot on insect injuries, the arsenical is an important, perhaps the most important feature of the earlier sprays.

Hazards of spraying and dusting. Stone fruits are particularly susceptible to spray injury, especially from arsenicals. The danger is lessened by adding 4 lb. of zinc sulphate per 50 gallons of spray containing arsenicals.   Zinc sulphate should never be used without adding an equal quantity of lime.   In any stone fruit spraying the directions should be carefully followed, excessive applications avoided, and the spray used as a fine mist, not a drench.

Arsenicals should not be used in applications within a month of fruit maturity, otherwise the fruit may carry enough arsenic to make it unfit for food according to the standards of the United States Pure Food and Drug Act.

Supplementary measures.   While spraying is most important in brown rot control, there is also value in sanitary measures, to remove sources of inoculum.   It may be impractical to attempt to remove the smaller twig infections, however the larger cankers can be cut out and burned, or surgically treated, and valueless, infected trees near the orchard can be removed.   More important is the removal of mummies.   These can be knocked from the tree at picking time.   Brown-rotted fruit should be culled out and destroyed, and the mummies on the orchard floor removed by raking or disking under, or eaten by hogs turned into the orchard for the purpose.   A disking in the spring just before the blossoms open is helpful in disturbing the mummies and thus markedly interfering with their ability to produce apothecia.   Brown rot storage and transit decay is minimized by selecting only sound fruit for the purpose, avoiding bruising in picking and packing, and maintaining the storage temperature as near to 32°F. as possible.

CHERRY LEAF SPOT (*Coccomyces hiemalis**).

The most frequent and destructive foliage disease of all common varieties of cherry is the leaf spot, sometimes known as shot-hole leaf spot or yellows.   The spots are circular, first purplish, later brown, then falling out to give the shot-hole effect (Fig. 62). Where the spots are numerous the leaves commonly turn yellow and fall by midsummer or earlier.   The fungus, *Coccomyces hiemalis*, overwinters as a saprophyte in fallen leaves.   In the spring it produces needle-like ascospores in sessile, disc-shaped perithecia. In moist weather, these produce the primary leaf infections, followed by the production of masses of summer spores (conidia) on the lesions, serving for secondary spread.   Control is aided by disk-

* More properly known as *Higginsia hiemalis*, but the name *Coccomyces* is more familiar in the literature on this disease.

ing under the fallen leaves before blooming, but the main control measure is the spray schedule, consisting of Bordeaux mixture (3–4–50) applied just at the end of petal fall, 2 to 3 weeks later, and just after harvest.   Lime-sulphur 1–40 is sometimes recommended, applied as for Bordeaux with an extra application 2 weeks after the second application.   Lead arsenate (1 lb. of powder or 2 lb. of paste per 50 gal.) may be added for insect control.

Figure 62. Cherry leaf spot showing various stages leading up to shotholing. (*Photo by Bureau of Plant Industry, U. S. Dept. of Agriculture.*)

ALFALFA LEAF SPOT (*Pseudopeziza medicaginis*).

One of the common leaf spot diseases of alfalfa is due to the ascomycete *Pseudopeziza medicaginis*. This can be distinguished from other alfalfa leaf diseases by the fact that the spots, although they may be numerous, are quite small (2 to 3 mm.), circular with irregular margins, black, and show, usually on the upper leaf surface in the center of the spot, a tiny round, raised disk, the apothecium. When young seedlings are attacked, they may be defoliated or entirely destroyed.   In older plants the leaves, especially the lower ones, are shed in the field or in harvesting, until the hay may consist largely of naked stems.

The only spores in the life cycle of *Pseudopeziza medicaginis* are the ascospores, produced in the apothecia on the leaf spots.   These serve both for primary infections and for secondary spread during the growing season.   The fungus overwinters either as mycelium or as apothecia in the dead leaves.   Infection is said to be relatively independent of weather but favored by cultural conditions that produce early shading of the ground.   Losses can be prevented by harvesting frequently, before leaf-shedding has become injurious.

Seed selection and seed treatment are of no value as the disease is not seed borne, and no resistant varieties of alfalfa, the only host, are known.

ANTHRACNOSE OF CANE FRUITS (*Elsinoë veneta* = *Plectodiscella veneta*).

Anthracnose or "gray-bark" is the commonest disease of raspberries, blackberries and related fruits. Canes of affected plants late in the season are light gray from the presence of numerous, small gray lesions, dotted over with black acervuli, or clusters of conidiophores and conidia (Fig. 63). In severe attacks the canes may crack open. The young lateral growth is attacked and often killed. On the leaves, the fungus causes tiny yellow lesions with raised brownish margins. When these are numerous the leaves may fall. Lesions similar to those on the canes also are found on petioles, peduncles, and pedicels, and rarely the fruit are

Figure 63. Anthracnose lesions on shoots of black raspberry. (*Courtesy of R. F. Suit, N. Y. Agr. Exp. Sta.*)

destroyed, becoming brown, dry, and woody. In the autumn primitive fruiting bodies are formed that mature ascospores, usually in the spring. These initiate the primary infections, while secondary spread occurs by means of the conidia during the earlier part of the growing season. Infections are favored by damp weather in the early part of the season, and losses are greatest when this is followed by unfavorable growing conditions the second year. Control depends on the use of a delayed dormant spray of lime sulphur (1–10) or Bordeaux mixture. Badly infected canes should be pruned out, and clean cultivation practiced.

BLACK SPOT OF ROSES (*Diplocarpon Rosae*).

The large, disfiguring lesions of black spot are familiar to every grower of roses, as the disease is almost universally present in rose culture (Fig. 64). The spots are up to ¼ inch or more in diameter, fringed in outline, and sprinkled with very tiny, inconspicuous fruiting bodies. In severe cases the leaves become yellow and fall, and even light attacks seriously impair the beauty and value of the plants. The fungus, *Diplocarpon Rosae* (= *Actinonema Rosae*) is an ascomycete, with non-sexual reproduction by means of conidia

formed in clusters (acervuli) on the new lesions, and with an ascospore stage developing on the fallen leaves in the spring after the fungus has hibernated in the leaves as a saprophytic mycelium. The disease develops most destructively under cool conditions (60°F. to 70°F.) when abundant moisture is available. Control out of doors is easily accomplished by occasional applications of a fungicide such as dusting sulphur (green colored if desired), Bordeaux mixture or its non-spotting substitutes, or red copper oxide spray, e.g. "Cuprocide." Fallen infected leaves should be raked and burned. In the greenhouse, a fungicide should be used and Selocide applied for red spider control instead of syringing with water for this purpose.

Figure 64. Black spot of roses. Two leaflets have fallen and the others are so disfigured that such plants would be worthless as ornamentals. (*Courtesy of P. P. Pirone, N. J. Agr. Exp. Sta.*)

PEACH LEAF CURL (*Taphrina deformans*).

History and distribution. Leaf curl is known as a serious disease wherever peaches are grown, and has been recognized as such since the earliest days of peach culture. In the United States it occurs in all important peach districts.

Importance. Leaf curl causes several types of losses. It destroys the new leaves in the spring, which necessitates a second foliation, draining the vigor of the tree. This renders the tree more susceptible to winter injury and reduces the fruit set the following year. Loss of leaves for several successive years will kill the tree

outright. The young fruits are attacked and fall prematurely.
These injuries lead to losses estimated at 2.5 to 3 million dollars
annually in the United States crop. With the general adoption of
spraying for leaf-curl control, the damage has been substantially
reduced, but the cost of spraying must be included in the loss caused
by this disease.

Host plants. *Taphrina deformans* attacks only the peach and its
derivatives, such as the nectarine and peach almond. A similar
fungus causes plum-pockets, a disease much like leaf curl in etiology
and control. Peaches differ in susceptibility to leaf curl, but varieties resistant in one place may be susceptible in another. Some of
the best commercial varieties are highly susceptible, and in view of
the ease and efficiency of control by spraying, no extensive use is
made of varietal resistance to leaf curl in peach culture.

Symptoms and signs. The young leaves are arched and reddened as they emerge from the bud. Soon they appear very much
curled, twisted, or puckered, thick and brittle. Affected portions
are first pale yellow or whitish, later covered with a silvery bloom.
The affected leaves die and fall, and symptoms are no longer
apparent as the season progresses, the new, second crop of leaves
being unaffected. New twigs may be swollen, pale, or even killed
back. Young fruits are dis-
torted, scabby, cracked, and
soon fall. In plum pockets, a
very smilar disease, the fruits
are transformed into large,
hollow, irregular bladders.

Etiology. *Taphrina deformans* differs from all of the
preceding ascomycetes in that
the asci are not found in a fruiting body but are in a naked

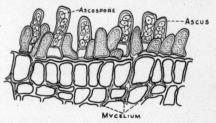

Figure 65. Peach leaf curl. Asci and
ascospores on the leaf surface and knobby,
jointed mycelium between the cells. (*After
Pierce and Atkinson.*)

layer over the surface of affected parts. There is no conidial
stage in the ordinary sense. The fungus oversummers and overwinters as ascospores on the bud scales. In very early spring
as the buds swell, the ascospores germinate, the germ tube penetrates the young leaves, and forms a peculiar, knobby intercellular
feeding mycelium that gives off a toxin stimulating the leaf to

distortion. Eventually a layer of asci appears on the leaf surface (Fig. 65). The ascospores are at first 8 per ascus but by yeastlike budding they become very numerous. They are discharged, and carried to the dormant buds of the next year's growth where they remain quiescent for the remainder of the year.

Epiphytology. Leaf curl is favored by cool weather, 50°–68°F., which at the same time slows down the development of the young shoots giving the fungus a longer period of activity. The ascospores are quite resistant to drying and summer temperatures, although a very hot summer reduces infection the following spring. High humidity in early spring favors the disease both by permitting the ascospores to germinate and by retarding the development of the young leaves. Any other factor retarding spring foliation, such as wet soil, also increases leaf-curl damage.

Control. Leaf curl and plum pockets are easily controlled by spraying at any time in the dormant season. Lime sulphur is usually recommended, the 32° Baumé concentrate being diluted 1–40 or if San José scale is a factor, 1–8. In absence of scale, Bordeaux mixture 5–5–50 or sulphur or copper carbonate dusts may be used. The application can be made at any time in the dormant season after leaf-fall, but freezing weather should be avoided. Delaying the spraying until spring is dangerous, since the ground in the orchard is often too soft to permit timely spraying in the spring, and the application is useless if delayed until the buds begin to swell. It is important to coat every part of the tree evenly and thoroughly with a fine spray or dust.

REFERENCES

1. Atanasoff, D.   Ergot of grains and grasses.   Mimeog., Off. Cer. Invest., U. S. Dept. Agr.   1920.
2. Gloyer, W. O.   Blister canker of apple and its control.   N. Y. (Geneva) Agr. Exp. Sta. Bull. 485.   1921.
3. Graf-Marin, A.   Studies on powdery mildew of cereals.   N. Y. (Cornell) Agr. Exp. Sta. Memoir 157.   1934.
4. Gravatt, G. F. and L. S. Gill.   Chestnut blight.   U. S. Dept. Agr. Farm. Bull. 1641.   1930.
5. Harter, L. L. and J. L. Weimer.   A monographic study of sweet potato diseases and their control.   U. S. Dept. Agr., Techn. Bull. 99.   1929.
6. Hesler, L. R.   Black rot, leaf spot, and canker of pomaceous fruits.   N. Y. (Cornell) Agr. Exp. Sta. Bull. 379.   1916.

7. Jones, L. K. Anthracnose of cane fruits and its control on black raspberries in Wisconsin. Wis. Agr. Exp. Sta., Res. Bull. 50. 1924.

8. Keitt, G. W. et al. The epidemiology and control of cherry leaf spot. Wis. Agr. Exp. Sta., Res. Bull. 132. 1937.

9. Lyle, E. W. The black spot disease of roses, and its control under greenhouse conditions. N. Y. (Cornell) Agr. Exp. Sta. Bull. 690. 1938.

10. MacInnes, J. and R. Fogelman. Wheat scab in Minnesota. Minn. Agr. Exp. Sta. Tech. Bull. 18. 1923.

11. Miles, L. E. Leaf spots of the elm. Bot. Gaz. 71: 161–196. 1921.

12. Pierce, N. B. Peach leaf curl: its nature and treatment. U. S. Dept. Agr. Bull. 20. 1900.

13. Reddick, D. The black rot disease of grapes. N. Y. (Cornell) Agr. Exp. Sta. Bull. 293. 1911.

14. Roberts, J. W. and J. C. Dunegan. Peach brown rot. U. S. Dept. Agr. Techn. Bull. 328. 1932.

15. Roberts, J. W. and L. Pierce. Apple scab. U. S. Dept. Agr. Farm. Bull. 1478 rev. 1935.

16. Welch, D. S. and D. L. Collins. Dutch elm disease and its control. N. Y. (Cornell) Ext. Serv., Ext. Bull. 437. 1940.

Chapter 7

DISEASES CAUSED BY IMPERFECT FUNGI

The classification of fungi is based on their mode of sexual reproduction. There is a large group of fungi in which the sexual stage
may be lacking or at least has not yet been discovered. These
are called "Imperfect fungi" (*Fungi imperfecti*). It is an artificial
grouping, a catch-all containing non-sexual stages of ascomycetes,
basidiomycetes, and phycomycetes. As the perfect stages of imperfect fungi are discovered they are transferred to their proper genera
in the ascomycetes, basidiomycetes, or phycomycetes. This is one
of the reasons we find duplication of technical names in fungi, where
the name of the imperfect stage was first given, and later the entirely
distinct name of the sexual stage after its discovery.

The imperfect fungi are classified first according to the presence
and type of non-sexual fruiting body, and second according to the
type of spore produced. We find among the imperfect fungi some
which have no spores at all (*Sterile mycelia*), and others in which the
conidia are borne at random over the surface of the mycelium
(*Hyphomycetes* or *Moniliales*), in tufts or clumps (*Melanconiales*), or in
flask-like pycnidia (*Sphaeropsidales*). Although many of the imperfect fungi are saprophytes, each of the classes contains destructive
pathogens, in fact the imperfecti rank as a major group in producing
plant diseases. Roughly subdividing the imperfect fungi according
to life history and methods of control, we will consider first those
that are primarily soil-borne, later those that are largely air-borne
and seed-borne.

I. Diseases Caused by Hyphomycetes (Moniliales)
Wilt Diseases (Species of Fusarium, Verticillium,
and Cephalosporium).

The wilts rank among the most deadly of plant diseases, not
only because they are killing diseases but also because the wilt

150

fungi can often live for long periods as saprophytes in the soil, and in general there is no control for them except the breeding of wilt-resistant varieties, a slow and sometimes unsuccessful measure.

The principal fungous genera involved are distinguished by the type of spore and its method of production (Fig. 66). All are *Moniliales*, bearing their conidia freely over the surface of the mycelium. In *Fusarium* there are two types of conidia. The larger, macroconidia, are generally borne in masses (sporodochia) and are banana- or sickle-shaped, clear, with several cells. The smaller, microconidia, are also clear, usually oval, and from one-

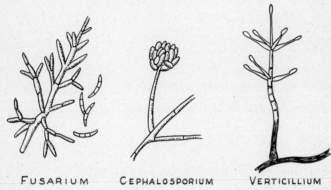

FUSARIUM   CEPHALOSPORIUM   VERTICILLIUM

Figure 66.   Three common genera of wilt fungi.   *Fusarium* species produce spores of both *Fusarium* and *Cephalosporium* types; *Cephalosporium* lacks the banana-shaped macroconidia but is otherwise like *Fusarium*. (*After Wollenweber and Reinking, and Rudolph.*)

to several-celled. Chlamydospores, thick walled swellings of individual cells of the hyphae, are sometimes found, alone or in rows of two to several. The mycelium and spore masses of *Fusarium* may be white, but are often bright colored, with various shades of pink, red, orange, and yellow depending on the species or strain. *Cephalosporium* is identical with *Fusarium* except that it lacks macroconidia. *Verticillium* is so named because of the verticillate or whorled method of branching of the conidiophores. The mycelium and conidia are colorless, and the latter are spherical or egg-shaped and one-celled.

COTTON WILT (*Fusarium vasinfectum*).

History and distribution.   There are two fungous wilts of cotton, the *Fusarium* wilt which is widespread in the United States, throughout the cotton belt, and also occurs in Europe, Egypt and India, and the *Verticillium* wilt, first discovered in Virginia in 1914, and since reported from Mississippi, Louisiana, Missouri, Texas, Arizona, New Mexico, Oklahoma, Tennessee, Arkansas, California, Greece and South America.   The two wilt diseases produce somewhat similar symptoms in cotton (see page 153), and although they are not likely to be confused by an experienced observer, they are most reliably distinguished by culturing the causal fungi on agar. Accurate identification is important because *Verticillium* wilt is not controlled by the measures that are effective against *Fusarium vasinfectum*.

Importance.   *Fusarium* wilt has long been known as a destructive cotton disease and was one of the earliest diseases to be combated by the breeding of resistant varieties.   Considering the cotton belt as a whole it causes greater losses than any other cotton disease, although in local areas other diseases are sometimes more destructive, as Texas root rot in Texas.   Wilt is estimated to cost American growers nearly half a million bales per year, or about 5 per cent of the crop.   Individual states report losses of 10 per cent or higher, and on individual farms the loss may reach 90 per cent.   Fields may be found in which every plant is killed by wilt before the first picking.   The losses are due to reduced yield and lowered quality of the lint harvested from dead or dying plants.

Host plants.   In general the various species of *Fusarium* causing wilts are each restricted to a few host plants.   That of cotton occurs only on cotton, tobacco, cassia, and okra, the watermelon *Fusarium* occurs only on melons and cucumbers, the cowpea *Fusarium* affects no other host, and other wilt *Fusaria* are similarly host-restricted. Among the various cottons, some of the Egyptian varieties are more resistant than ordinary Sea Island and upland varieties.   Thanks to intensive selection and breeding in the past 45 years, high quality, wilt-resistant cottons of several types are now available, and more are being developed.

Symptoms and signs.   Wilt is not as readily distinguished from a distance as root rot, since it more commonly occurs in individual plants scattered among healthy ones and not in large, well-defined spots of dead plants.   Plants dying of wilt are easily identified by cutting into the wood or peeling back the bark (Fig. 67).   The

A   B

C

Figure 67.   Cotton wilt.   Left, plant dying of wilt late in the season; B, healthy plant for comparison; C, discoloration of the wood due to the wilt pathogen: This is an advanced case, in earlier stages the discoloration is limited to a zone just under the bark.   (*Courtesy of V. H. Young, Ark. Agr. Exp. Sta.*)

tissues underlying the bark are discolored brown, often wet, the brown area usually appearing in the form of a ring under the bark when the stem is cut across. The discoloration extends up the stem and often far out into the smaller branches. The root system is not decayed, and affected plants are not pulled up easily, as in Texas root rot. In the stage preceding death, affected plants are stunted and yellowed, and single leaves and branches may wilt and die before the entire plant succumbs (Fig. 67). Wilt usually occurs most severely in soils deficient in potash, and the symptoms of potash deficiency or "rust," a browning of interveinal and marginal leaf areas, will often complicate the wilt symptoms on the leaves. The symptom of wilting is not altogether reliable, and may be less commonly seen in the field than stunting, yellowing, and death. The disease typically becomes noticeable between the time the plants are one to two feet tall and the first frost, however *Fusarium vasinfectum* is also at times a cause of seedling disease, damping-off, and poor emergence. After plants are killed, under moist conditions the bark and adjacent exposed tissues become covered with white mycelium bearing an abundance of macro- and microconidia.

Etiology. *Fusarium vasinfectum* is an imperfect fungus with no well known sexual reproduction although some related *Fusarium* species have ascomycetous stages. The fungus can persist in the soil for several years in the absence of a cotton crop, as a saprophyte or in the form of chlamydospores or conidia. The mycelium invades the seedlings or older plants through wounds in the roots. Within the plant it develops, especially in the xylem vessels, interfering with the water supply and ultimately causing death of the plant. The water supply is checked not so much by mechanical plugging of the vessels as by the action of a poison emanating from the fungus. Once the tissues are killed the mycelium grows to the surface of affected parts and produces masses of short cylindrical one- or two-celled microconidia and later four-celled, curved, spindle-shaped macroconidia. These are airborne but serve mainly to contaminate the soil and seed and not to initiate new infections during the current year. Thick-walled chlamydospores are also formed at tips of or along hyphae and these return to the soil with the decomposition of the cotton stalk. The disease is spread from place to place by any means that moves contaminated

soil, by drainage or irrigation water, and by air-borne conidia.   It
may be carried on the seed but there is very little evidence to indicate that infested seed are a common means of introducing the disease into new areas.

Epiphytology.   *Fusarium vasinfectum* grows between 50°F. and
104°F. with maximum growth at 77°–86°F. and maximum infection
at 82–90°F., temperatures that are also favorable for growth of the
cotton plant.   The fungus in culture is relatively independent of
variations in pH, developing well from pH 2.5 to pH 9.0., with the
best growth, however, in the acid range (pH 3.5).   Likewise, the
disease is of little importance in neutral soils, occurs rarely if ever in
alkaline soils, and is of major importance in acid soils.   The occurrence of the disease does not appear to be strongly dependent on
particular soil moisture content although the rapidity of the onset of
symptoms is conditioned by the amount of water available to the
plant.   In general, light, sandy soils are more conducive to the
disease than heavier soils.   The factor playing the most important
rôle is soil fertility, and experiments in numerous wilt locations show
that wilt is regularly associated with potash deficiency in the soil,
while the addition of potash alleviates or prevents the disease.
Nematodes also play a part in predisposing plants to wilt.   When
the root-knot nematode is present in the soil, even wilt-resistant
cotton varieties may succumb to wilt.   Cotton wilt often fluctuates
sharply in amount from year to year in the same field.   Whatever
may be the principal factor in this fluctuation is not clear; possibly
winter temperatures or spring rainfall influence these fluctuations to
a greater extent than now realized.

Control of cotton wilt rests on the facts that the causal organism
may live for years in the soil, that it is not seed-borne in important
amount, that it chiefly attacks plants in potash-deficient soils, and
that certain cotton varieties are wilt-resistant.   The procedure in
controlling wilt depends on the circumstances involved in each case.
Where the infestation is not severe, change to one of the better wilt-
resistant cotton varieties will suffice.   If the plants show signs of
potash hunger or "rust," enough potassium-containing fertilizer
should be added to correct this trouble (Fig. 68).   If the soil is
infested with both the wilt fungus and root knot nematodes, wilt-
resistant cottons should be grown in a rotation that will control the

nematodes, e.g. cotton following two years of cereal or grass crops or nematode-resistant legumes.   These control measures do not apply to the *Verticillium* wilt.

The U.S.D.A. Yearbook of Agriculture for 1936, pp. 682–686 gives an interesting account of the breeding of wilt resistant cottons, beginning in 1895 with the selections of two South Carolina farmers, aided and guided by the pioneer plant breeder for disease resistance, W. A. Orton, federal plant pathologist.   The selections gave us the variety Rivers, which was soon followed by Dillon, a systematically-obtained derivative from an Egyptian variety.   Apart from its

Figure 68.   Cotton wilt and potash hunger ("rust") in the plot at the left, controlled by application of potassium chloride ("muriate").   (*Courtesy of V. H. Young, Ark. Agr. Exp. Sta.*)

wilt resistance, Dillon had little to recommend it, but when crossed with Dixie, another wilt-resistant selection, it produced such desirable progeny as Triumph, Cook, Dixie-Triumph and others.   The work on breeding wilt-resistant cottons of other good qualities continues today with the efforts of state and federal experiment stations and private breeders in every cotton state.   Among the desirable wilt-resistant cottons thus far available and adapted to different regions are Stonewilt, Rowden 5056, Roldo Rowden, Clevewilt, 4 in 1, Miller, various Cook and Cleveland strains, Dixie Triumph and Acala No. 5.   Stoneville 2-B, Deltapine, Deltapine 12, and certain Acala strains are somewhat less resistant than other varieties listed, but may have enough tolerance to wilt for use in the Mississippi Valley.

TOMATO WILT (*Fusarium lycopersici*).

Fusarium wilt and the nematode disease root-knot, are the two leading tomato diseases of southern States but neither is of such great importance in the northern half of the United States except under greenhouse conditions.   Ten to thirty thousand tons of canning tomatoes and upwards of half a million bushels of market tomatoes are lost through wilt each year.   Losses in individual States of 10 per cent of the crop are common, and occasionally the State reports reach 20–35 per cent of the crop.   This of course means that in many individual fields the loss is total.

Tomato is the only known natural host of *Fusarium lycopersici* although successful inoculations followed by injury have been made into onion, Freesia, alfalfa, pear, and clover.   Tomato species and varieties vary in their susceptibility to wilt.   Some strains of the red current tomato, *Lycopersicon pimpinellifolium*, are immune and are being used in breeding as sources of resistance for the cultivated tomato.   Among the cultivated varieties, the following show more or less resistance to wilt: Marglobe, Pritchard, Break O'Day, Hastings Everbearing Scarlet Globe, Lloyd Forcing, Illinois Pride, Early Baltimore, Illinois Baltimore, Louisiana 16-4, Louisiana Pride, Louisiana Red, Michigan State Forcing, Marhio, Tennessee Pink, Tennessee Red, Norton, Marvel, Columbia, Arlington, Norduke, Marvana, Marvelosa, Livingston Globe, and Rutgers. None of these varieties is immune, but they show only few or relatively harmless infections under conditions fatal to susceptible varieties.

The **symptoms** of tomato wilt are similar to those of cotton wilt: yellowing, wilting, dieback, and death of the maturing plant from midseason onward.   A cut across the stem shows the darkened vascular ring characteristic of the *Fusarium* wilts.   The fungus sporulates abundantly producing both macro- and microconidia on dying and dead plants.   It can live for long periods as a saprophyte in the soil.   Infection occurs through the young roots; the xylem tissues are invaded, but the principal damage is due to a toxin excreted by the fungus.   All parts of the plant are attacked, even the seed.   The dissemination of the disease may occur through either infested seed or seedlings. Tomato wilt develops best at rather high soil temperatures, 82°–88°F., and is inhibited above 91° or below 70°F.   It is favored by a rapidly-growing, succulent condition of the host plant and any factors that stimulate this type of growth, as high fertility and abundant soil moisture.   Acid soil is most favorable.

Control of wilt depends primarily on excluding the disease from uninfested tomato plantings by using seed from a healthy crop and wilt-free seedlings.   Once the soil is infested only the varieties listed as resistant should be used, and in cases of heavy soil infestation it would be better to wait a year or two before using it again for tomatoes.   The root knot nematode appears to predispose even wilt-resistant varieties to wilt, and where the nematodes are in wilt-infested soil, a cropping plan should be followed to control them before undertaking the use of wilt-resistant varieties.

WATERMELON WILT (*Fusarium niveum*).

Wilt is by far the most serious disease of watermelons; at various times and in various localities in the past it has led to total abandonment of watermelon culture (Fig. 2).   It is so prevalent in all watermelon-growing sections that most growers sooner or later are faced with the choice of either turning to wilt-resistant varieties, moving the melon plot to a virgin field, or giving up watermelon culture altogether.   Fortunately intensive breeding in a number of states has given the grower a choice of wilt resistant varieties of various types, adapted to the grower's or the market preferences, long or round, large or "icebox size," green, gray, or striped, black or white seeded, with red or pink flesh, and with or without the hard rind adapted for shipping.

The main features of watermelon wilt are similar to those of the other *Fusarium* wilts.   Only the watermelon is attacked; wilts of other cucurbits are due to other organisms.   The fungus may be carried on the surface of the seed.   Once the soil is infested, it can remain so for 16 years or more.   The symptoms include seedling blight and later, wilting, yellowing, and dying of the runners, often one by one (Fig. 69).   The vascular ring is discolored near the crown, but this discoloration may not be seen farther out in the runners. Macro- and microconidia are produced on the dead vines, and chlamydospores within the infected tissues.

Control consists almost entirely of the use of adapted wilt resistant varieties, of which, thus far, the following are most important:

Hawkesbury: Medium size, oblong, gray, tough rind, pink flesh, brown seed.

Leesburg: Large, oblong, dark green, medium-tough rind, rose flesh, white seed.

Figure 69.   A plant of Tom Watson watermelon dying from wilt in typical fashion, seen by the dead, dying, and wilted runners at the left.   Resistant strains in the background show no wilt symptoms.   (*Courtesy of M. N. Walker, Fla. Agr. Exp. Sta.*)

Stone Mt. #5: Large, oval, green, medium-tough rind, scarlet flesh, seed light with black edge.

Stone Mt. #119: Medium-large, oval, green, medium-tough rind, scarlet flesh, seed light with black edge.

Kleckley #6: Large, oblong, dark blue-green, rind thin and brittle, bright red flesh, white seed.

Klondike R-7: Small, oblong, dark green, thin rind, red flesh, black seed.

Blue Ribbon: Medium-small, oblong, green-mottled, thin and brittle rind, deep red flesh, light brown seed.

Iowa King: Medium size, oblong, dark green, thick and medium-brittle rind, red flesh, white seed.

Iowa Belle: Medium size, oblong or round, mottled, tough rind, red flesh, light brown seed.

Pride of Muscatine: Large, oblong, dark green, thin rind, red flesh, light brown seed.

Promising results have been obtained in Tennessee in controlling watermelon wilt by spot disinfestation with chloropicrin, the gas being applied only to the hill in which seed are to be planted.

FLAX WILT (*Fusarium lini*).

Flax wilt, the most outstanding disease of this crop, is the reason why flax has always been a pioneer crop, ever moving in to new areas as the wilt fungus regularly laid waste the older fields. Until the development by Bolley of wilt-resistant flax varieties, a major turning point in the history of flax culture, there was no alternative but always to seek new land to replace the "flax sick" soil of earlier flax crops. Not only is the crop destroyed, but the oil from wilt-infested flax contains a poisonous substance.

The **etiology** of flax wilt is similar to those of the other wilts, except that *F. lini* is introduced into uninfested fields not only as spores on seed surfaces but also as mycelium within the seed hull. As in the other wilts the disease is recognized by browning of the vascular ring, accompanying wilting and death.

Control of flax wilt rests almost exclusively on the use of wilt-resistant varieties, of which Bison, Linota, Redwing, Buda, and Rio are in common use. The last is an Argentine variety that is moderately wilt resistant and immune from flax rust.

SWEET POTATO WILT OR STEM ROT (*Fusarium batatatis* and *F. hyperoxysporum*).

This is one of the major diseases of the sweet potato, similar to the other wilts, a killing disease recognized by dying of the runners with browning of the vascular tissues (Fig. 70). Here, however, the use of wilt-resistant varieties has not progressed to the extent seen in the other wilts. Many of the common varieties, such as Yellow Jersey, Red Jersey, Porto Rico, Nancy Hall, Gold Skin, Georgia, and Big Stem Jersey are highly susceptible, while others are but slightly injured by wilt, including Creola, Dahomey, Haiti, Key West, Pierson, Pumpkin, Red Brazil, Southern Queen, Triumph, White Yam, and Yellow Strasburg.   Control also benefits from the following practices:

1. Use of the same land for sweet potatoes not oftener than once in 3–4 years.

Figure 70. Stem rot or wilt of sweet potato. A plant obtained from the field and cut open in such a way as to show blackened fibrovascular bundles extending from the stem into the roots.   The fungus will grow from the stem into the roots in the field and from the potatoes into the sprouts in the seed bed. (*Photo by the Bureau of Plant Industry, U. S. Dept. of Agriculture.*)

2. Selection of disease-free mother potatoes for propagation, since the disease persists in the roots.

3. Use of vine cuttings instead of sprouts for field planting.

4. Use of sterilized soil for bedding.

5. Dipping cuttings or sprouts in a suitable fungicide, such as Semesan Bel, or adding a fungicide to the transplanting water.

OTHER FUSARIUM WILTS.

Fusarium wilts occur in numerous other crops.   The symptoms and etiology as seen in the preceding cases apply generally.   Among the important diseases of this group are cowpea wilt, Irish potato wilt (Fig. 71), banana wilt ("Panama Disease," the greatest limiting factor to banana production in Central America, with no control known), cabbage wilt (Fig. 196), pea wilt, and wilt of China asters.

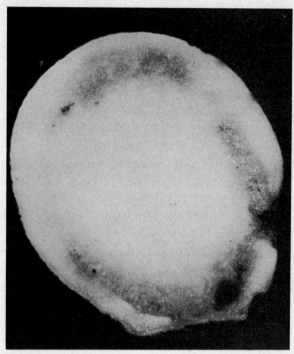

Figure 71.   Fusarium wilt of potato.   Darkening of the vascular ring, indicating invasion of the water-conducting tissues is a common symptom of the Fusarium wilts of potato.   Tubers such as this should be discarded and not planted.

CEPHALOSPORIUM WILTS.

Cephalosporium is so closely related to *Fusarium* that it may be regarded as a depauperate form of *Fusarium*, lacking macroconidia but otherwise identical.   Species of *Cephalosporium* are implicated in a few important plant diseases, best known of which are the wilt diseases of elm and of persimmon.   Both are primarily air-borne rather than soil-borne diseases.

Cephalosporium wilt of elm was discovered in searching for the Dutch elm disease (Fig. 72). It is widespread and fairly common and important both as a killing disease in itself, and because it so closely resembles the Dutch elm disease that culturing is necessary to distinguish the two, both of which cause a browning of the vascular ring. The American elm is highly susceptible, while the

Figure 72. *Cephalosporium* wilt of American elm. Note the similarity of symptoms to those of the Dutch elm disease in Figure 52. (*Courtesy of M. A. McKenzie, Mass. Agr. Exp. Sta.*)

Chinese elm, *Ulmus pumila*, is resistant to both diseases. Microconidia are produced on the surfaces of infected tissues, and these are air- or insect-borne to other trees, where the germ tubes enter through wounds. Within the tree the microconidia can pass through the conducting vessels thus spreading the infection. Control recommendations include: accurate diagnosis by culturing, eradication and burning of badly infected trees and all dead branches of trees left standing, with disinfection of the cut surfaces, regular spraying for insect and disease control, and measures to build up the vigor of the trees.

Cephalosporium wilt of persimmon, recently discovered in Tennessee, within a few years has come to occupy the greater part of the cotton belt, eastward to North Carolina and Florida and westward to Texas. It is a killing disease that spreads with great rapidity, destroying every persimmon tree over great areas; in fact there is some basis for feeling that it may prove as disastrous to the persimmon as the chestnut blight to the American chestnut, not halting until the species is practically wiped out. To some this may come as good news, the persimmon being regarded as a pest of the first order in range country, and the bane of every cattleman who has labored to grub out the sprouts. As soon as the news of this disease was released, letters to plant pathologists began to pour in, requesting cultures of the fungus and instructions on how to start local epiphytotics. Ethics prohibits such release of the pathogen, because the persimmon is highly regarded by others. It is the only tree of the ebony family in the United States, and its very hard wood is valued for golf clubs and other unusual uses. It is a valuable soil-binding tree for erosion areas, and its fruits are an important source of food for 'possums and other desirable wild life. Finally, the culture of persimmon for its fruit is becoming an industry in Florida and Texas. Here the Asiatic species of persimmon are used, and these are resistant to the fungus; however the American persimmon is valuable as an understock for the market varieties.

Persimmon trees are quickly killed by the *Cephalosporium*. Under the bark of such trees great masses ("spoonfuls") of microconidia are produced, and these are wind-disseminated to nearby trees. The vascular system is invaded, presumably through wounds. A dark ring results, but this alone is not reliable proof of the *Cephalosporium* wilt, because numerous other agencies will produce similar rings, e.g. fire injury or insects. Presence of the spores is needed for diagnosis. At present no remedial means are known, other than the substitution of the Asiatic persimmon.

VERTICILLIUM WILTS.

Wilts caused by *Verticillium albo-atrum* are common in many species of plants, and while generally less virulent than the *Fusarium* wilts, they often cause serious losses, and are also important in complicating diagnosis of *Fusarium* and *Cephalosporium* wilts.   In South America the *Verticillium* on cotton is a major pest, and in the United States and Europe *Verticillium albo-atrum* is fairly common on many plants including shade trees, particularly elm and maple, stone fruits, bush fruits, many ornamentals and weeds, and numerous truck crops, including potato, beet, cucumber, muskmelon, okra, peppers, tomato, rhubarb, and watermelon.   *V. albo-atrum* causes a discoloration of the xylem, similar to that due to *Fusarium* species.   The symptom of wilting is not as common as yellowing or browning of the leaves, and defoliation, followed by death of part or all of the plant.   In cotton a chlorotic marbling of the leaves is characteristic.   Sometimes trees recover. Infection takes place mainly from the soil, through the root system.

Verticillium wilt of cotton, in contrast to *Fusarium* wilt, is largely restricted to highly alkaline soils, and consequently rarely overlaps *Fusarium* wilt.   In neutral soils both may be found in the same field with *Fusarium* active on the sandy, acid spots and *Verticillium* in the heavy soils approaching alkalinity.   There are no records of *Verticillium* wilt occurring in acid soils.

Various practices aid in control of *Verticillium* wilt.   While the problem will ultimately be solved by the use of resistant varieties, few of these are available today.   Orchard and field sanitation is important, including removal and burning of dead and dying crop plants and weeds.   Rotation is useful but the large number of hosts complicates this.   Susceptible truck crops should not follow one another and perennials should not follow truck crops, particularly potatoes.   Measures to promote rapid growth, succulence, and well-developed root systems are useful.

Root Rots and Related Diseases

TEXAS ROOT ROT (*Phymatotrichum omnivorum*).

History and distribution.   Texas root rot, cotton root rot, *Ozonium* root rot, or *Phymatotrichum* root rot has been known since 1888 as the leading plant disease of the Southwest.   When first discovered, no spore stage was found, and the fungus was placed in *Ozonium*, a non-spore-bearing genus of imperfect fungi.   Later the discovery of the spore-mat stage required its transfer to the spore-producing genus *Phymatotrichum*. The bulk of the work on Texas root rot has been by state and federal experiment stations in Texas and Arizona, and their activities have included studies on host range, survival, spread, and attempts at control by rotation and fallowing, soil treatments, and barriers. The most recent work deals with the nature of resistance to root rot, and control by making use of biological antagonism in the soil.

Figure 73. Alfalfa field showing many spots infested with root rot. As the infested areas grow together their roughly circular shape is less apparent. (*Courtesy of R. B. Streets, Ariz. Agr. Exp. Sta.*)

Root rot occurs throughout the greater part of Texas except the Texas Panhandle, the adjacent states of Mexico, all of the Red River counties of Oklahoma except Harmon Co., and several of the counties north of these, the extreme southwestern corner of Arkansas, the southwestern and southern edges of New Mexico, the southwestern half of Arizona, the southwestern corner of Utah, and the southeastern edges of Nevada and California. (Cf. map of this area in Ariz. Exp. Sta. Bull. 71 (1937): 304.) It has a tendency to follow river valleys in finger-like projections. The disease has been in this area for at least 50 years and there is little indication that it will involve new areas to a serious extent.   Its apparent spread is due to introducing susceptible crops in locations that were formerly infested but showed no obvious sign of infestation because they were in native pasture or resistant crops.

Importance.   The disease is of utmost importance both because of its destructiveness in leading crops and its wide host range.   In all crops the loss in Texas alone is 10 to 15 per cent per year, estimated

Figure 74.   A large root rot spot in a cotton field.   Note that a few plants have survived although surrounded by dead plants.   Many trials have shown that the survivors have no resistance to the disease but have accidentally escaped the infection. (*Photo by the Bureau of Plant Industry, U. S. Dept. of Agriculture.*)

at $100,000,000 and there is probably some $50,000,000 loss in the other affected States.   Such enormous losses as these mean that root rot is often the deciding factor in the success of farming in the Southwest and particularly is this true in present day trends toward irrigation.   (Refer back to pages 12–14 discussing Texas root rot in relation to farm improvement projects.)

Among the types of loss occasioned by the root-rot disease are: killing of plants before a crop is produced; later killing reducing the amount of the crop; lower grade of the harvested crop; difficult picking in cotton; restriction of the crops that can be grown on

TABLE 4.—REACTION OF FIELD AND HORTICULTURAL CROPS TO TEXAS ROOT ROT
Field Crops

Susceptible: Alfalfa, alsike clover, cotton, cowpeas, hemp, peanuts, red clover, soybean, sweet clover, velvet beans, white clover.

Intermediate: Broad bean, flax, Kudzu, lespedeza, mung beans, tobacco, vetch.

Resistant: All grasses, barley, broomcorn, corn, crotalaria, millet, oats, rye, sesame, sorghums, wheat.

Fruit and Nut Crops

Susceptible: Apple, apricot, avocado, cherry, grape, Japanese persimmon, peach, pear, quince, walnut.

Intermediate: Blackberry, common persimmon, gooseberry, pecan, plum, raspberry, red currant.

Resistant: Black currant, strawberry.

Vegetable Crops

Susceptible: Beans, beets, carrots, chard, endive, horse-radish, Jerusalem artichoke, lima bean, okra, parsnip, pepper, rhubarb, salsify, sweet potato.

Intermediate: Eggplant, globe artichoke, Irish potato, lettuce, radish, rutabaga, tomato, turnip, watermelon.

Resistant: Asparagus, cabbage, cantaloupe, celery, cauliflower, cucumber, English pea, garlic, kale, mint, most squashes, onion, spinach.

Shade and Ornamental Trees

Susceptible and intermediate: Alder, ash, beech, black locust, catalpa, chestnut, chinquapin, chittam, cottonwood, cypress, elm (all but cedar-elm), filbert, hawthorn, hazelnut, honeylocust, hoptree, hop-hornbeam, locust, magnolia, mulberry (all but weeping mulberry), oak, pine (except Japanese red pine), poplar, redbud, sassafras, soapberry, spruce, sweet gum, Tree of Heaven, willow, witch hazel.

Resistant: Bois d'arc, cedar, cedar-elm (*Ulmus crassifolia*), hackberry, hickory, Japanese red pine, juniper, Kentucky coffee tree, Russian olive, sycamore, sycamore-fig, weeping mulberry.

Ornamentals

Susceptible: Amur and Chinese privet, common chrysanthemum, cotoneaster, dahlia, Euonymus, hollyhock, lilac, peony, poinsettia, redbud, rose, spiraea.

Intermediate: Arborvitae, box, butterfly bush, cactus, California privet, China aster, cosmos, florist's chrysanthemum, ivy, Japanese barberry, Japanese privet, laurel, morning glory, rhododendron, sunflower, trumpet flower, virginia creeper.

Resistant: Bamboo, calendula, calla, candytuft, carnation, coleus, columbine, crape myrtle, crocus, evergreen honeysuckle, ferns, gaillardia, geranium, gladiolus, gypsophila, hibiscus, iris, jasmine, lily, larkspur, mignonette, narcissus, nasturtium, pansy, petunia, phlox, poppy, pyracantha, sage, snapdragon, stock, sweet, pea, sweet william, tuberose, tulip, verbena, vinca, violet, zinnia.

Definitions

Susceptible: 30 per cent to 100 per cent of annuals, or 90 per cent to 100 per cent of perennials likely to succumb to root rot before maturity.

Intermediate: 5 per cent to 30 per cent of annuals or 50 per cent to 90 per cent of perennials likely to succumb to root rot before maturity.

Resistant: 0 per cent to 5 per cent of annuals or 0 per cent to 10 per cent of perennials likely to succumb to root rot before maturity.

infested land; and lowered market value of the land. Root rot infestation is as significant a property of soil as its fertility, its slope, or its water supply.

Host plants. *Phymatotrichum omnivorum* attacks more species of plants than any other known pathogen, more than 1700 species.

Figure 75. Infected cotton root magnified 4 diameters to show strands of the root-rot fungus on surface of root. (*Courtesy of R. B. Streets, Ariz. Agr. Exp. Sta.*)

The preceding table (Table 4) compiled from reports of tests in Texas and Arizona, indicates only the more important hosts and resistant crops.

Symptoms and signs. Root rot is apparent from July until frost. The disease kills plants in more or less circular spots from a few square yards to an acre or more in size (Figs. 3, 73, 74). The

plants die suddenly, often after having made excellent growth.
Just prior to showing severe symptoms the cotton plants have a

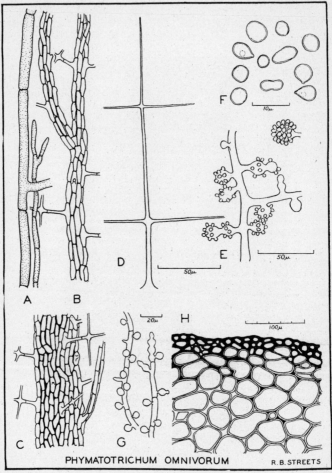

PHYMATOTRICHUM OMNIVORUM   R.B.STREETS

Figure 76. Morphology of *Phymatotrichum omnivorum:* A, large-celled and ordinary
mycelium; B, young strand; C, mature strand; D, needle-like hyphae from rhizomorph,
showing right-angle branching hypha; E, conidia and conidiophores from spore mat;
F, conidia; G, conidia borne laterally on vegetative hyphae; H, cross section of sclerotial tissues. (*Courtesy of R. B. Streets, Ariz. Agr. Exp. Sta.*)

"fever," or higher temperature than normal and this can be distinctly perceived by feeling the leaves in early morning. Death
occurs within a few days of the first wilting of the plants. In
affected plants, the whole root system is decayed and the plants

slip out of the soil without effort of pulling.   During the growing season and from year to year the spots of dead plants gradually grow larger as the root rot fungus spreads through the soil from diseased plants to adjacent healthy ones.   After slowly enlarging over a few years, there is a tendency for the spots to disappear suddenly but in the following seasons they reappear and again enlarge.

Affected plants show fine, brownish strands of fungus threads (rhizomorphs) sparsely covering the roots (Fig. 75).   Under the

Figure 77. Spore mats of root-rot fungus in alfalfa field.   The outer, younger zone is pure white and the inner zone after a few days becomes filled with a powdery mass of buff spores.   (*Courtesy of R. B. Streets, Ariz. Agr. Exp. Sta.*)

microscope the fibers clothing these strands have rigid needle-like side-branches at right angles to the main fibers, and these structures positively identify the root-rot fungus (Fig. 76).   Under moist conditions spore mats sometimes appear on the soil about diseased plants.   These are 2 to 12 inches in diameter, at first snow white and cottony, later tan and powdery from myriads of spores (Fig. 77).   On large roots and tubers there are often found numerous small cushion-like sclerotia or resting bodies, about the size of a pin-head, at first light-colored, later dark and warty (Fig. 78).

The various crops affected by root rot may die from other causes. Presence of the spore mats or the rhizomorphs with their character-

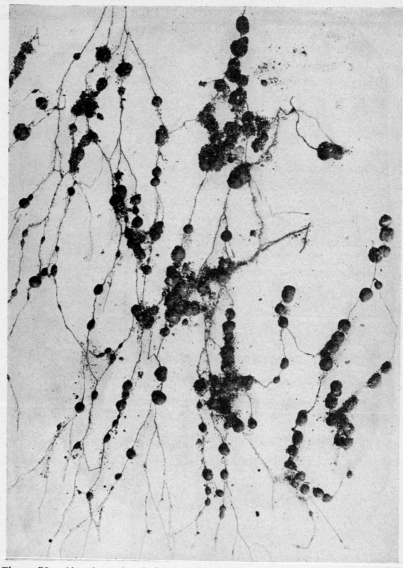

Figure 78. Abundant sclerotia formed in soil culture.   The soil was carefully washed away to secure a contrasting background.   (*Courtesy of R. B. Streets, Ariz. Agr. Exp. Sta.*)

istic side branches are positive evidence of the disease. The wilt diseases may be distinguished from root rot by the presence of the dark vascular ring accompanying wilt but absent in the case of root rot. Wilt diseases do not cause the extensive root decay found in the root rot disease. Although wilts at times occur in circular spots, they more often are scattered irregularly through the field. *Verticillium* wilt and root rot are frequently found in the same field since both commonly occur in alkaline soils; *Fusarium* wilt does not extend into the (alkaline) root rot regions except in rare instances.

Many farmers confuse root rot spots with alkali spots (Fig. 171) or spots where lightning has struck. In root rot the plants grow to healthy submaturity with no indication of disease, then suddenly die. Plants in spots of alkaline or poor soil are stunted or sickly from the start. Lightning can be ruled out by the fact that the root rot spots occur year after year in the same location.

Etiology. *Phymatotrichum omnivorum* can persist for many years in soil, as an active pathogen in the roots of plants or in the dormant condition as sclerotia. The rhizomorphs die with the host plant. Overwintering is accomplished in the roots of perennials or winter annuals or as sclerotia. The conidia (Fig. 76) appear to play no part in the life cycle; they have not been shown capable of germination. Spread of the disease from plant to plant is by growth of the fungus through the soil. There is little indication of dissemination of the disease into new areas outside the general area of infestation. A number of investigators have been unable to produce root rot in soil taken from root rot spots and moved to new locations. Despite the wording of some state quarantines, there is little or no evidence of any major dissemination of root rot through nursery stock from infested areas. Insects are not involved in root rot spread, and for some unknown reason the movement of soil by cultivation, appears to play no part in the spread of this disease.

The rate of spread from plant to plant is 2 to 8 feet per month in alfalfa and 5 to 30 feet per season in cotton and fruit trees. If a root rot spot is staked out and the development of the spot followed for several years it is seen that the spot slowly enlarges for 2 to 8 years, then suddenly or gradually breaks up leaving most of the spot bearing healthy plants but with a few separated foci of infection, each of which enlarges over the next few years, joining together and reforming the original spot (Fig. 79).   Breaking up of spots is unrelated to weather or cultural conditions, and there is some evidence that it is due to natural enemies of the fungus or competition in the soil between the root rot fungus and other soil organisms.

The advancing rhizomorphs come into contact with susceptible roots some 6 to 18 inches below soil level.   The root becomes sur-

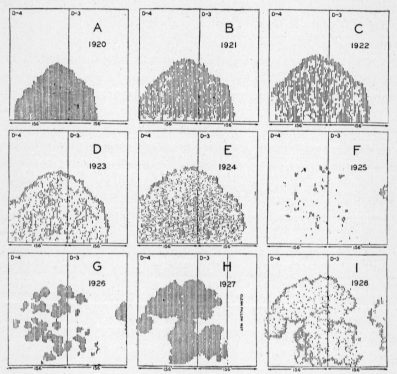

Figure 79.   Breaking-up of a root rot spot.   From 1920 to 1924 the spot increased in size; in 1925 it broke up and almost disappeared; then it reappeared in 1926–1927 with further, less complete breaking up in 1928.   The phenomenon is believed to be due to the antagonism of soil saprophytes which at times partially overcome the root rot fungus.   (*Reproduced from Circ. 173, U. S. Dept. of Agr., Bureau of Plant Industry.*)

rounded by a mantle of hyphae, the innermost ones contacting the root cells, pushing into the cortex, and then freely working through the root tissues, rapidly destroying them.   Symptoms appear above ground after about 6 weeks, or in trees, after as much as a year.

Epiphytology.   The limited and well-defined geographical area occupied by the root rot fungus leads one to think that its distribution is easily related to ecological factors, but this is not the case.   Temperature is clearly a limiting factor to the north of the area of infestation, as the disease develops only during hot weather and is inhibited by cold winter temperatures.   When temperatures are favorable, soil moisture is usually the limiting factor.   The disease flourishes with moderate moisture and is suppressed under either very dry or very wet conditions.   Although we commonly think of root rot as being associated with the heavy, black, waxy, calcareous soils of the Red River valley, it is by no means restricted to these but has been found in nearly every soil type in Texas.   It is most severe, however, on heavy, alkaline soils of high fertility.   The presence of abundant organic material in the soil lessens the disease incidence, probably through favoring the growth of soil saprophytes antagonistic to the root rot fungus.

Despite this information, the local distribution of root rot is often unaccountable.   In one of the Red River Counties, for example, the disease is found in every field to the east of a railroad line, and in no field to the west, although there is no single factor or group of factors that serves to explain this strange limitation.

As might be expected, root rot is not the type of disease that develops in periodic epiphytotics, but instead it is enphytotic, regularly occurring each year in the same areas, but varying in severity somewhat from year to year in relation to the amount of local rainfall.

Control.   1. *Rotation.*   Growers in root rot areas should not grow cotton or annual summer legumes on any given piece of infested land oftener than once in four years.   During the three intervening years the land can be used for small grains, corn, sorghums, broomcorn, or grass crops, or the vegetables listed above as "resistant."   Susceptible winter and spring legumes (vetch, Austrian winter peas, Canadian field peas, annual clovers) might be safely used in the intervening years provided the crop is harvested or turned under by late spring.

Such rotations will not rid the soil of the fungus, but will reduce root rot losses to a low level which will not seriously handicap the grower.   While this may seem like a long rotation, it is entirely practical and fits in well with the federal crop control program which ordinarily does not permit more than 25 per cent of cultivated land to be in cotton any given year.

2. *Avoid susceptible perennials.* Perennial crops rated susceptible on page 168 will generally result in failures on root-rot-infested soil. The prudent grower will not attempt to grow alfalfa, susceptible orchard crops or susceptible woodlot or ornamental trees or shrubs in root rot areas.

Figure 80. Peach orchard showing effective use of barrier to stop advance of root rot through the soil. When barrier was placed between the two rows, one year previously, all trees in the left hand row were alive. Root rot advancing from the infested area at left killed trees not protected by barrier. (*Courtesy of R. B. Streets, Ariz. Agr. Exp. Sta.*)

3. *Eradication and barriers.* Many direct methods for ridding soil of the Texas root rot organism have been tested, some with excellent results. These include chemical treatments of the soil to kill the fungus or make the soil uncongenial for its development, deep tillage, and the addition of large quantities of organic fertilizers. Under most conditions, it is doubtful whether any of these will justify the expense involved on a field basis. Walling off the spots with trenches or barriers as of several rows of sorghum, aids to keep the spots from enlarging and this is of value in some instances (Fig. 80).

Figure 81. Chart showing the effect of manuring in controlling Texas root rot. A, B, C, D represent the same plot during 4 successive years, 1932–1935. Shading indicates root rot occurrence in cotton. A photograph taken at the position of the arrow is reproduced in Figure 82. Note also the breaking up of root rot spots, e.g. in the top strips of B and C. (*Reproduced from Cir. 425, U. S. Dept. of Agr., Bureau of Plant Industry.*)

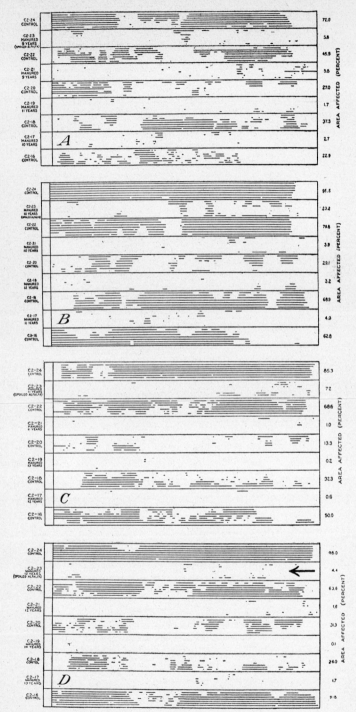

Figure 81. See opposite page for legend.

The use of organic fertilizers has special interest because here practical use is made of biological control: the inhibition of the root rot fungus by antagonistic organisms in the soil.   Soil saprophytes are ordinarily better adapted to a saprophytic life than plant pathogens that occasionally live as saprophytes.   King and Loomis in Arizona have demonstrated almost perfect control of root rot in irrigated cotton by heavy applications (15 to 30 tons per acre) of manure or spoiled alfalfa hay (Figs. 81, 82).   They interpret this control as due to the antagonism of the soil saprophytes, favored by

Figure 82.   The effect of manuring in controlling root rot.   A view of the plots diagrammed in Fig. 81 taken from the position indicated by the arrow in that figure. The center plot above has been manured with spoiled alfalfa hay for 12 years. Unmanured plots are at each side, with manured plots at their outer edges.   (*Photo by the Bureau of Plant Industry, U. S. Dept. of Agriculture.*)

the humus, against the root rot organism.   The increased fertility of the treated soils is not a factor in this means of control, since applications of commercial fertilizers to give equal availability of nutrients fail to effect the control obtained with the organic material.

4. *Weeds.*   Many weeds are susceptible to the root rot fungus. In any rotation program, every effort should be made to keep the land and fence rows free from weeds, as they can easily defeat the purpose of the rotation.   Among the most susceptible weeds are: bindweed, cocklebur, dock, ground cherry, horse nettle, jimson

weed, lamb's quarters, prickly lettuce, milkweed, ragweed, common sunflower, Russian thistle, goldenrod, wild aster, and spurge nettle.

5. *Ornamentals and fruit trees.* Select from the list of resistant plants so far as possible. The Arizona workers recommend as a treatment for saving affected trees, applying ammonium sulphate (1 lb. to 10 sq. ft.) to the soil, followed by a 3-inch to 4-inch irrigation. The full amount of water must be used and the trees should be headed back to give the root system a chance to recover. Soil disinfestants such as 1.25 per cent formaldehyde or .25 per cent organic mercury can be used to eradicate the fungus from small areas. The disinfestant must penetrate to a depth of 4 feet.

6. *Vegetables.* Select from the list of resistant vegetables as far as possible. Susceptible vegetables will escape injury from root rot if harvested by June.

HELMINTHOSPORIUM DISEASES OF GRAINS AND GRASSES

Helminthosporium is the most important genus of imperfect fungi affecting cereals and grasses. A few of the *Helminthosporium* species affect plants outside the *Gramineae*, but the majority are specialized on grain and grass hosts, where they cause seedling disease, foot and root rots, leaf diseases, and blighted grain. Among the more destructive species are:

Helminthosporium sativum, causing dry-land foot rot of wheat and spot blotch of barley;

Helminthosporium gramineum, the cause of barley stripe; and

Helminthosporium teres, which produces net blotch of barley. Each of these has a number of other hosts of less importance in the *Gramineae*. They are widespread and common in many parts of the world and throughout the entire grain-growing area of North America.

Mycology. *Helminthosporium* is a genus of imperfect fungi of the family *Dematiaceae* which includes imperfect fungi without special fruiting bodies, with dark spores borne at random over the surface of the mycelium. The family is spoken of collectively as the sooty molds. The genus *Helminthosporium* is distinct from other members of the family in that the conidia are long and divided into several cells by transverse cross walls. The common saprophytic genus, *Alternaria* (or *Macrosporium*), which includes species causing cotton boll-rot and tomato fruit rot, also belongs to this family.

The conidia of different *Helminthosporium* species range in length from 20 microns to 400 microns with much variability within species. The spores differ in color, ranging from almost colorless

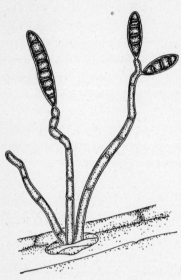

to dark brown, and in some species the spores are dark in the middle and paler at the ends. They also differ in shape, being straight or curved, cylindrical or ellipsoidal, or shaped like a snake's head, and they differ in the number of cells per spore. All of these characters are useful in identifying the 200 known species of *Helminthosporium*.

The spores are borne, one at a time, on dark conidiophores, which emerge through stomata or from the infected tissues directly. The conidiophore after producing the first spore, grows a short distance beyond it, pushes it aside and produces a second, and successive spores, until the end of the conidiophore is

Figure 83. Conidia and conidiophores of *Helminthosporium*, emerging from a stoma. (*After Dreschler.*)

marked by a series of knee-like bends, with the scars of earlier spore attachments. Usually only one spore is found on the conidiophore at any time (Fig. 83).

DRY-LAND FOOT- OR ROOT-ROT OF WHEAT (*Helminthosporium sativum*).

Dry-land foot-rot, caused by *Helminthosporium sativum* commonly affects wheat, rye, and barley, and also may be found on certain grasses, such as quack grass, Kentucky blue grass, wild oat grass, wild rye, and mouse barley.

In Oregon, the disease caused by *H. sativum* and other *Helminthosporium* species is known as Coastal foot-rot or crown rot. It is also spoken of as *Helminthosporium* blight or *Helminthosporium* disease.

Wheat from root-rot affected crops frequently is discolored at the germ end. This is called black-point wheat, and the trouble, the black-point disease. While various organisms may produce the trouble, the commonest and most important is *Helminthosporium sativum*.

The term "common root-rot" is applied collectively to the *Helminthosporium* disease and root-rots caused by other, undetermined species of *Helminthosporium* and *Fusarium*. The expression "foot-rot," as distinct from root-rot, refers to the stage in which the lower inch or two of the stem is discolored and eventually may decay, or cause failure to head or sterile heads. When wheat seedlings are destroyed before or soon after emergence the trouble is commonly termed seedling-blight or damping-off.

Helminthosporium sativum is only one of many fungi that attack the roots and stem bases of wheat plants. The discussion here, however, is limited to the disease caused by this fungus.

History and distribution. The dry-land foot-rot seems to occur only rarely in Europe but has recently been recorded from England, Germany, and Serbia, and also from Australia. In America it is one of the most important of the foot-rot diseases, yet *H. sativum* has only been known since 1910, when Pammei, King, and Bakke described it on barley, and it was not until 1919 and 1920 that its rôle as a wheat foot- and root-rot organism was recognized. The present known distribution includes most of the wheat areas of America. Experiments on the pathogenicity of *H. sativum* have been reported, demonstrating that this is a virulent parasite of wheat, but relatively little has been published on the control of dry land foot-rot.

Within the past few years studies on the wheat root-rots have been carried out particularly in Canada, in Minnesota, and in Kansas. The recent studies have been concerned with such subjects as: variation and specialization in *H. sativum*, cropping practices in relation to root-rot, influence of environment on root-rot, effect of the soil flora on the prevalence of the root-rot fungi, and the relation of seed infection to the disease in the field.

Importance. The foot-rots cause substantial losses in the wheat crop. For example, in Kansas alone the loss from all foot-rots in wheat was 4.5 per cent of the crop (11,901,000 bu.) in 1931, 4.5 per cent (5,943,000 bu.) in 1932, 6 per cent (4,727,000 bu.) in 1935, and 5 per cent (9,104,000 bu.) in 1937.   The average loss estimates for the United States usually range from .5 per cent to 1.5 per cent of the national crop.   In individual wheat fields that are heavily attacked, from 30 per cent to 70 per cent or more of the plants may be killed before harvest.   The greater part of these losses are due to *Helminthosporium sativum*, and one should not forget that wheat is only one of several crops attacked by this fungus.

The loss from foot-rots is of several types.   Young seedlings may be destroyed, giving a thin stand or necessitating replanting which is a twofold loss, consisting of the time, labor, and seed in replanting, and the fact that a replanted crop is rarely planted at the most favorable time, resulting in a subnormal crop.   As the crop approaches harvest the damage from foot-rots becomes most apparent, as the plants in large areas of the field die and blacken without setting grain, or produce weak, sterile, or partially filled heads with black-point or shrivelled grain.   Many of the plants which survive and produce are handicapped by a partial loss of roots, with a consequent subnormal yield.   To these losses must be added the cost of any measures which may be used in attempting to control foot-rot.

Symptoms and signs.   Foot- and root-rots have a tendency to appear in well-defined, round, oval, or irregular spots in the field. This may appear in the seedling stage of the disease but in the case of dry-land root-rot it is most pronounced at maturity of the crop when the great spots of sterile plants, overgrown with black, sapro-phytic molds stand out in striking relief against a golden background of ripened grain.   The spots may vary from a few square feet to an acre or more in size.   They are not restricted to either low or high parts of the field, but do have a tendency to be more abundant at the edges of the field, possibly indicating spread to the field from fence-row grasses or volunteer grain.   The spots may be distin-guished from spots of poor fertility by the sharp delimitation of the root-rot spots, the diseased plants being abruptly bordered by healthy ones, while in the case of poor or alkaline soil, the stunted plants show progressive stages of improvement as one passes from the center of the spot to nearby healthy grain.

The *Helminthosporium* seedling blight may be distinguished by the dark brown lesions of the cortical tissues, lesions that frequently extend into the coleoptile and seedling leaf.   This results in dead plants before or after emergence from the soil.   This phase of the disease is said to be more common in the spring wheat area than in winter wheat.

The fungus continues to cause a rotting of the roots of surviving plants.   In less severe cases dark-brown lesions develop on the roots at points of infection, causing but little apparent injury to the plant.   The coleoptile, basal leaf sheath, and stem may show various degrees of infection from small elongated lesions to a complete rotting.   In severe cases of root- or foot-rot the seedling leaves show a dark-green discoloration or sometimes a chlorosis and later the whole seedling usually dies.   In the case of older plants the type of root and culm injury is much the same as that occurring on seedlings, except that there seems to be less tendency for a complete rotting of the stems.

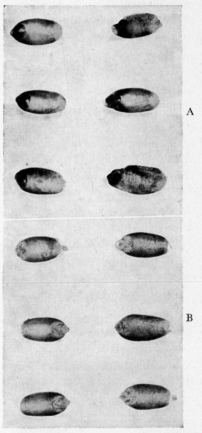

The fungus attacks the leaf blades, sheaths, upper culm, and head.   The kernels also become infected and develop a dark-brown to black tip at the germ end ("black-point") (Fig. 84).   So far as known, no part of the wheat plant is immune from infection by this parasite during its development.   Stem and foliage lesions tend to be elliptical in outline.   Usually these consist of a dark brown margin with a lighter brown

Figure 84.   A, Above, "black point" or internally infected wheat grains; B, healthy grains.

center.   On leaves, these centers frequently drop out, and in some cases lesions may involve the entire width of the leaf.

On the roots and stems of wheat seedlings *H. sativum* causes the tissues to develop a light to chocolate brown discoloration, which may easily be confused with discolorations due to other root-rot organisms.   The light brown discoloration of the lower inch or two of the culm is characteristic of the foot-rot phase of the disease.

Dark masses of *Helminthosporium* spores are not often seen on affected plants, although the mycelium and spores of secondary sooty molds, over the heads and leaves, are very typical of the disease at harvest time.   Whitened, shrivelled heads are also commonly the consequence of root-rot infection.

Etiology.   *Helminthosporium sativum* is a facultative parasite, and grows well as a saprophyte.on nutrient media and in soil debris. It survives between crops as spores or mycelium either in the soil and crop residue or in the "black-point" seed.   Conidia are produced from the saprophytic mycelium in the soil debris, which may initiate the early infections, or the roots of young plants may be invaded directly by the soil-borne or seed-borne mycelium, with consequent rootlet decay.   Ultimately spores are carried from the soil or affected bases of plants to the leaves, where they germinate and produce the first leaf lesions.   The leaf lesions produce successive generations of conidia which are air-borne to other leaves and heads and serve to multiply the disease during favorable weather conditions.   Many of these spores carry the infestation back to the soil. At the same time there is an onward march of the mycelium through the soil, continually enlarging the spots of infection.   The many cycles of infection continue till maturity of the plants and the production of black-tipped kernels in affected heads.   After harvest the soil is further contaminated by mycelium and spores in the stubble, straw, and chaff.

The part played by other hosts should be remembered.   *H. sativum* may include in its life cycle infections of rye, barley, and certain grasses, and these play a part in the survival of the fungus between wheat crops and in increasing the inoculum during periods in which wheat and these other hosts are growing together.

H. sativum is not a highly specialized parasite, as seen by its saprophytic life in the soil, and the fact that it attacks weakened

hosts in preference to vigorous ones.   Christensen has shown that
the fungus includes as many as 37 types or races, differing physiolog-

Figure 85.   Variation in *Helminthosporium sativum*.   The pair of pots at the extreme
right contain wheat plants in uninoculated soil.   The other pots contain soil inoculated
with various strains of *H. sativum* showing, from left to right, decreasing degrees of
virulence.   (*Courtesy of J. J. Christensen, Minn. Agr. Exp. Sta.*)

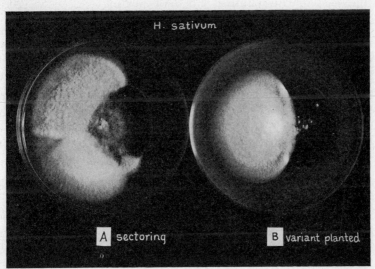

Figure 86.   Mutation and reversion in *Helminthosporium sativum*, cause of dry land
root rot of wheat.   The agar plate at A was planted with a pure strain of the dark fungus.   As the culture grew it mutated producing two or three white variants.   When
one of these was planted (B) it exhibited a reverse mutation, reverting back to the
original black type.   (*Courtesy of J. J. Christensen, Minn. Agr. Exp. Sta.*)

ically and structurally.   These variants also show differences in
pathogenicity, corresponding to an indefinite type of physiologic
specialization, in which some races are highly virulent on wheat

and barley, others much less so (Fig. 85).   He has shown that new races may arise through non-sexual mutation in pure cultures and that these may in time revert back to the parent form (Fig. 86).

Epiphytology.   *H. sativum* is tolerant of a rather wide range of temperature although it is favored by warmth.   The mycelium will grow at any temperature from 34°F. to 99°F. with an optimum near 82°F.   Likewise the spores will germinate from 43°F. to 102°F., with optimum germination between 72°F. and 90°F.   Infection can occur from 54°F. to 93°F. but is most severe at 72°F. to 93°F., and the disease develops most rapidly at the higher temperatures. Spores can withstand exposure to both low and high temperatures for considerable periods of time if the relative humidity is low. They can also withstand long periods of alternate freezing and thawing, and can overwinter as far north as Minnesota, although the percentage of surviving spores differs in different seasons. Within seed the mycelium is killed by heating the seed to 203°– 212°F., dry heat, for 30 hours.

High soil moistures favor root infection, especially at high temperatures.   The moisture optimum varies with the tempera-ture.   Extremely low soil moistures are unfavorable for infection at all temperatures, and at extremely low or high temperatures the moisture curves for infection are very irregular.   The ill effects of root infection are more severe in extremely dry and extremely wet soils than in soils containing an optimum amount of moisture for the growth of the plant.   Leaf and spike infections increase directly with the amount of moisture present, and are most abundant fol-lowing heavy dews and rains.

It is noticeable that the environmental conditions favoring growth and reproduction of the parasite are not necessarily those associated with the most severe disease.   This is largely due to the fact that the environment is also operating on the wheat plant, and any factor that weakens the wheat increases its susceptibility to root-rot, regardless of whether or not that factor at the same time favors the development of the fungus   Many such factors might be cited, for example, unfavorable temperature or moisture for wheat growth, competition due to overseeding or weeds, unsuitable soil, and attacks of insects or other diseases.   Since the fungus is tolerant of a wide range of environmental conditions, any analysis of the effect of environment on this disease will be largely concerned with the effect of environment in reducing host vigor and thus predisposing the host to the disease.   Wheat plants are most susceptible to *H. sativum* from the milk stage on, and this in turn may be correlated with their dwindling metabolic activity as maturity approaches.

In summary, *Helminthosporium sativum* has a tolerance for a wide range of environmental conditions.   Herein lies the reason why the dry-land foot-rot, unlike such diseases as rusts or downy mildews, is constantly with us, rarely if ever developing in epiphytotic proportions, but each year eating away at the crop and causing losses which vary to only a limited extent from one year to another.

Control.   As is generally true of soil-borne diseases, crop management is of first importance in controlling dry-land foot-rot. Fellows, a leading authority on root-rot, advises: "It may be controlled effectively by the proper date of planting.   It happens that the date recommended by the agronomist as the best for yield is the proper date for planting to avoid foot-rot.   I have found this true time and again from one end of the wheat belt to the other.   The agronomist worked out disease control without knowing it.   In general it is a retarded date as compared to that which the farmers ordinarily practice.   I avoid telling a farmer to plant late for the proper date really isn't late but retarded for him.   The farmer usually doesn't like a retarded date since it may permit blowing of the soil.   In Montana the proper date is around September 12 and in the Panhandle of Texas about October 15, with intervening dates in the intervening territory."

But the planting date is also dictated by many other factors such as available moisture, wind erosion, and avoidance of wireworms. Hence advantage must also be taken of other measures of aiding in root-rot control.

It has been shown that the weakest plants are the most susceptible to root-rot.   This implies that any steps which build up the vigor of the crop will at the same time predispose against root-rot. Thus application of phosphate fertilizers in the drill row in localities where moisture conditions permit, will promote rapid growth of the plants and the early establishment of a properly functioning root system, when this is most urgently needed in overcoming attacks of parasites.   In other cases the fertilization should follow the advice of soil specialists aiming at the balance of fertility that is most conducive to normal wheat development. Such fertilization does not prevent the disease from occurring; it appears to act as a means of control by stimulating plants in infected areas to a more vigorous development.

Proper depth of planting is also a factor. When seed are sown at a depth greater than 2–3 inches, the seedlings are weakened, and rendered more liable to attack by root-rotting fungi, both before and after emergence, while seedlings from shallow-sown seed are unable to establish themselves in time to forestall root-rot attack.

Insofar as possible, wheat fields and adjacent borders should be kept as free as possible of wild grasses and weeds. The grasses serve as reservoirs of root-rotting fungi, while weeds will compete with the grain for water, light, and nutrients, and predispose the grain to root-rot by lowering its vitality. As the wheat loses in its vigor from foot-rot, the weeds flourish, intensifying the trouble as the season progresses. It is also inadvisable to sow wheat on land directly after it has been in grass. If any grain crop must be used in this way, oats is preferable, but it is better to put the land into flax or some other non-gramineaceous crop for a few years after plowing the native or tame pasture.

Crop rotations including legumes or some other non-cereal crop will help to lower the concentration of cereal foot-rotting fungi in the soil. Such plants, together with summer fallowing, tend to starve the root-rotting fungi and allow other soil organisms to hasten their destruction. Oats is probably the least susceptible cereal crop to include in a rotation.

Seed treatments are not specific for root-rot but materially decrease the fungus load on infested seed, and also give some protection against soil-borne infection. Organic mercury dusts as "New Improved Ceresan," used as for bunt, are a standard recommendation. Formaldehyde, bichloride of mercury, and copper carbonate seed treatments are less effective. But black-point seed are internally infected with *Helminthosporium*, and the surface treatments will not control internal infections. These can only be eliminated by selecting for planting purposes seed that is free of black-point kernels.

There is little evidence on record which will help in combatting root-rot by the use of resistant varieties, although most investigators have observed variation in the reaction of different wheat varieties to root-rot.   Sallans, in Canada, reports that Reward and some new varieties of Reward parentage are constantly more resistant than such varieties as Marquis, Apex, Thatcher, and Ceres, and McKinney also speaks of the high susceptibility of Marquis.   Doubtless there are corresponding differences in the winter wheats, but for

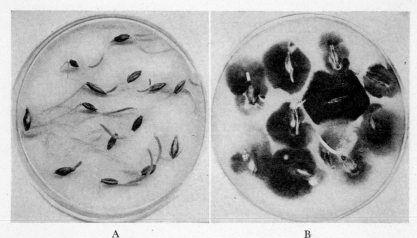

A   B

Figure 87. . Germinating barley seeds.   Left: Healthy seeds; right: seeds infected with *Helminthosporium* blight, showing the black mycelium growing out on the agar from each seed.   (*Courtesy of W. E. Brentzel, N. D. Agr. Exp. Sta.*)

the present this desirable control measure is still in the experimental stage.

The natural microflora has a marked inhibitory action on the growth of *H. sativum* in soil.   Bacteria and fungi isolated from the soil show a suppressive action on the pathogen.   Although *H. sativum* sporulates well in certain sterilized soils it will not if the soils are unsterilized.   The evidence suggests that sporulation is inhibited by saprophytic soil organisms.   The fact that root-rot diseases of wheat are less severe when the crop is grown on fallowed land than on land cropped to wheat for several years, may be related to the growth of soil saprophytes, which in bare fallow have an advantage over the pathogens in competition for food.   Whether or not this natural control may be used directly in controlling root-rot, as has

TABLE 5—DISTINGUISHING CHARACTERISTICS OF HELMINTHOSPORIUM DISEASES OF BARLEY

Character	Stripe	Spot blotch	Net blotch
Causal organism	Helminthosporium gramineum	Helminthosporium sativum	Helminthosporium teres
Host species	Barley (wheat, rye, oats, corn).	Barley, wheat (rye, millet, sorghums, grasses).	Barley (oats, rye, corn, Sudan grass, grasses).
Resistant barley varieties	Wis. Pedigree 38 (Wis. Barbless) and 39, Chevron, Korsbyg, Nepal, Black Hulless, Lion, Tystofte Kors, Spartan, Leiorrynchum, Glabron, Trebi.	Manchuria, Minsturdi, Nepal, Glabron, Minn. 184 (a Manchuria sel.), Peatland, Velvet.	No detailed data available but differences in susceptibility exist.
Highly susceptible barleys	Oderbrucker, Minsturdi, Manchuria, Velvet, Peatland.	Two-row barleys as a group and many six-row barleys.	
Nature of infection	Systemic, killing the immature plant.	Local on leaves and roots.	Local on leaves.
Symptoms and signs a. Effect on plant	White or yellow streaks on all leaves of the plant, as in ribbon grass; leaves later splitting as streaks become brown and dry, sprinkled with black mycelium and spores. Plant dead and inconspicuous by harvest time. No seedling blight.	Oval, chocolate-brown, uniform, well-defined leaf spots, followed by dying-back of the leaf tip. Spots becoming covered with dark mold. Appearance of spots variable on other host species. Seedling blight common and serious.	Elongate, lens-shaped leaf lesions showing a net- or ladder-like appearance of dark veins when seen with transmitted light, often with a yellowish halo about the spot, followed by die-back of the leaf tip. Seedling blight rare.

b. Effect on crop	No grain produced by affected plants.	Reduced yield, sometimes shrivelled or basally blackened grain ("blighted barley").	Reduced yield; basally discolored kernels uncommon; light brown hull discoloration ("blighted barley").
Mycology	Spores light brown, up to 8-celled, thin-walled, straight, not constricted at the septa (cross-walls). No perfect stage recognized.	Spores dark brown, up to 13-celled, thick-walled, curved. No perfect stage recognized.	Spores light brown, up to 8-celled, thin-walled, straight or slightly curved, constricted at the septa. Ascosporic stage with perithecia on old stubble.
Life history	Much as in bunt. Survival between crops as mycelium between hull and seed coat. Infection of seedling as seed germinates, mycelium invading all parts of the plant. Spores produced on leaf streaks wind-borne to healthy seed, where they germinate and produce mycelium in and under the hull. Little or no soil survival or direct leaf-to-leaf infection.	Survival between crops as a saprophyte in crop debris or as "black point" (internally infected) grain. Primary infection of roots by soil mycelium or of leaves by conidia from soil debris followed by successive leaf-to-leaf or leaf-to-head generations from air-borne conidia. Primary infection also due to seedlings from "black point" kernels.	Survival between crops on surfaces of seed and in soil debris, where ascospores are an important source of spring infections, followed by leaf-to-leaf generations due to air-borne conidia. In cool climates some over-summering on volunteer barley in conidial stage.
Epiphytology	Normally enphytotic; favored by weak plant growth, poor soil, cool temperatures (under 68°F.) at planting time, ample moisture at blossoming.	Normally enphytotic; favored by weak plant growth, very dry or very wet soil, high temperatures (72°–86°F.) and ample moisture. Tolerant of wide environmental variation. Virulence of the fungus strain is important.	Normally enphytotic; favored by cool temperatures (50°–60°F.). (Net blotch is normally replaced by spot blotch as the warm season advances).

TABLE 5.—DISTINGUISHING CHARACTERISTICS OF HELMINTHOSPORIUM DISEASES OF BARLEY.—(Continued)

Character	Stripe	Spot blotch	Net blotch
Control	Seed dusting is entirely effective. "New Improved Ceresan" proved best of 75 treatments. Methods as for bunt control (see page 62). Avoid "black point" seed. Sanitation and rotation of no direct value. Use of resistant varieties listed above.	Early and thorough cultivation to destroy crop debris. Two to three year rotation *with nongramineous crops* in intervening years, best including one soil-building crop. Eradication of grasses and volunteer grain near or in barley fields. Seed dusting and avoidance of "blighted barley" for seed are important accessory measures. Use of resistant varieties listed above.	Early and thorough cultivation to destroy crop debris. Two to three year rotation *with any other crop than barley.* Seed dusting and avoidance of "blighted barley" for seed are important accessory measures. This is the most difficult of the three diseases to control.

been done with Texas root-rot and the pineapple nematode, in any case our knowledge of this natural control aids us in understanding the disease and its control by cultural practices.

OTHER HELMINTHOSPORIUM DISEASES.

Many other species of the grain and grass family become attacked by species of *Helminthosporium*, usually in the form of root decay or leaf spot diseases.   Representative of these is the leaf spot of wheat shown in Figure 88, a disease of minor importance found only when wheat has been subjected to extremely moist conditions.

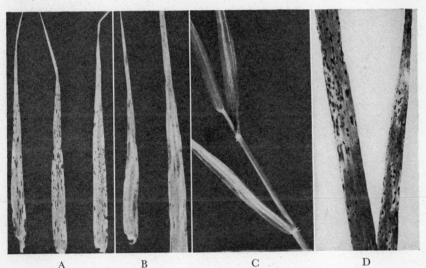

A   B   C   D

Figure 88. Helminthosporium diseases of cereals. A, barley spot blotch (*H. sativum*); B, barley net blotch (*H. teres*).   C, barley stripe (*H. gramineum*); D, an uncommon *Helminthosporium* spot disease of wheat growing in a very humid environment.

HELMINTHOSPORIUM DISEASES OF BARLEY.

Barley is attacked by 5 species of Helminthosporium.   Three of these, causing stripe, spot-blotch, and net-blotch are common and at times quite destructive.   Each of these diseases has its own peculiarities in etiology, epiphytology, and control, as is seen in the preceding table (Table 5).

Leaf and Shoot Diseases

GRAY MOLD NECK ROT OF ONIONS (*Botrytis allii*).

The genus *Botrytis* includes some 200 species, a number of which are important pathogens causing "gray-mold" diseases of lilies, peonies, lily of the valley, lilac, onions, various fruits, tobacco, lettuce, cabbage, and other hosts.   There are three closely related species on onions, of which *B. allii* is commonest and regularly found in white market onions, less often in colored ones, as a leading cause of storage rot in this crop, the storage and transit losses sometimes exceeding 50 per cent of the crop.

Botrytis is a genus of hyphomycetes, imperfect fungi having the conidia borne at random over the surface of the mycelium on

Figure 89.   Gray mold or mycelial neck rot of onions.   (*Courtesy of J. C. Walker, Wis. Agr. Exp. Sta.*)

branched conidiophores, resembling bunches of grapes.   The conidia are clear, egg-shaped, and one-celled.   In some species sclerotia are formed.   Some of the *Botrytis* species are imperfect forms of ascomycetes of the genus *Sclerotinia*, related to the fungus causing brown rot of stone fruits.

Neck rot becomes apparent after harvest time, with a softening of the neck that slowly or rapidly spreads until the entire onion is decayed and covered with a gray, powdery mold (Fig. 89).   Later the onion dries, becoming a mummy.   The mold bears countless conidia that are air-borne to other onions, rapidly spreading the disease by infection through the necks.   Overwintering is by mycelium in the bulbs and, in related species, by sclerotia.   The

Botrytis species are facultative parasites and can flourish as saprophytes on waste onion debris.

Botrytis allii exhibits an unusual environmental relationship in that it develops rapidly at cool temperatures, even in refrigerators, at temperatures inhibitory to many other storage decay organisms, while high temperatures do not allow neck rot.   Moisture is essential.   The resistance of red and yellow onions is due to the inhibitory effect on the fungus of water-soluble pigments, protocatechuic acid and catechol, that are present in the red and yellow papery scales.   The inner flesh of such onions is as susceptible as that of white onions.

Control of gray mold neck rot depends on:

1. Use of red and yellow varieties in preference to white ones.

2. Thorough curing after harvest in cool dry storage or artificial curing by exposing the bulbs to hot air (100° to 120°F.) until the necks are thoroughly dried.

3. Storage at temperatures from 32° to 35°F. in a dry, well ventilated compartment.

PEACH   SCAB   (*Cladosporium carpophilum*).

Scab is one of the common diseases of peach, occurring nearly everywhere that peach crops are grown with the exception of the Pacific states where it is rarely seen.   However, it need not be

Figure 90.   Scab spots on peach.
(*Photo by Bureau of Plant Industry, U. S. Dept. of Agriculture.*)

considered a serious menace since it can be efficiently controlled by spraying.   To a lesser extent it is found on plum, nectarine, apricot, and cherry.   Scab occurs on twigs and leaves but is most important on the fruits, where it causes numerous round olive-green to black lesions, sometimes called "freckle" (Fig. 90).   In severe cases the lesions run together and the fruit may crack open, often paving the way for brown rot.   The fruits may be reduced in size, misshapen, and worthless, but in many cases the injury is mainly or entirely to the appearance of the fruit.

The surface of each lesion is covered with brown, jointed conidiophores each bearing at its tip a brown, oval or slipper-shaped condium.   No perfect stage is known.   Spread of the disease during the growing season is by means of wind-blown conidia.   Overwintering occurs in tiny (⅛ inch) cankers on the twigs, in a mycelial state.

Scab is controlled by spraying as for brown rot (see page 142), but beginning a little earlier.   Two applications are commonly recommended, the first about 3 weeks after petal fall, the second 3 to 4 weeks before harvest.   The same fungicides as used for brown rot are effective against the causal fungus of scab.   Pruning and orchard sanitation are not essential parts of peach scab control.

II. Anthracnose Diseases, Caused by Melanconiales

"The *Melanconiales* are a large order of the *Fungi Imperfecti* containing many important parasitic species.   The mycelium grows within the host tissue.   The fruiting mass, consisting of a flattish or shallow cup-like basal layer of fungous tissue—the stroma—with the conidia, often borne on short, narrow conidiophores, is called an *acervulus*, meaning a little heap.   The expansion of the acervulus ruptures the cuticle or epidermis permitting the escape of the spores" (Dearness).   See Figs. 6 and 93.

"The common term *anthracnose* is applied to any disease caused by a member of this order" (Stevens).

"The anthracnoses come next to the rusts and smuts in importance as producers of plant diseases" (Dearness).   Dearness recognized about 350 anthracnose diseases, some of great importance, in Canada and the adjacent United States.

The two leading genera of anthracnose fungi are *Colletotrichum* and *Gloeosporium*, both with clear, one-celled, round or oblong conidia.   In *Colletotrichum* the acervuli are distinguished by the presence of long, dark bristles (setae) among the conidia; these are lacking in the otherwise similar *Gloeosporium* (See Fig. 93 on page 204).

CEREAL ANTHRACNOSE (*Colletotrichum graminicolum*).

History and distribution.   The fungus causing cereal anthracnose was first described, as a fungus on corn by Cesati in Italy, 1852,

and in America (South Carolina) by Ravenel, 1855.   In its early
study its characteristics were imperfectly understood, and the fungus
was described under several names.   The most extensive pathological study is that of Selby and Manns in Ohio, 1909.   The
fungus was determined to be a cause of shrivelling of grain and
reduced yields in rye and wheat and was also found on oats and
certain grasses.   In 1935, Sanford in Canada showed that the
fungus is important as a cause of root and stem rot in oats.   The
remaining literature dealing with the diseases due to *C. graminicolum*
is limited to brief reports of the occurrence of the fungus on species
of grasses and notes on the injury to cereals observed in various
areas.

  Colletotrichum graminicolum has been observed·in western Europe:
Germany, Italy, and France, in Canada, and in the United States
from southern New England south to Florida and west to the 100th
meridian including Oklahoma, the eastern half of Texas, most of
Kansas, up to eastern South Dakota.

  Importance. The statement is frequently encountered that
cereal anthracnose is a disease of minor importance and in dry
seasons and locations this is doubtless true.   The disease lesions are
less conspicuous than those of rusts, smuts, and other cereal diseases.
However, the outbreaks recorded in the "Plant Disease Reporter"
indicate that under favorable conditions, especially in the central
and southern cereal areas it may be very destructive.   Fields of
wheat and rye have frequently been found with 100 per cent of the
plants affected and showing losses due to anthracnose from a trace
up to total failure as in Kentucky in 1932.   In 1918 the disease
was epiphytotic; the losses in individual rye fields were as high as
33 per cent in Minnesota, 50 per cent in Missouri and 50 to 60 per
cent in Oklahoma.   The same year the wheat in Virginia suffered
a 10 per cent loss from anthracnose and the Ohio wheat crop 4 per
cent with 2 to 26 per cent infestation in every county inspected.
Again in 1923 there was a severe outbreak with several states
reporting anthracnose as the worst rye disease of the year, the state
losses reaching 10 per cent in Mississippi and 15 per cent in Ohio.
Ten per cent losses were suffered again in 1924 in the southern rye
areas.   By 1926 Ohio had come to the conclusion that over the
preceding 9 years anthracnose had been one of the most destructive

diseases in the state, and also in Pennsylvania it outranked any other two rye diseases put together. Serious losses in oats were seen in Mississippi in 1926 and in Arkansas in 1931. Missouri in 1928 found anthracnose severe on Sudan grass with a 5 to 10 per cent loss for the state. Losses are due to both lowered yield and poorer quality of affected grain crops.

Host plants. The fungus *Colletotrichum graminicolum* has a wide host range among 8 tribes of the *Gramineae*. Of the cultivated hosts, rye is most important followed closely by wheat, oats, and sorghums, including Johnson grass and Sudan grass. Corn and barley are less severely attacked. Among the grasses it has been recorded on species of *Tripsacum, Andropogon, Chrysopogon, Anthaenantia, Brachiaria, Brachypodium, Poa, Beckmannia, Cenchrus, Echinochloa, Panicum, Syntherisma, Agrostis, Calamogrostis, Phleum, Arrhenatherum, Bromus, Dactylis, Festuca, Melica, Poa, Lolium,* and *Arundinaria.* It has also been reported on clover, but apparently is unimportant on this host.

Varieties of cultivated cereals differ in susceptibility to anthracnose but lists of resistant varieties are not available. In wheat, Turkey, Kanred, Fultz, Harvest Queen, and Marquis have all been found highly susceptible. Some of the oat hybrids of recent origin have been observed to be free of the disease in Arkansas although adjacent to other, heavily infested varieties.

Symptoms and signs. In wheat and rye the disease is distributed among plants in the field at random; in oats where root decay is a prominent feature of the disease, the affected plants may occur in well-defined spots. Infection is most commonly observed at the foot or base of the stem, especially just below the nodes and on the leaf sheaths. The affected tissues are dark and speckled with numerous black acervuli (Fig. 91). The heads may be attacked directly, much in the fashion of scab. The spikelets are darkened, the glumes are dotted with dark acervuli, and the grain within may be shrivelled and dark, or in rye the entire head above the point of attack may be bleached and blighted. Premature ripening often occurs. A certain amount of root decay accompanies these above-ground symptoms in oats, especially in the seminal roots, later formed roots escaping injury to a greater degree. *Colletotrichum graminicolum* also attacks the leaves directly, producing spots that vary in appearance with the host species.   On corn they are oval or elliptical, brown, studded with acervuli, while on sorghum they are oval to spindle-shaped and brilliant red or stained

brown or of the same color as the light brown dead leaf, depending on the sorghum variety. As a consequence of stem, leaf, and root infections, plants are stunted in size, the grain is poorly filled, and the general picture, resembling that of a leaf rust attack, is one of malnutrition or starvation. On orchard grass the spots are round-ish, small, reddish-brown, often fusing to form long necrotic streaks, and on the grass *Brachypodium mucronatum* the spots are white with a narrow brown margin.

Etiology. The organism caus-ing anthracnose is an imperfect fungus, *Colletotrichum graminicolum,* also known in the past by several other names: *C. cereale, C. lineola, C. Bromi, C. sanguineum,* and species of *Dicladium, Psilonia, Vermicularia,* and *Steriochaete.* A reason for this synonymy was imperfect knowledge of all of the morphological charac-ters requisite to exact placement in the proper genus and species of the imperfect fungi.

Figure 91. Anthracnose on wheat. Discoloration of stem joints is a characteristic of the disease, as is also the presence of black specks on stems, sheaths, and glumes. Severely in-fected plants ripen prematurely and bear shrivelled grain. (*Courtesy of Illinois Natural History Survey.*)

C. graminicolum has no known sexual or perfect stage, although in related species of *Colletotrichum* the perfect stages, where known, fall into the ascomycetous genera *Glomerella* (e.g. the cotton anthracnose fungus to be considered later) and *Pseudopeziza* (kin to the alfalfa leaf spot fungus). The only spores produced are conidia, which are spindle- or boat-shaped, about 6 times as long as broad, clear (hyalin), with 2 or more oil droplets ("2 plus guttulate"), borne on very short sporophores. The sporophores and conidia are grouped in circular or oval acervuli up to 1 mm. in diameter, arising from a compact layer of fungus tissue. They are dark due to the presence of numerous brown spine-like setae, visible as black hairs under low-power magnification.

C. graminicolum overwinters as a saprophytic mycelium or in the form of resting, sclerotium-like bodies in the soil (Sanford) or in stubble and straw from previous crops (Dickson), as spores on the surface of seed grain (Selby and Manns), or as active, parasitic mycelium in winter grains (Valleau and others). In the spring, conidia are liberated from overwintered lesions, are spread by wind and rain to healthy plants, and induce primary infection. On the lesions thus formed, groups of conidia-bearing acervuli soon form, the spores serving for secondary spread, first from stem to stem, later to the heads when these appear.

In oats, a distinct type of life history is seen (Sanford). Here the fungus may be soil-borne. The first roots formed by the germinating seed are highly susceptible; these are rapidly invaded by the soil-borne mycelium and their tissues broken down. The vessels of these roots are plugged with mycelium, and the poor functioning of the roots produces stunting and suffering in the seedling. On the rhizome and base of the stem are formed dark, compact sclerotium-like fungus masses (see illustrations in Sanford; Sci. Agr. 15 (1935): 370–376). These do not produce spores unless above ground. The roots formed subsequently appear to be more resistant to the fungus and escape serious injury, but the disease progresses in the culm, in typical fashion.

There is a little indication of physiologic specialization in *C. graminicolum* although detailed studies of this point are needed. Sanford found that his oat isolate failed to attack wheat, barley, or flax.

Epiphytology. There is little exact information on the relation of environment to cereal anthracnose. The disease is favored by warm temperatures but tolerant of a wide temperature range as indicated by its distribution from Canada to Florida and Texas with greatest losses from Tennessee southward. Moisture is plainly an important factor, restricting the disease to areas east of the 100th meridian, and to moist locations and years.   Anthracnose is so commonly seen coexistent with cereal rusts that it appears that a similar sequence of rainy or dewy weather favors both types of disease.

Little is known of the relation of soil conditions to anthracnose. Dickson suggests that attention to adequate soil fertility is useful in anthracnose control, but this may merely be as partial compensation for devitalizing due to the disease.   Coexistence with rusts implies that well-fertilized plants are anthracnose-susceptible.   A number of workers indicate that the effects of anthracnose are most pronounced in combination with malnutrition and simultaneous attacks by other diseases.

Control. Because of the many points in connection with anthracnose that lack sufficient study, recommendations on control are theoretical, based on available information on the life history and not well supported by critical tests.   These recommendations include:

1. *Seed treatment.*   Formaldehyde treatment is commonly suggested to kill surface-borne spores.   This is probably due to dependence on Selby and Manns' early data (1909) before mercury dusts and copper carbonate came into general use.   It is probable that any of the surface treatments used for smut control would be effective in destroying infestation on seed surfaces.   Fanning seed to remove light kernels is also recommended.

2. *Sanitation and rotation.*   Considering the wide host range of *C. graminicolum* among the cereals and lack of knowledge on physiologic specialization, it is advisable to alternate cereals with noncereal crops wherever practicable.   One of the most destructive outbreaks of anthracnose on record, complete killing of winter wheat in Kentucky, was in wheat planted on disked corn stubble, although corn and barley are less subject to the disease than wheat, oats, and rye.   Thorough turning under of cereal debris, allowing it to decompose well before replanting cereal crops, would doubtless effect important reduction of inoculum.

3. *Resistant varieties.*   Hope for the future in anthracnose control rests largely on the varietal differences in susceptibility that have been frequently noted.   No specific recommendations on resistant varieties can be made at present, but growers should be alert to

detect differences in susceptibility of the major cereal crop varieties, and be governed accordingly.   There is need for a careful study of the resistance of cereal varieties to this disease.

MELON ANTHRACNOSE (*Colletotrichum lagenarium*).

This disease is mainly important on watermelons and musk-melons where it ranks as a major disease; cucumbers, pumpkins,

Figure 92.   Cucurbit anthracnose on watermelon (advanced stage) and Honey Dew melon.   (*Courtesy of C. J. Nusbaum, S. C. Agr. Exp. Sta.*)

squashes, and gourds are less commonly affected.   Its destructiveness is illustrated in an outbreak involving two-thirds of the Mississippi watermelon crop in 1930 (Plant Disease Reporter) where 75 per cent of the 3,500 acres involved showed 5 to 100 per cent of the melons affected, lowering the market grade of one-fifth of the carloads shipped, a loss amounting to several thousand dollars.   Fruit may be completely destroyed before maturity but more commonly the principal loss is from poor appearance and decay in transit. The disease prevails throughout the melon areas east of the Rocky Mountains. The symptoms include irregular, brown or black, dry leaf spots, eventually causing the leaf to shrivel up and die, and sunken, circular to irregular rotten areas on the fruit from pin-point size to very extensive patches (Fig. 92). Elongate stem and petiole lesions occur. Under moist conditions the fruit lesions are dotted with masses of pink conidia. These rapidly spread the infection in moist weather. The fungus overwinters in decaying vines and on seed from diseased fruits. Temperatures above 63°F. are favorable with optimal spore germination at 72° to 80°F.

Control depends on (1) seed treatment with 1:1000 bichloride of mercury (5 to 10 minutes followed by water rinse); (2) spraying with Bordeaux mixture (2–3–50, 3–6–50, and 4–4–50 have all been recommended) or dusting with copper lime dust (20–80), or other copper and sulphur dusts; and (3) practicing a 3-year rotation with non-cucurbits. Practically all commercial varieties of watermelons exhibit some anthracnose susceptibility, but high resistance occurs in 5 African varieties, and Dayton in Iowa has recently produced resistant hybrids between these and the commercial, wilt-resistant variety, Iowa Belle.

ANTHRACNOSE OF BEANS AND COWPEAS (*Colletotrichum lindemuthianum*).

This major bean disease, often incorrectly called "rust," is worldwide and occurs in every state in the Union. It is most destructive in the North Central and Eastern states, and rarely is important on beans in the semi-arid western areas in the Southwest, where bacterial blight is a correspondingly great problem. Cowpeas, however, are sometimes severely attacked in the Southwest. Anthracnose is most noticeable in the pods, as sunken, irregular, brown lesions exuding flesh-colored spore masses when moist (Fig. 93). On beans, leaf lesions are on the under sides, along the veins, and on cowpeas they are rather large dead spots with a pale center and reddish, wavy rim. Dark, sunken cankers occur on stems and petioles. The dry beans show dark-discolored spots that are most obvious on white-coated beans (Fig. 94). These lesions may involve as much as half the seed surface, and may reach downward into the cotyledons. The fungus overwinters primarily in such

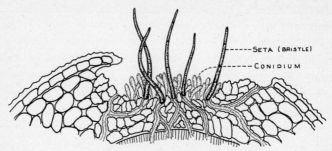

Figure 93. Acervulus of the bean anthracnose fungus. The ruptured host tissues are a constant feature of anthracnose lesions, and the presence of the setae distinguishes anthracnose fungi of the genus *Colletotrichum* from other closely related organisms. (*After Whetzel and Schwarze.*)

seed; it is short lived in the soil. Spores produced on the lesions are spread mainly by splashing rain, infection being favored by cool

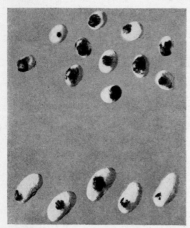

Figure 94. Bean anthracnose on the seed. The seed is infected through the cankers on the pods. Infected seed serves as a means of infesting the new crop and should never be planted. (*Photo by the Bureau of Plant Industry, U. S. Dept. of Agriculture.*)

temperatures (72° to 73°F. is optimum for growth of the fungus and none occurs above 86° to 93°F.). The fungus exhibits physiologic specialization; 34 strains in 3 groups having been recognized. In spite of this there has been some success in selecting and breeding beans for anthracnose resistance, the varieties with more notable resistance including: Perry Marrow, Genessee, Wells Red Kidney, White Imperial, Idaho Refugee, Wisconsin Refugee, Corbett Refugee, Sugar Pearl and pea bean No. 22.

Control depends first on the use of anthracnose-free seed. This can be obtained from areas in which anthracnose does not become prevalent, notably Colorado, Idaho, and California. For the best results, this should be assisted by a rotation, using beans on the same land only once in 3 or 4 years, and avoiding picking or handling the vines when wet, a precaution that is also paramount in controlling bacterial blight of beans. Seed treatments and spraying or dusting are of little or no value in controlling this disease. Other factors being equal, preference should be given to the anthracnose-resistant varieties in areas of common infestation. In cowpeas, selection of seed from anthracnose-free fields, which occur frequently in cowpea areas, and crop rotation are the principal control measures.

CLOVER-ALFALFA ANTHRACNOSE (*Colletotrichum trifolii*).

Anthracnose has been the principal limiting factor in red clover production in the southern part of the region of adaptation of red clover, which comprises the greater part of Tennessee, Kentucky, and Missouri, western Virginia and North Carolina, the southern parts of Ohio, Indiana, and Illinois, and the eastern edge of Kansas. The losses involve both reduced hay and seed yields and value in soil building, and killing out of the stand. The disease also attacks alfalfa, sweet clover, crimson clover, bur clover, and subterranean clover. Other similar anthracnose fungi are sometimes found on these and other leguminous hosts.

Any green part of the plant is susceptible. Leaf lesions are dark or black, from tiny up to areas involving the entire leaf blade. Petioles are often attacked, causing the leaflets to wither and fall off. On larger petioles and stems the lesions are zoned, light gray with a dark border, dotted with tiny black acervuli, exuding pink spores in moist weather. The stem or petiole usually bends at the point of infection, and parts above this wilt and die. The crown may be affected with a rotting of the crown and dark lesions on the tap root finally encircling and killing the root. The flowers and heads droop, and become dry, giving the field a scorched appearance. The disease must be carefully distinguished from other clover and alfalfa troubles, as leaf spots, sun scorch, winter injury, and bacterial diseases.

C. trifolii is a typical *Colletotrichum*, with clear, oval, one-celled conidia, borne in acervuli distinguished by the presence of black setae, similar to those in Fig. 93. No perfect stage is known. The fungus develops between 41° and 97°F. with maximum growth from

77° to 86°F., i.e. in moderately warm but not hot weather, such as favors the growth of its hosts. In the absence of crown infections, infected plants may recover during cool weather. Moisture is necessary for infection to occur but once this is accomplished the damage is accentuated by dry weather. Spread is by means of the abundant conidia produced on both living and dead plants and borne by splashing rain. The incubation period, from infection to spore production, is surprisingly short,—only 4 days, allowing many

Figure 95. Destruction by anthracnose of red clover of several strains (A, C, D, E, and F, from Italy, Netherlands, Poland, Oregon, and Denmark, respectively), while the resistant Tennessee strain (B) was uninjured. (*Photo by the Bureau of Plant Industry, U. S. Dept. of Agriculture*).

secondary cycles during the season. Overwintering and introduction into legume fields is chiefly by the agency of infested wind-borne and seed-borne leaf and hay fragments, less commonly through seed itself, since the nature of the infection usually prevents seed formation in badly infected plants.

In clover, the major means of control is the use of the anthracnose-resistant clover strain developed in Tennessee (Fig. 95). Accessory measures include the use of well-cleaned seed, preferably from anthracnose-free fields, and a 2 or 3 year rotation. No specific control measures have been worked out for alfalfa, but the sanitary measures of clean seed and an interval between one alfalfa crop and the next would probably be beneficial.

OTHER ANTHRACNOSE DISEASES.

Cotton anthracnose (Glomerella gossypii) is considered in Chapter 9.

Flax anthracnose (Colletotrichum lini) is not ordinarily a very serious disease but is capable of destroying plants much as wilt. It is outstanding in being internally seedborne and is controlled by the use of bright, plump, clean seed from disease-free crops.

Onion smudge (Colletotrichum circinans), while not a major onion disease, is remembered as one of the few cases for which we have a clear-cut picture of the nature of resistance, due in red and yellow onions to the pigments, protocatechuic acid and catechol.

Colletotrichum falcatum is unusual in attacking the inner tissues of the sugar cane stem, causing a destructive disease, "red rot." Resistant varieties have provided the major means of effective control.

Pestalotia species, distinguished by conidia equipped with hair-like appendages, are common on many kinds of woody plants, but are generally considered weak parasites or saprophytes.

Marssonina populi, with two-celled conidia, causes the very common leaf spot disease of poplar and cottonwood.

Many other anthracnose fungi, particularly species of *Colletotrichum* and *Gloeosporium* might be mentioned. In fact there is hardly a major crop that does not suffer at one time or another from pathogens of this group.

III. Diseases Caused by Sphaeropsidales

The *Sphaeropsidales* are those imperfect fungi in which the conidia are produced in dark, flask-like pycnidia, from which the spores often ooze in long tendrils.

APPLE BLOTCH (*Phyllosticta solitaria*).

The word "*Phyllosticta*" means "leaf-spot," and there are some 800 species of the imperfect fungus genus *Phyllosticta*, associated with leaf spot diseases of many species of plants. The genus *Phoma*, containing 1200 species is indistinguishable from *Phyllosticta* except that it occurs on woody or fleshy tissues rather than leaves. Both genera are characterized by clear, one-celled conidia, produced in simple, flask-like, black pycnidia sprinkled over the surface of the spot. Apple blotch is typical of this type of disease.

History and distribution. Apple blotch was discovered in Indiana in 1893 and the organism correctly named shortly after. During this early period it was frequently confused with scab and other apple diseases. That the disease was important from the outset is indicated by attempts at control by spraying and dusting in Illinois, 1903, and Arkansas, 1906. In 1907, two Arkansas workers, Scott and Rorer, showed by infection experiments that the leaf spot, fruit blotch, and bark canker are all stages of the same disease. They also investigated the etiology and control of the disease and the mycology and life history of the causal fungus. Since their time most of the work on the disease has concerned control by spraying. The most extensive monograph on apple

TABLE 6.—RELATIVE SUSCEPTIBILITY OF APPLE FRUIT TO PHYLLOSTICTA SOLITARIA

Very Susceptible

Arkansas Black	Gilpin	Paradise Sweet
Arkansas Red	Harvest Pippin	Red Astrachan
Ben Davis	Hawthornden	Rhode Island Greening
Benoni	Huntsman Favorite	Rome Beauty
Bentley Sweet	Krauser	Royal Pearmain
Chenango	Lansingburg	Schockley
Clayton	Lawver	Smith Cider
Domine	Limbertwig	Sops of Wine
Duchess	Maiden Blush	Stark
Early Harvest	Mann	Tolman Sweet
Ewalt	Missouri Pippin	Wagener
Fameuse	Northwestern Greening	White Winter Pearmain
Gano	Oliver (Senator)	Yellow Transparent

Moderately Susceptible

Aiken Red	Mammoth Black Twig	Rambo
Baldwin	May of Myers	Roman Stem
Bradford	McAfee	Salome
Champion	McIntosh	Shannon
Fink	Minkler	Willow Twig
Golden Russet	Northern Spy	Yellow Bellflower
Ingram	Ralls Genett	Yellow Newton

Resistant or Slightly Susceptible

Delicious	Jonathan	Stayman Winesap	York Imperial
Grimes Golden	Red June	Wealthy	Winesap

blotch is the thesis of Guba in 1925 (Ill. Agr. Exp. Sta. Bull. 256) to which you are referred for a detailed discussion.

Blotch occurs in a rectangular area extending from Pennsylvania to Nebraska and south to include all southern States except Florida. It appears to be a native disease of the American crab apple.

Importance. Blotch is most destructive in the Ozark section of Missouri, Arkansas, Oklahoma, and in Texas, where it frequently outranks scab and becomes the leading apple disease. Losses up to

TABLE 7.—RELATIVE SUSCEPTIBILITY OF APPLE BARK TO PHYLLOSTICTA SOLITARIA

Very Susceptible		
Benoni	Duchess	Missouri Pippin
Bentley Sweet	Fameuse	Northwestern Greening
Chenango	Lawver	Smith Cider
	Mann	

Moderately Susceptible		
Baldwin	Maiden Blush	Rhode Island Greening
Ben Davis	McIntosh	Rome Beauty
Gano	Oliver (Senator)	Stark
Limbertwig	Red Astrachan	Yellow Transparent

Resistant or Slightly Susceptible		
Aiken Red	Ingram	Red June
Champion	Jonathan	Sops of Wine
Delicious	Mammoth Black Twig	Stayman Winesap
Early Harvest	May of Myers	Wealthy
Fallawater	Minkler	Willow Twig
Fink	Northern Spy	Winesap
Grimes Golden	Ralls Genett	Yellow Newton
Huntsman	Rambo	York Imperial

Susceptible to Bark Infection but Degree of Susceptibility Doubtful		
Arkansas Black	Golden Russet	Salome
Arkansas Red	Harvest Pippin	Schockley
Bradford	Hawthornden	Shannon
Clayton	Lansingburg	Tolman Sweet
Domine	McAfee	Wagener
Gilpin	Roman Stem	White Winter Pearmain
	Royal Pearmain	

10 per cent annually are reported by individual States, and the losses in the national crop range from 500,000 bushels to more than 4,000,000 bushels annually.   The loss is composed of the following factors: lowered market value of the fruit because of disfiguring blemishes, predisposition to fruit decay, defoliation with ensuant weakening of the tree, to a lesser extent injury to the tree from bark cankers, rejection of affected nursery stock, and cost of control measures.

Host plants.   *Phyllosticta solitaria* is limited in its attack to apples and crabapples.   Guba gives us the preceding list of apple varieties showing their degree of susceptibility or resistance to blotch (Tables 6, 7).

Symptoms and signs.   Blotch symptoms occur on leaves, fruit, and bark (Fig. 96).

Leafspots due to the blotch fungus are small, about 1 mm. in diameter, although often very numerous on the leaf, round, white, usually with a tiny, solitary black pycnidium in the center of each spot, occasioning the name *Phyllosticta solitaria*.   They vary somewhat in size depending on the apple variety.   Larger, elongate lesions occur along the veins and midrib.   The leaf areas between the spots are usually normal green, but where the spots are very numerous the leaf falls prematurely.

Fruit blotch occurs as brown patches, very irregular in outline, sometimes star shaped, feathery at the margin.   These lesions are studded with numerous tiny, black pycnidia.   They are superficial, not extending into the apple flesh, but often opening the way for decay organisms that rot the fruit more or less extensively.   When the fruit is affected in a very early stage the fruit lesions may develop into deep cracks, a three-directional crack being common.

Bark lesions on the twigs at first are lens-shaped or oval, light in color, smooth, sprinkled with numerous pycnidia.   They are biennial; after the second year the wood under the lesion heals and the area becomes rough.   Meanwhile a new lesion area develops around the edges of the old lesion, and this may continue year after year until large rough areas are produced on the branches.

Etiology.   *Phyllosticta solitaria* is an imperfect fungus having as its only spore form clear, one-celled, oval conidia borne on slender conidiophores and produced in large quantities within simple,

Figure 96. Apple blotch. Left, cankers on apple twig, enlarged, showing the tiny black pycnidia that initiate spring infections; right, above, typical blotch leaf lesions, at the center of each of which is a tiny black pycnidium, not visible in the photograph; below, typical superficial fruit lesions.

globular to irregular-shaped pycnidia.   The formation of pycnidia is sometimes preceded by the heaping together of mycelium to form sterile, dark, overwintering mycelial masses on the lesions, known as pycnosclerotia.   The following season these become pycnidia. Ordinarily pycnidia formed early in the season develop spores directly, while those initiated later in the season pass through the pycnosclerotial stage.   The spores of *P. solitaria* are unusual in sometimes having a long or short gelatinous appendage that partly envelopes the spore (figured in Guba's monograph).   *P. solitaria* is a facultative parasite, growing well on various artificial media.

Overwintering occurs in the form of pycnosclerotia mainly on bark cankers but to some extent on fallen leaves and fruit, and as dormant mycelium in the bark cankers.   Conidia are produced in the spring and these are largely spread by splashing rain, to a less extent by wind, initiating the new infections on leaves and at the bases of buds or bud scars, later on the fruit.   The secondary infections normally occur rather late in the season, several weeks after petal-fall.

Man is the principal agent of dissemination from one orchard to another, infected nursery stock constituting the leading means of introducing the disease into new localities.   Neglected orchard or windbreak trees and wild species of *Malus* may serve as reservoirs from which the disease may spread to nearby orchards year after year.

Epiphytology.   The pycnidia swell and discharge their spores only when thoroughly wet, following abundant rains.   Light rains of short duration and dews are insufficient.   Even under favorable moisture conditions pycnidia may retain many spores until later in the season.   Germination of the spores is dependent on warm temperatures.   They germinate promptly at 77°–86°F. and more slowly at 59°–68°F.   Well-fertilized trees are most susceptible due to their increased succulence, although it is sometimes necessary to fertilize and stimulate trees that have suffered devitalization from blotch, even at the expense of increasing their susceptibility, and to depend on spraying for control of the disease.   Juvenile tissues are more susceptible than more mature ones, in fact fruits become quite resistant to new blotch infections after midseason, and the healing of twig lesions after the second year of infection illustrates the same point.

Control. 1. *Exclusion.* In starting new orchards, care should be used to secure only blotch-free nursery stock, and to remove any neglected cultivated or wild apple trees from the vicinity of the orchard. The protection given by most state nursery inspection services helps appreciably to minimize danger from infected nursery stock.

2. *Spraying* is the principal means of blotch control. Three or four applications suffice, beginning about 2 weeks after petal fall and thereafter at intervals of 3 or 4 weeks. The material commonly used in these applications is Bordeaux mixture, 3–4–50 for the first application, and 4–4–50 for the later ones. Spraying must be thorough, the entire tree being coated with a fine mist (Fig. 205). This is impossible unless the trees are pruned to give an open, well-aerated top, easily penetrated by the spray. Excessive applications with coarse streams under high pressure may produce serious spray injury. Lime-sulphur is less likely to injure the trees and although it is not quite so effective against blotch it may be used (1¼ gal. lime sulphur, 33° Baumé, in 50 gal. water) where infection was light (less than 10 per cent loss) in the previous crop.

These applications are also useful in controlling bitter rot. Lead arsenate (1 lb. in 50 gal. spray) may be added for controlling the codling moth and other chewing insects. Where scab, San José scale, canker worms or other pests are troublesome, the blotch sprays may constitute only a part of the spray schedule. A complete spray schedule suggested by the U. S. Department of Agriculture (Farmers Bulletin 1479, 1936) for scab, blotch, and minor fungous diseases consists of 6 applications:

A. Dilute lime-sulphur just after blossom buds open.
B. Dilute lime-sulphur just after petal fall.
C. Bordeaux mixture two weeks after "B."
D. Bordeaux mixture 2 to 3 weeks after "C."
E. Bordeaux mixture 2 to 3 weeks after "D."
F. Bordeaux mixture 2 to 3 weeks after "E."

The advisability of using several or all of these applications and insecticide applications in addition to or in combination with these, is a local problem, depending on seasonal, geographical, and local environmental conditions, the cost of spray applications, and the value of the expected crop; it must be worked out for each orchard as an individual matter.

3. *Pruning* as an accessory control measure is useful to produce the type of tree development that is easily and efficiently sprayed. Pruning to remove most or all of the bark lesions is impractical except in the case of lightly infested nursery stock. Surgery to remove larger cankers is also impractical.

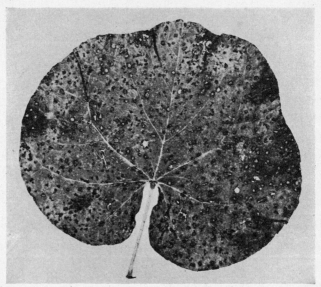

Figure 97.   Representative of the many *Phyllosticta* leaf spots of trees is this one of the redbud.

4. *Fertilization* and other cultural methods to promote vigor in the trees are often needed in older, blotch-weakened orchards, although this increases susceptibility to blotch.

5. *Resistant varieties.*   In areas of regular blotch losses, wherever possible varieties for new orchards should be selected from the list of those resistant to blotch, especially the bark-canker phase.

PHYLLOSTICTA LEAFSPOTS OF OTHER HOSTS.

A great many plants suffer from leaf spot diseases due to various species of *Phyllosticta* and other related imperfect fungi (Fig. 97). These are often quite noticeable on shade and ornamental trees.

They are sporadic in occurrence, largely dependent on current moisture conditions for their development.   Because of the uncertainty of their appearance in any given year, and the fact that once the spots appear it is too late to control the disease that season, control methods other than burning fallen leaves are rarely recommended.   Where the value of such trees is high, they can usually be protected from these leaf spot diseases by repeated applications of Bordeaux mixture or other copper sprays.

ROSE CANKERS (*Coniothyrium species*).

Coniothyrium differs from *Phyllosticta* principally in that the conidia are brown instead of colorless.   Two species attack roses, *C. fuckelii* causing stem canker and graft canker, together called common canker, and *C. wernsdorffiae* which produces brand canker.   Two other similar types of disease on roses are brown canker, caused by an ascomycete, *Diaporthe umbrina*, and crown canker (*Cylindrocladium scoparium*).   These four types of canker are distinguished as follows:

Stem canker; graft canker; Pale yellow or reddish spots enlarging and joining to form extensive cankered areas, sometimes girdling the stem, in which case it dies back to the lesion.   Black, fringed leaf lesions, similar to black-spot lesions occur (Fig. 98).

Brand canker: Small, pale brown, oval spots with purple borders enlarging to surround the stem, sharply contrasted against normal green stem tissues between the lesions.   Long canes may die back to girdling lesions.

Brown canker: Small, raised, circular purple spots becoming grayish white and developing into large brown cankers the second season, sometimes surrounded by a reddish border.

Crown canker; On greenhouse roses only; extensive, black, water-soaked, punky cankered areas at the graft union or just above; plants not killed, but weak with poor blossom production (Fig. 98).

Rose cankers are a sure sign of poorly handled roses.   Well nourished, vigorous rose plants have a high degree of resistance to canker, but roses which are weakened by poor culture or marketing methods are readily susceptible to canker.   Proper culture and handling constitute the best of all methods for keeping the canker problem to a minimum.   Prevention of rose cankers, consequently, may be accomplished by the following measures:

1. In buying rose bushes, reject any that show discolored or dead areas on the canes.   It is much preferable to buy plants directly

Figure 98.   Rose cankers.   Above, typical cases of crown canker; below, common cankers showing the tiny, dark fruiting bodies (pycnidia) bursting through the epidermis.   (*Courtesy of P. P. Pirone, N. J. Agr. Exp. Sta.*)

from the nursery, to avoid the weakness of plants that are marketed by those department stores that are not equipped properly to care for plants.   Plant rose bushes in their permanent location as promptly as possible.

2. If it becomes necessary to plant cankered rose bushes, all dead parts should be pruned out and burned. The cut surfaces resulting should be covered with tree-paint or shellac. The pruning shears should be disinfested from time to time by dipping in a solution of formaldehyde (1:20) or kerosene or gasoline to which a little lubricating oil has been added.

3. The new growth should be dusted at intervals throughout the season using a sulfur-arsenate dust. This fungicide will also control mildew and black-spot, the two other common and destructive rose diseases. The dust is a mixture of nine parts finely-powdered (325 mesh) dusting sulphur plus one part dry arsenate of lead. Green-colored forms of the mixture are available, and are less noticeable than the ordinary dusts. The dust may be applied with any of a variety of dusting devices, the choice of equipment depending on the number of plants to be treated. The first application is made as soon as the leaves begin to develop, and this is repeated at intervals of 2 to 3 weeks throughout the season.

4. No control methods will be satisfactory without adequate attention to the nutrition and watering of the plants. Every effort should be made to insure that the plants are provided with an adequate supply of water and nitrogenous fertilizer, and that they are properly pruned back in the spring.

SEPTORIA DISEASES OF WHEAT.

Septoria is an important genus of imperfect fungi characterized by long, threadlike, many-celled conidia produced in black, globose pycnidia. There are over 900 species, many of considerable economic importance. Two occur on wheat, *S. nodorum*, cause of glume blotch, and *S. tritici* which produces speckled leaf blotch.

Speckled leaf blotch (*Septoria tritici*). This trouble is often confused with winter injury, since it results mainly in a killing of leaves during late fall, winter, and early spring. The causal fungus is adapted to low temperatures and ordinarily disappears by jointing time. Rye and blue grass are also attacked. The leaves of affected plants show oval, light brown spots, often with a yellow margin, speckled with minute, dark brown pycnidia which liberate threadlike conidia in large numbers. As the spots increase in number they cut off the water supply of the leaf tips and a progressive dying back of the leaves results (Fig. 99).   It is not uncommon to find 30 per cent or more of the leaves killed at the critical time when winter wheat is emerging from its dormant period, resulting

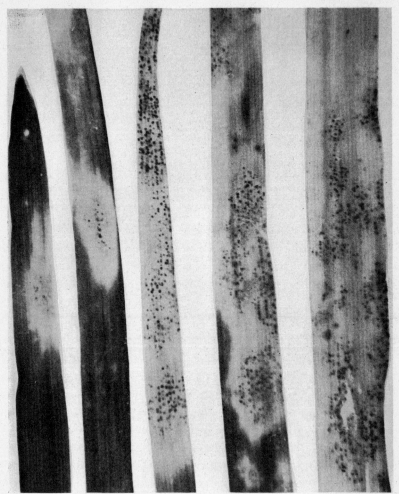

Figure 99.   Speckled leaf blotch of wheat.   Note the many small black pycnidia and the killing resulting from infection.   (Enlarged about 3x.)

in a material retardation in spring development.   Occasionally plants may be killed outright.   Boewe in Illinois ranks the disease as second in importance on wheat, its damage being exceeded only by leaf rust.   In 1941 the disease was epiphytotic in the winter wheat areas, continuing the destruction of wheat leaves until 40 to 50 per cent of the foliage was destroyed by heading time. This outbreak occurred in a cool, moist spring, and the widespread damage was somewhat obscured by the favorable effect of the abundant rains.

The fungus oversummers on volunteer wheat, rye, and blue grass, and in infested debris from the wheat crop. The spores retain viability for a year. In the cool, fall weather primary infections occur, and secondary cycles may follow, while with the advent of winter the fungus remains dormant in the wheat leaves.

Little information is available on control. The following precautionary measures may be suggested: the use of well cleaned seed, suppression of volunteer grain and grasses during the summer, care in threshing to avoid blowing of infected leaf fragments to new fields, plowing soon after harvest, where soil conditions permit, to hasten decomposition of infested debris, and crop rotation with at least one year intervening between wheat crops.

Glume blotch (*Septoria nodorum*). Glume blotch is ordinarily a disease of minor importance, but may be fairly injurious when there is excessive rainfall between blossoming time and harvest. The fungus also attacks volunteer rye and blue grass (*Poa pratensis*). Various parts of the plant may be attacked but the disease is most conspicuous on the glumes, taking the form of irregular chocolate-brown spots, sprinkled with tiny, black pycnidia, which serve to distinguish glume blotch from other diseases attacking the glumes of wheat (Fig. 100). In severe attacks the kernels may become shrivelled and the heads reduced to one-half normal size. Leaf spots with brownish margins and light centers dotted with pycnidia sometimes occur, and the fungus also attacks the stems, turning the nodes dark brown and the internodes light brown, resembling late freeze injury.

Septoria nodorum, in contrast to *S. tritici*, is adapted to high temperatures. The black pycnidia contain countless spores that are carried by the wind from one plant to another. The fungus oversummers principally in wheat straw and chaff. No special control measures are required beyond those already suggested for speckled leaf blotch.

Figure 100.   Glume blotch of wheat.   The fungus attacks the nodes most often, discoloring them and producing tiny, black pycnidia.   On the glumes small, dark spots are produced, on which pycnidia are rarely seen.   (*Courtesy of Illinois Natural History Survey.*)

Figure 101.   Late blight of celery (*Septoria apii*).

These and other species of *Septoria* are often found associated with leaf spots of pasture grasses.

CELERY LATE BLIGHT *(Septoria apii)*.

Even in areas where celery is not commonly grown, its most important general disease, late blight, is often seen in the market where it causes heavy losses as well as in the field.

The disease takes the form of small or large leaf spots, gray or brown with a darker border, sprinkled with black pycnidia (Fig. 101). Petioles, stems, and flower parts are attacked, showing small spots. Under moist conditions the pycnidia exude threadlike conidia that efficiently spread the disease in the field or in storage or transit. The fungus overwinters in crop debris and to some extent in the seed. Control is somewhat aided by disposal of crop refuse, but principal dependence is on spraying with Bordeaux mixture or dusting with copper-lime dust, starting in the seedbed and continuing at frequent intervals through the growing season.

REFERENCES

1. Barrus, M. F.   Bean anthracnose.   New York (Cornell) Agr. Exp. Sta. Memoir 42. 1921.
2. Cochran, L. C.   A study of two *Septoria* leaf spots of celery.   Phytopath. **22:** 791–812, 1932.
3. Edgerton, C. W. and C. C. Moreland.   Tomato wilt.   La. Agr. Exp. Sta. Bull. 174. 1920.
4. Guba, E. F.   *Phyllosticta* leaf spot, fruit blotch, and canker of the apple: its etiology and control.   Ill. Agr. Exp. Sta. Bull. 256. 1925.
5. Harter, L. L. and J. L. Weimer.   A monographic study of sweet potato diseases and their control.   U. S. Dept. Agr., Tech. Bull. 99. 1929.
6. Layton, D. V.   The parasitism of *Colletotrichum lagenarium* (Pass.).   Ell. & Halst. Iowa Agr. Exp. Sta. Res. Bull. 223. 1937.
7. McKenzie, M. A. and E. M. Johnson.   *Cephalosporium* elm wilt in Massachusetts. Mass. Agr. Exp. Sta. Bull. 368. 1939.
8. Monteith, J.   Clover anthracnose caused by *Colletotrichum trifolii*.   U. S. Dept. Agr. Tech. Bull. 28. 1928.
9. Rudolph, B. A.   *Verticillium* hadromycosis.   Hilgardia **5:** 201–353. 1931.
10. Streets, R. B.   *Phymatotrichum* (cotton or Texas) root rot in Arizona.   Ariz. Agr. Exp. Sta. Tech. Bull. 71. 1937.
11. Walker, J. C.   *Botrytis* neck rots of onions.   Jour. Agr. Res. **33:** 893–928. 1926.
12. Weber, G. F.   *Septoria* diseases of wheat.   Phytopath. **12:** 537–583. 1922.
13. Young, V. H. et al.   (A series of technical bulletins on various phases of the cotton wilt problem.)   Ark. Agr. Exp. Sta. Bulls. 226, 234, 269, 272, 358, 410. 1928–1941.

Chapter 8

DISEASES CAUSED BY PHYCOMYCETES

The phycomycetes are the lowest class of fungi, probably evolved from the aquatic algae and ancestral to the ascomycetes and basidiomycetes. They are very diverse in habit, structure, and methods of reproduction, but as a class they show characteristics that readily distinguish them from the higher fungi. Ordinarily the mycelium lacks cross walls except those that set off the sexual organs. The mycelium may be thought of as a complex, branched but single, multinucleate cell (*coenocyte*), and in this non-septate mycelium, which is often irregular in diameter, the granular and highly refractive cytoplasm can often be seen surging through the hyphae in a powerful and regular streaming. In the lower phycomycetes, non-sexual reproduction is usually by means of free-swimming *zoospores*, liberated from *zoosporangia*, while in higher forms the zoosporangia may function as wind-blown conidia, germinating either by a germ tube or by the production of zoospores. In the highest phycomycetes of all, the zoospore-forming habit has been discarded entirely, and the sporangia produce air-borne, non-motile *sporangiospores*. Sexual reproduction is through the union of gametes. In the simplest forms two zoospores may act as gametes, fusing to form a *zygote*, usually a resting body which may later germinate. Higher up the phycomycete scale we find the gametes, male and female being either alike or dissimilar, consisting of special cells, separated by cross walls from the main mycelial system. These unite when growth processes bring them into contact, and a zygote, usually a thick-walled resting spore, is formed. If the two gametes are alike, as in the common bread mold, the resulting fertilized cell is a *zygospore*, while if male and female elements are distinct, the fertilized egg cell is an *oospore*.

The phycomycetes for the most part are adapted to humid conditions, and frequently an important part of their life cycles requires the presence of standing water.   We find them associated with destructive plant diseases under these conditions, the downy mildews of potato, tobacco, spinach, grape, cucumber, and sugar cane, damping-off of seedlings in wet soil, and storage decays in moist environments.   Some of them have unusual habits, as the *Entomophthorales* many of which are parasites on insects and often serve for the natural control of insect epizootics, the *Chytridiales*, primitive fungi often parasitic on algae or other fungi, and the *Saprolegniales*, primarily parasitic on fish and other aquatic animals, sometimes seriously jeopardizing fish populations.

Downy Mildews

The term "downy mildew" is given to members of the phyco-mycete family *Peronosporaceae*, including several related genera causing numerous plant diseases a few of the most important of which are:

POTATO LATE BLIGHT (DOWNY MILDEW) *Phytophthora infestans*.

History and distribution.   The early history of this classic disease that inaugurated the science of plant pathology was recounted in Chapter 1, the introduction of the disease from its ancestral home in America to European potato fields, and the disastrous epiphytotics in the 1840's, resulting in the Irish murrain and famine of 1845, and eventually in the discovery of late blight control by the use of Bordeaux sprays.   Since that time severe epiphytotics have occurred, but less destructive than that of 1845, until with the universal use of Bordeaux mixture today, late blight destructiveness need be largely a thing of the past.

Late blight occurs in nearly every potato-growing area: The United States, Canada, Europe, India, Australia, and New Zealand, and at rather long intervals it breaks out in transient epiphytotics.   Today its importance as a disease of potato tubers in storage and of tomatoes in the field compares with its depredations in potato fields.

Importance.   Ordinarily late blight is most destructive in the cooler potato-growing areas, such as the northeastern United States, eastern Canada, and northwestern Europe, and relatively unimpor-

224   NATURE AND PREVENTION OF PLANT DISEASES

tant in the southern states. That this is not always the case was
seen in 1918 when Arkansas lost nearly half its crop from late blight
or 1919 when the loss in two counties of Florida alone was $300,000.
Despite very general spraying for late blight control, the losses from
this disease are often high. The destructiveness of the disease and
its variation from season to season are seen in the following United
States loss estimates from the Plant Disease Reporter (Table 8).

TABLE 8.—ANNUAL ESTIMATED UNITED STATES LOSSES FROM POTATO LATE BLIGHT,
1918–1938

Year	Late blight loss (bushels)	Year	Late blight loss (bushels)
1918	8,745,000	1929	1,753,000
1919	20,978,000	1930	5,169,000
1920	43,257,000	1931	4,430,000
1921	2,106,000	1932	9,230,000
1922	11,288,000	1933	1,303,000
1923	623,000	1934	3,409,000
1924	21,980,000	1935	9,170,000
1925	14,278,000	1936	3,637,000
1926	27,013,000	1937	7,141,000
1927	26,269,000	1938	54,573,000
1928	30,998,000		

These figures show that late blight has lost none of its potentiali-
ties of destructiveness. In 1938, nearly a hundred years since the
great European epiphytotic and the discovery of Bordeaux mixture,
more than one eighth of the United States crop was needlessly
destroyed by late blight. In that year 45 per cent of the New York
crop, 10 per cent of the Maine crop, 35 per cent of the Vermont
crop, 15 per cent of the Pennsylvania crop, and 20 per cent of the
Virginia crop was sacrificed to the disease that raged from Maine to
Texas. And everywhere the reports agreed that the losses were all
exacted from the growers who, indifferent because of the lighter
losses of 1929–1937, failed to spray in 1938. (See Plant Dis. Rep.
Supp. 119, "Diseases of plants in the United States in 1938,"
1939.)

The losses consist first in the destruction of the vines, resulting
in a short crop, and second in the decay of infected tubers, in the
field or in storage. This disease alone does not produce extensive

tuber decay, but it is regularly followed by secondary decay organisms that rapidly rot the tubers.

Host plants. *Phythopthora infestans* affects only plants of the nightshade family, the *Solanaceae*. It is principally important on potato and tomato, and to a minor extent occurs on petunia and eggplant. It affects various wild *Solanaceae*, sometimes becoming quite destructive on these, as on the kangaroo apple, *Solanum aviculare*, in Australia.

There is considerable variation in susceptibility to late blight among potato varieties and species, however in the past the commercial varieties grown in America have all been quite susceptible. Thanks largely to intensive breeding in Maine we now have two acceptable blight-resistant commercial varieties, Sebago, a cross between Chippewa and Katahdin, a late variety similar to Green Mountain in type and yields, and also resistant to mild mosaic, and No Blight, earlier known as Foster's Rustproof. No Blight is more highly resistant than Sebago and is also a high-yielding late variety, but its tubers are not equal to Sebago in size and quality. Intensive breeding is continuing to produce additional, desirable blight-resistant types and to combine drought resistance (a lack in Green Mountain types) with blight resistance.

Symptoms and signs. The picture of late blight as seen by the layman is brought out in the following description in a letter from Canada to Dr. Bellingham of Dublin, 1844 (Clinton, 1910).

"Toward the close of the month of August I observed the leaves to be marked with black spots, as if ink has been sprinkled over them. They began to wither, emitting an offensive odor; and before a fortnight the field, which had been singularly luxuriant and almost rank, became arid and dried up, as if by a severe frost. I had the potatoes dry out during the month of September, when about two-thirds were either positively rotten, partly decayed and swarming with worms, or spotted with brownish colored patches resembling flesh that had been frost-bitten. These parts were soft to the touch and upon the decayed potatoes I observed a whitish substance like mold."

The disease often occurs in rapidly expanding circular areas in the field. On individual plants the necrosis passes upward from the lower leaves, and petioles and stems as well as leaves become black

and dry (Fig. 102).   The tuber lesions are pit-like, not deep until
secondary decay sets in.   The frost-like mildew, occurring especially on the lower surfaces of leaves at the margins of the lesions
consists of multitudes of white, branched conidiophores, tipped with
ovoid conidia.

On tomatoes a similar rapid necrosis kills the leaves and eventually the vines.   Stem lesions are dull-brown cankers that may

Figure 102.   Late blight of potato.   A, underside of blighted potato leaf showing
watersoaked spots from which the cobwebby growth of the fungus develops; B, sunken
areas on the tubers indicate early stages of late blight rot; C, penetration of late blight
rot into the flesh of the tuber.   (*Courtesy of J. H. Muncie, Mich. Agr. Exp. Sta., from
negatives made by G. H. Coons.*)

split open.   The fruits are attacked when green, with large, poorly
defined, brownish lesions, involving up to half the fruit or more.
Affected areas do not ripen, and thus contrast sharply with the
remaining part of the fruit.   The rot is firm, not ordinarily deep
seated.   Conidiophores appear on the foliage lesions but less commonly on the fruits unless these are under very moist conditions.

Etiology.   The fungus overwinters as mycelium in affected
tubers, and perhaps also in the soil as mycelium or oospores.   The
primary infections ordinarily develop from infected shoots produced

by diseased seed tubers. On the surface of these first infected sprouts a mouldy coating of conidiophores appears. In cool weather (54°F.), within the egg-shaped conidia (zoosporangia) are produced a quantity of free-swimming, biciliate zoospores. These are distributed largely by splashing rain. On coming to rest in a suitable infection court, the zoospore or swarm spore resorbs its cilia and protrudes a germ tube or infection hypha that grows through a stoma and on coming in contact with cells of the mesophyll commences its parasitic feeding. This is intracellular, the mycelium penetrating the cells and ingesting their substance through long, coiled, threadlike haustoria. Further development of the mycelium occurs and more and more cells are invaded and destroyed until in about five days necrosis is obvious to the unaided eye.

Under warmer conditions at 75°F. no zoospores are formed, but instead, the conidium as a whole breaks off, and is blown or washed about, ultimately germinating by an infection thread.

The infected foliage soon produces a crop of secondary conidia, and the process of infection is rapidly repeated until large areas of the field are destroyed.

Some of the zoospores find their way into the soil and in contact with the developing tubers, where they germinate and initiate the tuber lesions that result in overwintering of the fungus. There is evidence to indicate that the fungus may also develop to some extent as a saprophyte in the soil on the decaying remains of the crop, and perhaps even overwinter in that condition, but this is not of sufficient practical importance to require consideration in the control program.

The perfect stage, oospore production, occurs but rarely in *Phytophthora infestans*, in contrast with most other downy mildews, and seems to play but little part in the life history of the pathogen. It occurs in culture but has not been found in the potato plant itself. According to Clinton, who first thoroughly studied them in 1909–1910, the *oogonia* or female organs appear as swollen thick-walled hyphal tips, single or double. Within the oogonium is the egg or *oosphere*. The male organs, *antheridia*, appear even more rarely than the oogonia. These are thin-walled, club-shaped protrusions of the mycelium that come into contact with the oogonium, and fertilize it, by the passage of nuclei from antheridium to oosphere. Following this the fertilized oosphere becomes thick-walled and acts as a resting spore.

De Bary prior to 1876 proved the causal relationship of *P. infestans* to blight, fullfilling the requirements of Koch's rules of proof. The fungus evidently exists in more than one physiologic form, those on potato and tomato each being particularly adapted to its host.

Epiphytology. Reference to the figures on annual losses show clearly that late blight is a disease that fluctuates in severity from year to year, depending on the seasonal weather. The most important conditions favoring epiphytotic development are continued humid weather and cool temperatures, 60°F. or lower, especially at night. Germination of the sporangia is most active at 50°–55°F. and infection most rapid at 75°F. These conditions are ideally realized when cool, dewy nights are followed by moderate, cloudy days. High summer temperatures and dry weather check the disease. These factors account both for the seasonal prevalence and geographic distribution of the disease, and its late development (July and August) in northern areas. The relation between vigor or succulence of the host and its susceptibility to late blight is not clear. Heavy soils predispose potatoes to late blight, probably largely through their water-holding capacity which favors both infection and secondary decay of the tubers.

Control. 1. *Tuber selection.* Planting tubers should be free from late blight lesions, obtained by use of certified or selected seed. Most states include late-blight infection as a cause for disqualification of potatoes for seed purposes.

2. *Spraying or dusting.* Applications of Bordeaux mixture, 4–4–50 to 6–4–50 are standard for late-blight control. Where late blight is a problem, spraying should start when the vines are 6 to 8 inches tall and continue at 10-day intervals until harvest. Applications must be thorough, preferably with a sprayer delivering a fine mist under 200 lb. pressure (Fig. 204), and are best given before, rather than after rains. The cost of spraying is offset not only by disease control, but also by a stimulating effect of the copper spray on potato growth often observed, and by protection afforded by Bordeaux mixture against tipburn and hopper burn. The spray

repels leafhoppers and by its shading effect reduces sun injury (tipburn). Instead of spraying, copper-lime dusting is often practiced, using 20 lb. dehydrated copper sulphate to 80 lb. hydrated lime, best applied early in the morning when the vines are wet with dew. Heavy and strong spraying at harvest is sometimes practiced to prevent infection of the tubers during digging.

3. *Cultural methods.* In some regions it is recommended that potatoes be hilled, that digging be delayed until 10 days after the vines die down, and that the potatoes be allowed to dry out in the sun before storing, in order to reduce tuber infection. These practices may apply in northern areas, but in the South they cannot be followed without serious damage from heat injury and loss of the brief price advantage before more northern potatoes are harvested.

4. *Storage* to reduce secondary decay is most satisfactory at 40°F. Tuber treatment of potatoes from infected crops with mercury before storage is recommended in Ireland, but this applies only to tubers saved for seed; it would render them unfit for food.

5. *Resistant varieties.* The rapid progress in development of blight resistant potatoes such as Sebago and No Blight gives increasing opportunity to combat the disease by varietal resistance. It is probably only a matter of a few years before blight resistant varieties well adapted for each potato region will be generally available.

6. *In tomatoes* the disease is controlled by spraying or dusting just as in potatoes and during epiphytotics by storing the crop in dry open sheds a few days and then culling before marketing.

DOWNY MILDEW OF CUCURBITS (*Pseudoperonospora cubensis*).

This is an important disease, especially of cucumbers, in the Atlantic states and everywhere in greenhouse cucumber culture. The foliage undergoes rapid necrosis, the lesions bearing conidia that are wind borne and may germinate directly or by the production of zoospores (Fig. 103). The disease is favored by cool temperatures (68°F.) and humidity. It is controlled by weak Bordeaux spraying or better, copper-lime dusting, and to some extent by resistant varieties such as crosses of a Chinese cucumber with Early Black Diamond, and certain recent Puerto Rican selections.

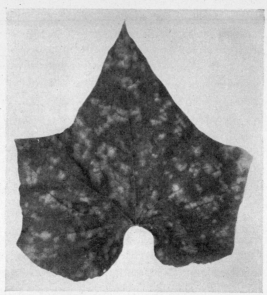

Figure 103. Downy mildew of cucumber. (*Courtesy of C. J. Nusbaum, S. C. Agr Exp. Sta.*)

Figure 104. Spinach leaves severely infected with downy mildew or "blue mold," viewed from the under surface. The tip of the leaf on the right shows necrotic spots caused in mildew-infected leaves by a secondary weak parasite, *Heterosporium variabile.* (*Courtesy of M. A. Richards, from Cornell Agr. Exp. Sta. Bull 718.*)

DOWNY MILDEW ("BLUE-MOLD") OF SPINACH (*Peronospora spinaciae*) occurs in all parts of the United States, and in the mammoth spinach industry of Texas it is a vital production factor. The disease is a yellowing, stunting, distortion, and killing of the leaves in the field, often advancing in a very destructive manner during storage and transit to market (Fig. 104). The fungus

Figure 105.   Downy mildew or "blue mold" of tobacco.   (*Photo by Va. Agr. Exp. Sta.*)

hibernates mainly on overwintered spinach plants, thence is spread to the spring crop by wind and rain under cool conditions (45°–65°F.).   While spinach is the only host, no resistant varieties are known.   Control is mainly accomplished by separating overwintered crop or volunteer spinach from spring plantings.   Spraying is ineffective or impractical, partly because it is disfiguring to the foliage, but mainly because of the impossibility of applying a spray to the under surfaces of the leaves where it is needed.   Control by addition of fungicides to irrigation water is promising but still experimental.   Such methods introduce the danger of poison residues on the crop, which would eliminate the heavy metals as fungicides for a leafy crop like spinach.

DOWNY MILDEW ("BLUE MOLD") OF TOBACCO (*Peronospora tabacina*) is the leading seedbed disease of tobacco. It appears as a bluish-gray mold that overruns the seedbed and in a

Figure 106. Downy mildew or "blue mold" of tobacco. Top, healthy seedlings; bottom, a bed severely attacked. (*Courtesy of P. J. Anderson, Conn. Agr. Exp. Sta.*)

very short time may ruin thousands of seedlings with a rapid necrosis (Fig. 105, 106). No zoospores are produced but instead the conidia regularly germinate by infection threads. These can be wind-borne for considerable distances. Oospores are produced in the dead tissues and these serve to overwinter the fungus. The disease is favored by cool temperatures and abundant moisture. While the disease can be prevented by red or yellow copper oxide plus cottonseed oil sprays, both prevention and cure are accomplished by the unusual but highly effective practice of fumigating the seedbeds with benzol vapor or with paradichlorobenzene (Fig. 207). The benzol is allowed to evaporate over night from a wicktype evaporator or a flat pan while the paradichlorobenzene is sprinkled on a cloth over the seedlings. In either case the bed is covered with cloth or canvas during the night.

DOWNY MILDEW OF GRAPES (*Plasmopora viticola*) has been the most devastating disease in the commercial wine industry of Europe where it was brought from America on Phylloxera-resistant understocks. In America it is most destructive to European varieties. The disease appears on grape leaves as yellowish, then necrotic spots bearing on the under surface a white mold of conidiophores and conidia (Fig. 107). Young fruits are very susceptible and drop when infected. Oospores develop within the leaves, and these, together with mycelium in the buds and crowns, serve to overwinter the fungus. The conidia germinate by means of zoospores, most abundant infection occurring at temperatures between 77°–83°F. and under humid conditions. Control depends on destroying the fallen leaves by burning and applying 4–4–50 Bordeaux mixture 5 or 6 times during the growing season.

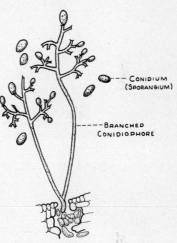

CONIDIUM
(SPORANGIUM)

BRANCHED
CONIDIOPHORE

Figure 107. Conidiophores and conidia of the downy mildew of grape. (*After Smith.*)

DOWNY MILDEWS OF GRAINS AND GRASSES (*Sclerospora* species).

In moist and especially tropical regions, downy mildews of the genus *Sclerospora* are common and often serious on corn, sorghums, millet, sugar cane, and other *Gramineae*. The diseases are primarily necrotic, with more or less extensive destruction of the foliage. In millets an abnormal stimulation of dormant buds and leafy proliferations of the floral organs follow infections. Conidia are produced on the necrotic areas although often sparsely, sometimes only at night.   The tissues become filled with thick-walled oospores (*Sclerospora* = "hard spore") that are very resistant to unfavorable conditions and often germinate with difficulty.   In the Southwest during moist seasons, the rare *Sclerospora Farlowii* may become

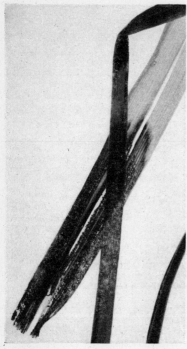

abundant on Bermuda grass, causing short black dead areas that prune off the tips of the leaves and do a fairly efficient job of mowing Bermuda grass lawns without any serious damage to the grass (Fig. 108).   The control of the downy mildews of cultivated *Gramineae* consists mainly in breaking the sequence of host culture by rotations or fallowing.   Seed treatments are sometimes beneficial, and in many cases downy-mildew resistant cereals have been developed.

OTHER DOWNY MILDEWS of occasional importance occur on cabbage and other crucifers, alfalfa, clover, carrots and other umbellifers, hops, lettuce, beet, lima bean, pea, onion, violet, pansy, rose, coffee, and cocoa.

Figure 108.   Downy mildew of Bermuda grass.   Leaves much enlarged showing one breaking over, characteristic of the disease, and in the larger leaf, the dark oospores occupying the diseased tissues.

White Rusts

While closely related to the downy mildews, the white rusts differ in that the conidia are produced in chains within compact sori resembling those of true rusts. The only genus is *Albugo* with about 15 species, chiefly noted as pests of cruciferous plants, spinach, sweet potato, salsify, and pigweed.

WHITE RUST OF CRUCIFERS, *Albugo candida*, is common in plants of the family *Cruciferae*, including cabbage, cauliflower, cress, mustard, horse radish, radish, rutabaga, turnip, salsify, wallflower, stocks, and weeds such as shepherd's purse and pepper grass.   It is not ordinarily very destructive but occasionally may be serious on mustard greens, turnips, and radishes.   Affected plants show yellow spots on the leaves and, eventually, on the under side, white powdery pustules of conidia burst through the epidermis (Fig. 109). The conidia are in chains of 5 to 10 spores (Fig. 110).   These are wind-carried, and germinate on moist leaves liberating 6 to 18

Figure 109.   White rust of mustard.   (*Courtesy of G. F. Weber, Fla. Agr. Exp. Sta.*)

zoospores which, after a swimming period, come to rest and protrude an infection thread.   Affected stems are frequently distorted, curled, or swollen, and floral organs may be hypertrophied.   As the affected tissues die, thick-walled oospores are often formed within them, which after a resting period may germinate liberating 50 to 100 zoospores.   Overwintering is accomplished by oospores in the refuse of infected crops and as mycelium in the crowns of perennial crucifers.   Several host-specialized races of the fungus have been detected.   Disease development occurs chiefly at low temperatures that favor dew formation and germination of conidia (50°F.).   Standing water is necessary for spore germination, but once infection is accomplished it progresses under dry conditions.   Control measures are rarely called for but where indicated should consist of crop rotation, destruction of cruciferous weeds near cultivated crucifers, and destruction of affected crops.   Spraying is required only in exceptional cases.

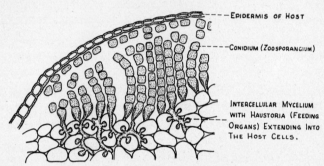

EPIDERMIS OF HOST

CONIDIUM (ZOOSPORANGIUM)

INTERCELLULAR MYCELIUM WITH HAUSTORIA (FEEDING ORGANS) EXTENDING INTO THE HOST CELLS.

Figure 110.   Reproduction in white rust of crucifers.   Section through a fruiting lesion showing mycelium and spores.

WHITE RUST OF SPINACH, *Albugo occidentalis*, was first recorded on spinach from Texas arriving in the New York market in 1937.   The following season it was epiphytotic in Texas, the most destructive spinach disease of the year, present in every field examined, and reducing the huge Texas crop by one fourth.   The white, powdery spore masses resemble those of *A. candida;* later the leaves are killed.   The parasite was previously known only on the goosefoot or pigweed, *Chenopodium capitatum*, which occurs in North Texas, and from which it has evidently spread to spinach.   The fungus appears to hibernate in overwintering spinach and to spread thence to the spring-planted crop.   When 120 spinach varieties were tested for resistance the damage varied from 10 per cent to 90 per cent in different varieties.   Of the important varieties, Bloomsdale Long Standing was much more severely affected than Viroflay, many fields of which yielded normal crops.   Other varieties with less than 20 per cent damage were Broad Flanders, King of Denmark, Victoria, Zwann's Dark Green Bloomsdale, Zwann's Darkie, Prickly Winter, Harlem Market, and Dark Green

Giant Prickly.   Control, so far as present knowledge goes, depends on separating overwintering spinach from the spring crop, and the use of the more resistant varieties.   Texas experiments on control by airplane dusting are under way.

Zygomycetes

SWEET POTATO RING ROT AND STRAWBERRY LEAK
   (*Rhizopus nigricans*).

Rhizopus nigricans is the black bread mold of which the coarse, cobwebby mycelium and little black balls of spores are familiar to everyone.   The fungus is primarily a saprophyte, but under conditions of high humidity it can actively invade plant tissues.   As a pathogen it is best known for its ability to cause rots of storage organs, especially fruits, although it is capable of producing rapid necrosis of leaves in saturated air.   The decays of sweet potato (soft rot or ring rot) and strawberry (leak) are the best known of the *Rhizopus* diseases.

History and distribution.   *Rhizopus nigricans* is worldwide, but has been recognized as a pathogen of sweet potatoes and strawberries only since 1914.   Since that time it has attained major importance as cause of storage, transit, and market losses of these and other crops especially when grown in the South and shipped to the northern States.

Importance.   Cars of sweet potatoes reaching the Chicago and New York markets show from 1 to 70 per cent of infection with *Rhizopus* rot, the average infection being about 10 per cent and the loss in individual cars sometimes exceeding 25 per cent.   Leak is practically always present in overripe, bruised, or improperly refrigerated strawberries with many market lots showing 10 to 20 per cent infection.

Rhizopus rot ranks with brown rot as one of the two most serious market diseases of peaches.   Cars may occasionally show 25 per cent loss from this cause.   It is destructive, with losses up to 20 per cent, in overripe tomatoes, especially those shipped from Mexico, Cuba, and other distant points.   In peppers and pimentoes *Rhizopus nigricans* is the most important cause of market decay, with market losses recorded from 3 to 30 per cent.   *Rhizopus* rots are common in grapes, beans, and cucumbers, and occasionally serious in avocado, pineapple, prunes, and prickly pear.   These losses are taken from data in the Plant Disease Reporter referring only to the losses of the distributor and ultimate consumer.   In addition there are the considerable losses experienced by the grower between harvest and marketing, and by the shipper.   Nor should we forget the important destruction of plant products, especially prepared foods, due to this ubiquitous fungus.

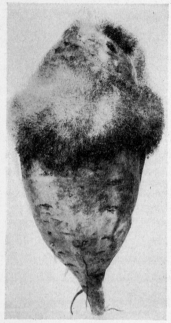

Figure 111. Soft rot or ring rot of sweet potato. If the skin is ruptured, the mycelium develops on the surface producing numerous sporangia. (*Photograph by the Bureau of Plant Industry, U. S. Dept. of Agriculture.*)

Host plants. The crops mentioned above are only a few of the more important plants affected by *R. nigricans*. Almost any kind of stored fruits, vegetables, and field crops can be attacked under storage conditions favorable to the fungus. It is also associated with root decay or damping-off of many kinds of plants, and is one of the principal causes of cotton boll rots.

Symptoms and signs. In all plants affected, the principal symptom is a rapid, soft, watery decay. In sweet potatoes the roots are not markedly discolored. While the skin remains intact, the internal tissues become mushy and stringy, and watery exudate often wets adjacent roots. Frequently the end of the potato may be attacked (soft rot) or the rot may form a depressed belt around the root, referred to as ring rot.   Ultimately the potato shrivels and dries to form a mummy.   Under very moist conditions, the coarse, white mycelium protrudes through ruptures in the skin, bearing erect sporangiophores surmounted by black balls of sporangiospores (Figs. 5, 111).

On strawberries and grapes, *Rhizopus* rot is often called "leak." It is a rapid, wet, soft decay, the affected fruit being overrun with the familiar *Rhizopus* mycelium and dark sporangia.

The signs of *Rhizopus* decay include the odor of fermentation, described in sweet potato as being at first yeast-like, later resembling the odor of wild rose or geranium. In apples and peaches, and in the later stages of decay in sweet potatoes the tissues are dark-discolored, but this does not occur in strawberries and grapes.

Etiology. The rots considered here are generally ascribed to *Rhizopus nigricans* although other varieties or species of *Rhizopus* are sometimes involved. In the case of sweet potato, nine *Rhizopus* species cause similiar soft rots, although the majority are due to *R. nigricans* operating at cool temperatures and *R. tritici* which is favored by warmth.

Rhizopus is a genus of higher phycomycetes exhibiting non-sexual reproduction by means of air-borne sporangiospores and sexual reproduction through the union of similar gametes. The vegetative mycelium is coarse, with relatively few cross walls, and filled with granular protoplasm and vacuoles that can easily be seen streaming along the hyphal stretches. The hyphae assume three habits: there are root-like feeding hyphae buried in the host tissue, erect hyphae (sporangiophores) tipped with the spore-filled sporangia, and horizontal stoloniferous hyphae that reach out laterally, "strike root," and spread the mycelium in vegetative fashion, much like the runners of strawberries. The sporangium is a round spore case with fragile wall, containing great numbers of tiny, dark sporangiospores surrounding the swollen apex of the sporangiophore. At maturity the sporangial wall weathers away releasing the spores (Fig. 5).

Occasionally sexual reproduction occurs. The fungus is *heterothallic*, i.e. two sexes of mycelium are found, designated as $+$ and $-$. When hyphae of these two sexes come in contact, each produces a short side branch. The $+$ and $-$ side branches unite, each cuts off a reproductive cell (gamete) and the two gametes fuse to form a thick-walled sexual *zygospore*, as illustrated on page 22. This stage is not commonly seen in nature but it may be easily demonstrated by "planting" a culture dish of nutrient agar with the $+$ and $-$ strains of *R. nigricans*.

The sexual stage appears to play little part in the natural distribution of the fungus. In contrast, the sporangiospores are produced in enormous numbers, so much so that the air everywhere constantly contains them, and susceptible substrates develop growths of *Rhizopus* with great regularity when exposed to the air. It is no wonder, then, that bruised fruits and vegetables held in environments favorable to the fungus, invariably develop *Rhizopus* infection from the omnipresent air-borne spores.

Epiphytology.   Infections ordinarily take place through fresh wounds.   The various *Rhizopus* species that produce storage decay flourish at different temperatures.   There is a high temperature group with optimal development at 90° to 95°F., and a low temperature group including *R. nigricans* that develop best from 68° to 75°F.   The extremes of temperature between which any of these species can operate are 38°F. and 108°F.

Saturated air or condensed moisture are not necessary for *Rhizopus* development; in fact, at 74°F. sweet potatoes show a higher percentage of infection at 75 to 84 per cent relative humidity than in nearly saturated air.

Control.   The details of *Rhizopus* control differ with the crop but similar principles apply to all crops.

1. *Storage conditions.*   The leading single factor in preventing *Rhizopus* decays is storage temperature.   For sweet potatoes the recommended temperature is 55°F. after curing 10 days to two weeks at 80° to 85°F.   Strawberries are best shipped at or below 50°F., with *Rhizopus* danger beginning two to three degrees above this.   Strawberries should be picked in the cool part of the day and refrigerated and shipped without delay.   The storage conditions should also include adequate aeration.   For sweet potatoes the ventilated storage house is much preferable to pits or cellars and for berries, other fruits, and vegetables the crop should be packed and stored in such a way as to provide free circulation of air.

2. *Sanitation.*   It is futile to hope to create a harvesting and storage environment free from *Rhizopus* spores, since the fungus is ubiquitous.   This is no excuse, however, for increasing the concentration of spores by allowing mouldy heaps of cull fruits and vegetables to lie about.   Proper sanitary measures to lessen the danger of this and other storage decays include disposing of culls, occasional disinfestation of storage houses and containers as by spraying with formaldehyde, and general cleanliness about the packing shed and storage house.

3. *Varietal resistance.* Sweet potato varieties differ in their susceptibility to *Rhizopus* decay. The most susceptible varieties are Gold Skin, Yellow Jersey, Belmont, Red Brazil, Haiti, Yellow Yam, and Dooley. The more resistant varieties are Nancy Hall and Southern Queen. Varieties intermediate in their resistance include Porto Rico, Big Stem Jersey, Triumph, Pierson, Florida, and Dahomey.

Chytrids

BROWN SPOT OF CORN (*Physoderma Zeae-maydis*).

History and distribution. Brown spot, also known as measles, pox, and dropsy of corn, is primarily a disease of the moister southern states, from the eastern halves of Kansas, Oklahoma and Texas eastward and extending north with less destructiveness to Minnesota and New Jersey. It also occurs in India, China, and Japan. The disease was first noted in the United States in 1912 but had doubtless been present prior to that time. It was first extensively studied by Tisdale in 1919, and later important contributions to our knowledge of the disease are those of Eddins and Voorhees in 1933–1935 regarding the relation of environment to brown spot and its control by varietal resistance.

Importance. Brown spot is not regarded as a major corn disease in the corn belt, where it rarely causes important losses. In the warm, moist southern and subtropical areas, however, it frequently becomes destructive, causing losses up to 10 per cent. Even as the drier prairies are approached, we find occasional instances of sufficient damage by brown spot to arouse the concern of growers. The loss is due to devitalizing of the plants and to lodging caused by the disease.

Host plants. Corn and the closely related teosinte are the only hosts of *Physoderma Zeae-maydis*. While all corn varieties are susceptible to some extent, they differ in their degrees of susceptibility, and Eddins and Voorhees in Florida have recently had success in reducing the severity of the disease by use of resistant inbred lines of corn.

Symptoms. Brown spot is most apparent in the leaf sheaths just above the nodes, although it also occurs on leaf blades and stalks (Fig. 112). The spots are small, 1 to 5 mm. in diameter, rounded, and numerous, at first watersoaked, then bright yellow, and finally chocolate brown.   Many may fuse to form large irregular dead areas at the base of the leaf sheath.   The spots are most evident on the inner face of the sheath.   This position of the injury, when superficially examined, might be confused with the work of chinch bugs or aphids that often congregate in the space between leaf sheath and stem.   As the lesions mature, the epidermis ruptures, liberating powdery masses of spore-like sporangia.   At this stage the disease resembles a rust.   Ultimately the sheath may dry and

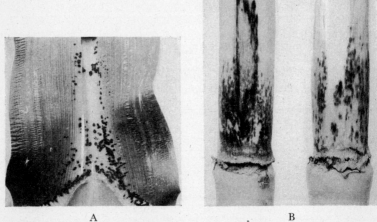

A   B

Figure 112.   Brown spot of corn.   A, upper surface of affected leaf base; B, affected stalks, just above the nodes.   Both views illustrate the tendency of brown spot to develop in the moist funnels between leaf base and stalk.   (*Photo by La. Agr. Exp. Sta.*)

shred and the stalk may break over at an infected node.   A certain amount of abnormal reddening of leaves, sheaths, and stalks commonly accompanies the appearance of lesions.

Etiology.   *Physoderma Zeae-maydis* is one of the chytrids, the most primitive group of phycomycetes.   The brown spore-like bodies, which are formed inside the infected corn cells, are in reality sporangia.   Each sporangium is equipped with a circular lid, like a trap-door, and this structure distinguishes these sporangia from any other type of spore (Fig. 113).

By means of these sporangia, which are highly resistant to unfavorable environments, the fungus overwinters in refuse from a preceding corn crop. In the spring moisture the overwintered sporangia germinate: the lid is detached, and the contents of the sporangium, a protoplasmic mass, oozes out, and at once separates into individual one-celled zoospores. The zoospores swim about actively, being each equipped with a long whip-like cilium. Ultimately the zoospore comes to rest, resorbs its cilium, and becomes amoeba-like. It then extends a fiber-like hypha which is able to penetrate the corn epidermis through the stomata or cuticle and invade the epidermal cells. Instead of germinating by means of a fiber-like hypha, the zoospores occasionally come to rest, and

produce a slipper-shaped sporangium in place of a hypha. This thin walled sporangium liberates about 300 smaller zoo-spores of uncertain function.

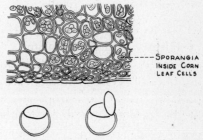

Within the infected host cell there is formed an enlargement of the infecting fiber ("Sam-melzell"), and from this, new fibers pass out to nearby cells and repeat the process. Within each infected cell the swollen

Figure 113. Brown spot of corn. Above, appearance of infected corn tissues; below, sporangia showing the characteristic lid.

hyphae become transformed into the brown, thick-walled resting sporangia, several to a cell, and these are liberated from the dead host cells as the tissues decompose or the epidermis weathers away.

Epiphytology. The resting sporangia are highly resistant to physical and chemical agencies. They can survive one or possibly two winters in the field, and can withstand freezing from 32° to 18°F. They are also resistant to digestive fluids and can pass through the alimentary tracts of farm animals without injury. Germination of the sporangia requires saturated air, as is often found between leaf sheath and stem, and proceeds best at 82°F. They will not germinate under 74°F. Twelve to 48 hours are required for germination. The combined temperature and mois-ture requirements condition the south-eastern and sub-tropical range of *P. Zeae-maydis*. The sporangia are spread primarily by wind, aided by rain and surface water and the movement of soil.

Control. No extensive studies on the control of brown spot have been made. Judging by the nature of the disease, it should be reduced in severity by (a) rotation with one or preferably two years intervening between corn crops, (b) early, deep, and thorough plowing to dispose of infested corn debris, and (c) avoidance of using manure for corn land from animals fed on infested corn stalks. These are the same measures as used for controlling the common corn smut, which doubles their value. At the Florida Agricultural Experiment Station certain inbred lines of corn have been selected as resistant to brown spot, but no resistant varieties or hybrids are yet available commercially.

CLUB ROOT OF CRUCIFERS (*Plasmodiophora brassicae*).

History and distribution. Club root, also known as finger-and-toe disease, hernia, and clubbing, is a classic plant disease in many respects. Although first recorded in England in 1736, it probably existed in Europe much earlier than that. It appears to be the same trouble that was known as the beginning of the 15th century in Spain as "cabbage syphilis." During the 1700's it caused much injury to turnips in Scotland. It was a problem in the United States by the middle of the 19th century, but prior to Woronin's masterful study in 1877, the cause of club root was unknown, and it was variously attributed to insects, excessive manure, reversion to wild types, or environmental disturbances. By 1872 club root was so destructive in Russia that a prize was offered by the Russian Gardening Society for its solution. Independently of this inducement, the brilliant young Russian scientist, Woronin, in 1873 began an intensive study of club root, and in 1877 he published such a complete account of the life history of *Plasmodiophora brassicae* that comparatively little has been added in spite of intensive subsequent researches. Woronin's paper, which every student of this disease should consult, is available as Phyto-pathological Classic 4 (1934). More recent researches, particularly in the United States, England, and Germany, have been especially concerned with doubtful points in the life history of *P. brassicae* and control of the disease by soil treatments and the use of varietal resistance.

The present distribution of club root includes nearly all parts of Europe where cruciferous crops are important, the United States, Canada, Alaska, Australia, New Zealand, South Africa, and India. In the United States it occurs in 36 states and is important in 21 of them.

Importance. The losses from club root are very considerable but difficult to estimate. Infestation in the seedbed produces seedlings that are worthless as transplants. In the field the root injury may lead to partial or complete crop loss, cabbages failing to head, and root-crop crucifers exhibiting stunting, yellowing, wilt, absence of fleshy root, malformation, and premature death. Added to the direct damage due to water shortage is the decay that regularly follows club root infection. Also there may be a loss from the fact that once land is infested, susceptible crucifers cannot be safely grown on that land for many years. This is particularly important because of the peculiar soil requirements of some of the crucifers, notably cabbage.

Host plants. Club root occurs only on plants of the Cruciferae, wild and cultivated. Within this large family there are many highly susceptible species and a few that are immune. Nearly all of the cultivated cruciferous crops are in general highly susceptible: cabbage, turnips, radishes, rutabagas, cauliflower, brussels sprouts, rape, mustards, alyssum, and pepper grass. Among the cultivated varieties of susceptible crops are numerous resistant varieties, e.g.:

Cabbage: Hollander, Stone Mason, Henderson's Early Summer, Large Late Flat Dutch, Early Jersey Wakefield.

Radish: Early Giant Stuttgart, Early Scarlet Turnip.

Turnip and rutabaga: Yellow, firm-fleshed, rutabaga types; Early White Milan, Early Snowball, Yellow Stone, Yellow Egg, Sweet German, White Swede, Sweet Russian, Purple Aberdeen, Yellow Rutabaga.

Certain of the crucifers are club-root tolerant, i.e. they may be heavily infected but still produce a saleable crop, as the American Savoy and Perfection Savoy cabbages and certain varieties of radishes in which the edible taproot is uninjured, the disease being confined to the lateral roots.

Symptoms and signs. Club root may be apparent at any stage in development of the host, from seedling stage until the first frost.

Above ground, infected plants exhibit symptoms of chronic water deficiency, wilting during hot, sunny days with recovery at night, yellowing of the outer leaves, and failure of cabbages to head, these symptoms being often followed by premature death.   When such plants are pulled up, the root system is found to be a grossly dis-

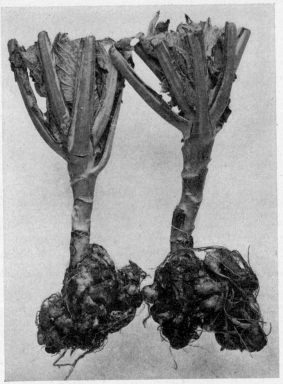

Figure 114.   Club root of cabbage.   Compare with figures 139 and 160.   (*Courtesy of C. T. Gregory, Ind. Agr. Ext. Serv.*)

torted mass of large and small irregular swellings (Fig. 114). There may be a single massive gall, or more often several sweet-potato-shaped galls, the reason for the name "finger and toe." Either the tap root or the lateral roots or both may be affected. The swellings are often associated with more or less extensive decay, or the infection may result in scabbing, fissuring, or decomposition of the roots.   The only other trouble likely to be confused with club

root is the nematode disease, root knot. While the two troubles
are superficially similar, root knot can be distinguished by the
presence of the pearl-like female nematodes buried in the tissues.
Moreover clubroot is limited to cool growing conditions while root
knot is a high temperature disease. Rarely similar swellings are
produced by root-feeding insects or genetic abnormalities.

The swollen roots are not discolored nor hollow, but are white
and firm until secondary decay occurs. Microscopic sections
through an infected root show that the water-conducting xylem
elements are very poorly developed, and here and there are seen
groups of very large, dark-staining cells filled with the protoplasmic
mass or tiny spores of the pathogen.

Etiology. *Plasmodiophora brassicae* was formerly held to be a
myxomycete or slime mold but is now generally considered to be a
fungus of the primitive group of chytrids, kin to the corn brown spot
organism.

It persists between crops, often for many years, as resting spores
in the soil. Alternate periods of freezing and thawing do not kill
them but even aid their later germination. In the spring, with the
occurrence of favorable conditions of temperature, moisture, and
soil, the resting spores germinate, each producing a motile swarm
spore. These are at first equipped with a flagellum but soon this is
absorbed, and the swarm spore becomes amoeba-like, moving
about by means of protoplasmic streaming. On reaching a root
hair or other suitable infection court the amoeboid swarm spore
penetrates into the host tissues. Root hairs are generally the
portals of entry, although wounds or even uninjured cuticle may
serve for points of infection. The amoeba passes down to the base
of the root hair and by penetration to adjacent cells, division of the
amoebae, and division of infected cells, a large number of infected
cells results. According to one account (Cook) the amoebae in the
root hairs become sporangia, liberating 4 motile zoospores which go
through the sexual stage of fusing in pairs before beginning their
general invasion of the root. Meanwhile the number of nuclei in
each swarm spore is greatly increased. After a period of occupa-
tion of a host cell by the fungus, its protoplasm collects about each
nucleus, which then rounds off and becomes a minute resting spore,
thousands in a single cell. These have no special means of dis-

tribution, but are finally returned to the soil with the decomposition of the root.

During invasion of the root the host cells are stimulated to excessive development, food materials are drained away from the aboveground parts, and the swollen clubs result.

Epiphytology. Temperature, moisture, and soil reaction are all important in the development of club root. Disease development occurs between 54°F. and 80°F. with maximum at 77°F. Spores germinate between 43°F. and 80°F. with maximum also at 77°F. Club root occurs throughout the range of its hosts, but develops best at temperatures somewhat higher than optima for host root development. Soil moisture is even more important than temperature, with infection taking place between 50 and 100 per cent moisture-holding capacity of the soil, particularly at the higher points. Thus rainy seasons and poorly drained soils predispose plants to club root. Soil reaction is a limiting factor, the disease occurring only in neutral to acid soils approximately pH 5.0 to 7.2 or 7.4.

Spread of the disease is brought about by any means of moving infested soil, manure, or plant refuse, or by drainage water from infested fields. Movement of infected seedlings serves principally for long-distance spread. Wind dissemination is unimportant except in very light soils.

Control. 1. *Sanitation.* As club root is usually introduced into new areas with infected seedlings, careful inspection and supervision of seedlings and their source is indicated. The refuse from infected crops is another important danger and should be disposed of in such a way as to avoid future soil contamination. The resting spores pass through animals' bodies uninjured, resulting in the hazard of using infested manure. Where infested and uninfested fields are nearby, the grower must be alert to avoid transferring the pathogen from one field to another on machines, tools, and feet.

2. *Rotation.* The club root organism can be eliminated from soil by a long rotation, at least 6 years in which no susceptible cruciferous crops or weeds are allowed to grow on the soil.

3. *Soil disinfestation.* Where danger of soil infestation exists, seedbeds can be rendered safe by chemical soil disinfestation, as with corrosive sublimate, 1 oz. in 10 gallons of water, Semesan, or

Uspulun. Heating soil to boiling temperature is also effective. In the field, liming has long been recognized as the chief preventative of club root, its action being primarily due to killing of the inoculum. Hydrated lime is most effective but other forms can be used, the dosage varying with the pH and character of the soil. At the same time the use of barnyard manure or superphosphate

Figure 115. The slime mold, *Spumaria alba*, while not a true parasite, becomes troublesome by climbing over and smothering young shoots of various plants; here it is seen on strawberry, which is frequently overrun by the slime mold in this fashion.

increases the disease. The striking effects of lime in club root control were brought out in Vermont where the yield of cabbage was increased from 672 lb. to 23,182 lb. per acre following liming.

4. *Drainage* and lightening the soil are accessory means of lessening club root damage.

5. *Varietal resistance.* It has been pointed out that certain varieties of cultivated crucifers are resistant to club root. These may be given preference, but our lack of knowledge regarding physiologic specialization in *P. brassicae* indicates the possibility

that under some conditions they might prove susceptible. Our ignorance on this point is also a hindrance to effective breeding for club root resistance.

Slime Molds

Formerly the club root organism was classified as a slime mold. Today it is considered a phycomycete and this leaves the slime molds with but very few members of pathological importance.

The slime molds or myxomycetes have an amoeba-like feeding stage, and reproduce by heaping up slimy masses of protoplasm which become converted into spores. One of the group, *Spumaria alba* has the habit of climbing over the foliage of strawberries, grasses, and nursery cuttings. It is recognized as large, oval, powdery, steel-gray spore masses (Fig. 115). Under moist conditions it can be quite a nuisance, and cause injury by smothering the plants. No information is available on its control, but in all probability a dusting or spraying with sulphur or Bordeaux mixture would be effective as a repellent.

REFERENCES

1. Crosier, W. Studies in the biology of *Phytophthora infestans* (Mont.) De Bary. N. Y. (Cornell) Agr. Exp. Sta. Mem. 155. 1934. (Includes extensive bibliography of the early literature, and the student of this disease should particularly consult the papers there cited of de Bary, Melhus, Reddick, and Jones et al.)

2. Doran, W. L. Downy mildew of cucumbers. Mass. Agr. Exp. Sta. Bull. 283. 1932.

3. Harter, L. L. and J. L. Weimer. Soft rot and ring rot. *In* A monographic study of sweet-potato diseases and their control. Pp. 63–66, U. S. Dept. Agr. Tech. Bull. 99. 1929.

4. Heald, F. D. "White rust of crucifers" and "Downy mildew of grape." *In* Manual of plant diseases, pp. 432–449. McGraw-Hill Book Co., New York. 1933.

5. Kincaid, R. R. and W. B. Tisdale. Downy mildew (blue mold) of tobacco. Fla. Agr. Exp. Sta. Bull. 330. 1939.

6. Melhus, I. E. et al. A study of *Sclerospora graminicola* (Sacc.). Schroet. on *Setaria viridis* (L.) Beauv. and *Zea mays* L. Iowa Agr. Exp. Sta. Bull. 111. 1928.

7. Richards, M. C. Downy mildew of spinach and its control. N. Y. (Cornell) Agr. Exp. Sta. Bull. 718. 1939.

8. Tisdale, W. H. Physoderma disease of corn. Jour. Agr. Res. **16:** 137–154. 1919.

9. Wellman, F. L. Clubroot of crucifers. U. S. Dept. Agr. Tech. Bull. 181. 1930.

10. Wiant, J. S. et al. White rust of spinach. Phytopath. **29:** 616–623. 1939.

Chapter 9

DAMPING-OFF AND RELATED TROUBLES

DAMPING-OFF (*Pythium debaryanum, Rhizoctonia solani*, etc.).

From time to time growers of every type of crop are confronted with the problem of poor stands with need of replanting, often at a less favorable date than the original planting, or with a resultant poor yield from broken stands and weakened plants. Poor stands may be due to the use of seed of low viability or to the direct effects of adverse weather, but in most cases they are the result of invasion and destruction of the seedlings by soil pathogens, operating under the influence of excessive soil moisture and temperatures unsuitable for best seedling development.

History and distribution. There is little doubt that damping-off or seedling blight, whether recognized or not, has been prevalent and destructive since time immemorial. Seventy years ago, de Bary and his student Hesse observed damping-off in greenhouse plantings, associated with the fungus named by Hesse for his master, *Pythium debaryanum*, and even before this, other German workers had studied a similar trouble caused by a species of *Rhizoctonia*. In America, damping-off first received attention in connection with losses in nursery stock some thirty years ago, following observations of similar troubles in Bavaria and England. At about the same time attention was focussed on seedbed losses in truck crops. The earlier researches were largely directed at identification of the damping-off organisms and their control by soil disinfestation and modifications of culture, but quite recently much attention has been given to the use of chemical seed treatments in preventing damping-off of vegetables and cotton, with uniform seed treatment tests being performed at many points in the United States.

Damping-off is worldwide, probably occurring wherever plants are cultivated. It has been studied as a serious problem in many countries of the temperate zone and tropics.

251

Economic importance.   Estimates of losses from damping-off are not available but many isolated observations of damping-off in nurseries, seedbeds, greenhouses, and fields, and in many crops, indicate the great destructiveness of damping-off.   Losses of 50 to 100 per cent in plantings are common experiences to every grower, and many cases might be cited comparable to Horsfall's account of the complete destruction of 200,000 tomato transplants nearly ready for sale at $1000.

The losses from damping-off take various forms: destruction of saleable seedlings, cost of replanting, loss from replanting at unfavorable late dates, loss from broken stands, poor yields from surviving but injured plants, and consequent effects of the damping-off organisms such as stalk, ear, boll, and fruit rots, and various leaf and stem diseases.

Host plants.   Almost any type of plant may be affected by damping-off but some crops suffer much more than others.   Among the more susceptible crops are spinach, legumes, cruciferous vegetables, tomatoes, salsify, cucurbits, sugar beets, cotton, tobacco, corn, sorghums, and forest tree seedlings both coniferous and deciduous.   Plants are susceptible to damping-off only in the seedling stage, and the importance of the disease in nursery stock relates to the long seedling period in woody plants.

Symptoms and signs.   a. *Germination failure.*   In the early stages of germination the swelling seed may be invaded by damping-off organisms and destroyed without sprouting.   In some cases seed decay is due to seed-borne damping-off organisms, in others it is the effect of soil-borne pathogens.   Under conditions favorable to damping-off even the best of seed may fail in this way.

b. *Pre-emergence damping-off.*   Before the young seedling reaches the sunlight, as it pushes upward through the soil, it is highly susceptible to damping-off attack.   At this time it may be destroyed by swift decay.   The failure to get a good "come-up" does not necessarily indicate poor seed, although the grower often blames stand failures on the seed (Fig. 116).

c. *Post-emergence damping-off.*   The most common manifestation of damping-off is the toppling over and death of seedlings after they have emerged from the soil.   Soft, succulent seedlings usually show a watersoaked zone at the soil level; this soon becomes necrotic and shrunken and the plant falls over, often before it wilts.

With woody seedlings the plant remains erect but wilts and dies, following the development of a dark necrotic lesion at the soil line. More or less extensive decay of the root system is seen in either case. If the stem is not completely girdled by the lesion, the plant survives, but the injurious effect of the lesion remains and the plant is often stunted and injured for life. This condition in cotton is termed "sore shin."

Damping-off, like other soil-borne diseases, tends to occur in well-defined, ever-widening spots in the planting, the spot contain-

Figure 116. Damping-off and its control by soil treatment with formaldehyde dust. The soil in the right half of each flat has been treated; the left halves are untreated checks. (*Courtesy of P. E. Tilford, Ohio Agr. Exp. Sta.*)

ing only affected plants and bordered abruptly by healthy ones. Many of these spots may give the planting a "moth-eaten" appearance. The spots appear very suddenly and spread so rapidly that no more than two or three days may elapse between the first appearance of the disease and the total destruction of large plantings.

Etiology.   Damping-off may be caused by any one of a number of different fungi, the principal ones being:

a. *Pythium debaryanum, P. ultimum, P. aphanidermatum,* and certain species of *Phytophthora,* all closely-related phycomycetes that are common inhabitants of soil, reproducing by swimming zoospores and by thick-walled resistant oospores (Fig. 4).

b. *Rhizoctonia solani,* the same fungus as produces black scurf of potato, described on pages 99–105, the imperfect, sporeless stage of the crust-like basidiomycete, *Corticium vagum* (Fig. 119);

c. *Fusarium moniliforme* and other *Fusarium* species, imperfect fungi with oval microconidia, banana-shaped macroconidia, and thick-walled chlamydospores (Fig. 119);

d. *Botrytis* species, imperfect fungi with egg-like conidia on branched conidiophores resembling bunches of grapes; and

e. *Sclerotium bataticola*, a black, sporeless, imperfect soil fungus persisting through the means of tiny, round, black sclerotia.

Of these, *Pythium debaryanum*, which flourishes principally at high soil temperatures and *Rhizoctonia solani* which prefers cool soil, are usually considered the most important.

The various damping-off organisms are all facultative parasites, and are so successful in their saprophytic existence in the soil that they may be found with great regularity in almost all soils that have not been disinfested. With the exception of some of the species of *Fusarium*, these damping-off fungi are not ordinarily seed-borne, but persist between crops in the soil or the plant refuse that it contains.

Plants are usually susceptible only in the seedling stage but during this period they may be readily invaded and destroyed with a rapid necrosis by mycelium of one or another of the damping-off fungi. The damping-off fungi produce highly active enzymes that break down the various cell constituents converting them into substances that can be assimilated by the pathogen. Wounds are not ordinarily necessary for fungus penetration.

Overwintering of the damping-off organisms and their persistence in the soil for long periods is accomplished by resting bodies in the soil, oospores in *Pythium* and *Phytophthora*, sclerotia in *Rhizoctonia* and *Sclerotium* and chlamydospores or conidia in *Fusarium*, or as active, vegetating mycelium. Mycelium plays the principal rôle in infection and spread of damping-off. Spores have only a minor part in dissemination of these fungi, and in some cases they are entirely lacking. Spread of the damping-off fungi from one field or planting to another depends largely on the movement of infested soil as on machinery or feet or clinging to transplants.

Epiphytology. Most natural soils contain damping-off fungi, but the disease is highly dependent on a favorable environment and only appears when conditions of moisture, temperature, and soil reaction are suitable. Some damping-off fungi, such as *Pythium debaryanum*, are favored by high temperatures, others such as

Rhizoctonia solani are destructive in cool soils, but all are most injurious when soil moisture is abundant. Damping-off occurs in soils of various types and reactions as might be expected of a trouble due to any of several organisms, some of which are rather tolerant of environmental extremes. In general the disease is most severe in heavy, poorly drained soils and in well-fertilized soils. In heavy clay soils that crust over easily, damping-off is sometimes so severe as to lead to complete stand failure. It is commonly suggested that in such soils the seedlings are physically too weak to break through the crust, but pre-emergence damping-off of the retarded seedlings in the poorly aerated, moist zone under the crust is more likely the principal cause of this type of damping-off. The problem of soil fertility in relation to damping-off must also be considered as a biological problem. The soil organic material favors the saprophytic life of the damping-off fungi as well as that of other soil organisms, some of which are known to be antagonistic to *Pythium* and *Rhizoctonia*. Soil sterilization raises a special problem, where the removing of antagonistic soil inhabitants opens the way for unrestricted and deadly development of damping-off fungi when such soils become reinfested. This whole problem of soil competition as it affects the damping-off fungi is almost a virgin field for further productive study and experiment.

Control of damping-off is approached primarily in three ways: the use of treatments to surround the seed with a protectant coating of disinfestant chemical, soil disinfestation, and soil management. There is little information on the resistance of various crop varieties against damping-off.

1. *Seed treatments*. Most damping-off fungi are soil-borne, not seed-borne. Seed treatments for damping-off control are rarely intended to kill inoculum on or in the seed, but instead are used with the purpose of surrounding the seed with a chemical that disinfests a small volume of soil about the seed after it is planted, giving the seed a temporary protection against soil-borne fungi. To accomplish this it is necessary to use a chemical that is not washed off after the treatment, as is done with corrosive sublimate. It is also desirable that the chemical be slowly volatile, so that its fumes will pass out from the seed and effectively destroy or repel soil pathogens in the vicinity of the seed. A number of chemicals meet

these requirements, in particular the organic mercury dusts and the organic, metal-free "Spergon." The oxides of copper and zinc are also useful for this purpose, although they are not volatile and depend on diffusion of their solutions with soil water, for their soil-disinfestant action.

The value of seed dusting for damping-off control is so well established that it should be regularly practised in growing most crops. The following recommendations and limitations are based on general usage of the present time:

For small grains use "New Improved Ceresan" or copper carbonate dust according to the manufacturer's directions.

For corn use "New Improved Semesan Jr." according to the manufacturer's directions.

For cotton use "New Improved Ceresan" or "2% Ceresan" according to the manufacturer's directions, without or preferably with previous acid delinting of the seed.

For vegetables and ornamentals use "Semesan," red or yellow copper oxides, such as "Cuprocide," "Curedamp," "Metrox" etc., or zinc oxides such as "Vasco-4" each according to the manufacturer's directions, with the following limitations:

> Zinc oxide is very injurious to peas and less effective than the copper and mercury compounds for cabbage, beets, and cucumbers.
>
> Copper oxides are less effective than organic mercury dusts for cabbage and peas.
>
> "Spergon" has proven superior to the other dusts for peas.

For small seed lots the dusts are shaken up with the seed in a bottle or can. For larger quantities, use commercial treaters or one of those shown in Figure 28. Further details of seed treatments are given in Chapter 20. In legume seed treatments, certain of these chemicals may interfere with bacterial nodulation, but it remains to be seen whether this is a serious handicap or one that can not be overcome.

Seed treatments for damping-off control are most effective under conditions of moderate disease occurrence (moderate "inoculum potential"). Where the disease is very severe, even seedlings from treated seed will succumb, and where there is little display of damping-off there may be no advantage seen in the plants from treated seed.

2. *Soil disinfestation* for control of damping-off and other diseases will be discussed in much more detail in Chapter 20. Soil disinfestation with steam or dry heat should be a routine practice in controlling damping-off in greenhouses and small seedbeds. Where heat is not available, formaldehyde, tear gas, organic compounds such as "Semesan," "Uspulun," or "Germisan" or copper oxide may be used (Fig. 116). Soil disinfestation for damping-off control is practical only on small areas of soil.

3. *Post-emergence treatments.* Control of damping-off is mainly a program of prevention. Little can be done to save a crop once the disease has appeared, however, valuable seedlings in the early stages of damping-off can sometimes be salvaged by watering the seedbeds with a copper oxide, zinc oxide, or organic mercury solution.

4. *Acidifying the soil.* In forest nurseries the problem of damping-off is a very serious one. Good results in control have been obtained by drenching the nursery bed soil with sulphuric acid, acetic acid, or ferrous or aluminum sulphate, which have acid reactions. Extreme care must be used in these practices because of the danger that seedlings will be unable to grow normally in highly acid soil.

5. *Greenhouse and seedbed management.* We have seen the strict dependence of damping-off on excessive soil moisture. Much can be accomplished in damping-off control by regulating the water supply to avoid excessive soil moisture, and the value of seed or soil treatments can be greatly enhanced by this means. Other cultural devices that aid the same end are the use of lightened, easily drained soils for seedlings, sand or sphagnum mulches over the seedbed, and improved subsoil drainage by use of gravel or tiles.

THE COTTON SEEDLING BLIGHT AND BOLL ROT COMPLEX.

It is a common experience for cotton growers to have planting followed by poor stands, the seed failing to germinate, or the seedlings dying before or soon after they emerge from the ground. The trouble may be due to any one of several seed- and soil-borne fungi, of which *Glomerella gossypii*, the anthracnose organism, is most common and virulent. These same organisms may also bring about boll-rot and lint- and seed-decay later in the season.

The name "cotton anthracnose" is applied only to the disease caused by *Glomerella gossypii* in any phase. It is also called "pink-boll" or "pink boll rot." The black boll rots due to *Aspergillus niger*, *Diplodia gossypina*, and *Rhizopus nigricans* are sometimes called "smut," but the name should be avoided as it does not apply to a true smut fungus, especially as cotton does have a true leaf smut (*Doassansia gossypii*) in Equador and the West Indies. In most of the current literature the troubles considered here are grouped together, the seedling phases being referred to as seedling blight, seedling disease, or damping-off, often with the prefix "pre-emergence" or "post-emergence" to indicate whether or not the seedlings emerge before being destroyed. The various boll diseases are classed as "boll rots," including boll spots and lint-stain. The common damping-off caused by *Rhizoctonia solani* in its later stages is usually called "sore-shin."

Host plants. The anthracnose fungus is limited in its host range to cotton, as is also the bacterial blight organism, which is responsible for some of the seedling disease in this crop. On the other hand, certain other seedling-disease fungi are each common to a number of hosts. *Rhizoctonia solani*, the most important cotton damping-off organism west of Louisiana has many other hosts as was indicated in the discussion of the black scurf disease of potatoes caused by the same fungus (page 100).

Fusarium moniliforme is a principal parasite of corn as well as cotton, and the other species of *Fusarium* involved in cotton seedling disease are also parasites of other plants. *Fusarium vasinfectum*, the cotton wilt organism, which occurs primarily on cotton, is also capable of causing seedling blight in this crop. *Sclerotium bataticola*, originally described on sweet potatoes is now known to be a parasite of such varied crops as sorghum, peppers, cowpeas, strawberries, chrysanthemums, and cotton. *Rhizopus nigricans*, *Aspergillus niger*, and *Alternaria spp.* are common saprophytic molds occurring on various kinds of decaying organic material, however, these fungi are quite important as causes of cotton boll rots, although their effect on seedlings is negligible. *Diplodia gossypina* is primarily a cotton organism, occasionally associated with either seedling disease or boll rots.

History and distribution.   Cotton anthracnose has probably been present in cotton fields for many years.   The disease was first described in its non-sexual or imperfect stage by E. A. Southworth of the U. S. Department of Agriculture in 1890, and the organism named *Colletotrichum gossypii*.   Atkinson of Alabama, working independently, published a paper in 1891 in which he verified Miss Southworth's work.   Edgerton of Louisiana discovered what he interpreted to be the perfect or sexual stage in 1909 and proposed the name *Glomerella gossypii*.   The perfect stage has rarely been found since that time, although Shear of the U. S. Department of Agriculture obtained it in pure culture.   Barre of South Carolina has contributed much to our knowledge of the disease, especially of the growth of the causal organism in cotton bolls and seed and of control measures.

During succeeding years, cotton seedling diseases were under study in a number of the experiment stations, and this work has been stimulated by spectacular results in recent years with the use of organic mercury dusts in controlling seedling disease.   In 1935 was formed the Cotton Disease Council of the American Phytopathological Society, embracing all cotton disease workers in the South.   From the outset this council has taken great interest in the seedling-disease problem.   Uniform experiments on seed-treatments for cotton are performed each year in most of the experiment stations of the cotton states and a laboratory is maintained in South Carolina for identifying the seedling disease organisms collected by collaborators in all cooperating states.   The U. S. Department of Agriculture has also cooperated by sending a representative of the Plant Disease Survey on thorough seedling-disease and boll-rot surveys throughout the South each year.

This intensive study has focussed attention on the prevalence and importance of other organisms than the anthracnose fungus in causing seedling disease and boll rots.   An account of the separate histories of these organisms is omitted, as they generally have been found associated with other hosts, and our knowledge of their rôle as cotton parasites for the most part is limited to the recent studies of the Cotton Disease Council.

Cotton anthracnose is widespread in most of the cotton-growing regions of the world.   Edgerton mentions it as being reported from Trinidad, British Guiana, West Indies, and possible India and Natal.   In the United States it has been reported in most of the cotton growing States, and is most prevalent in the area east of the 97th parallel of longitude (which corresponds approximately with the longitude of Dallas, Texas), with a progressive decrease passing from the southeastern states to Arkansas and Louisiana and thence to Oklahoma and Texas.

Importance.   The cotton seedling blight and boll rot complex is one of the major cotton disease problems.   The losses are brought about in a variety of ways, including expense of overseeding with increased cost of thinning; cost of replanting and loss from the boll weevil and drought in the late, replanted crop; weakening and stunting of surviving plants; direct loss from boll rot; and expense of control treatments.   The estimated losses range up to 15 per cent of the annual crop or 188,000 bales in North Carolina and 13 per cent or 944,000 bales in Texas with losses of 10 to 20 per cent of the crop in a number of other states, totalling a loss of a million and half bales in 1937 and 1938 from seedling disease and boll rot.   The greater part of this loss was due to other pathogens than the anthracnose organism.

Symptoms and signs.   *Seeds* infected with seedling blight organisms may fail to germinate, the seed contents being decayed to a greater or less extent.   When placed in a germinator such seed are soon overgrown with white, pink, or dark mycelium of the pathogens.

Seedlings may be attacked and killed at any stage after germination of the seed, before or after emerging from the soil.   The roots and lower part of the stem of affected seedlings are decayed and shrivelled.   In the case of *Rhizoctonia* damping-off or sore shin, the lesions are well-defined, sunken, and reddish brown at the soil line (Fig. 117).   The anthracnose organism causes tissues to redden somewhat and shrink in longitudinal lines.   On the cotyledons of young seedlings, anthracnose produces irregular diseased areas around the edges.   Seedling blights due to various other organisms are difficult to distinguish from one another and from anthracnose and it is usually necessary to culture the tissues on nutrient agar in order to determine which organism is present in any given case.

Stems of maturing cotton plants are sometimes attacked by anthracnose. The infected areas are at first dull red, then black, and finally become pink if spores are produced. The stem lesions, while unimportant in themselves, serve as sources of boll infection.

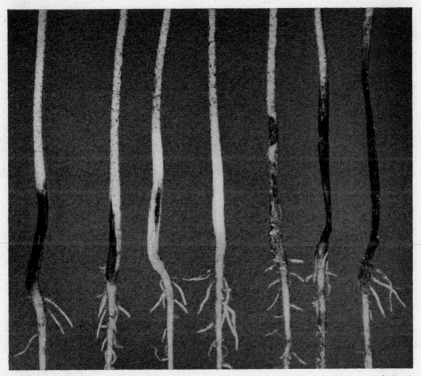

Figure 117. Damping off of cotton seedlings caused by *Glomerella gossypii* (left of healthy plant in the center) and *Rhizoctonia solani* (right). (*Courtesy of R. Weindling, Bureau of Plant Industry, U. S. Dept. of Agriculture.*)

Plants that survive seedling attacks of *Rhizoctonia* have black cankers, that partly surround the stems near the soil. As the plant matures, these become callused and probably do not seriously interfere with the functions of the stem, although surviving "sore-shin" plants do not make as vigorous growth as normal plants.

Leaves of mature cotton plants, frequently harbor the anthracnose fungus, especially those that are sickly or injured, and this is probably an important source of infection for bolls. The other seedling and boll fungi are not responsible for primary leaf damage.

Bolls of cotton exhibit characteristic symptoms of decays due to the various organisms under consideration. Anthracnose is most typical on bolls of nearly mature size. The disease first appears as small dull red spots that enlarge until they may cover one fourth to

Figure 118. Cotton bolls collected from a field showing an unusual amount of anthracnose boll rot. Note the watersoaked early stages and abundant mycelium and spores covering the lesions in advanced stages. (*Courtesy of R. Weindling from negative made by Paul Miller, Bureau of Plant Industry, U. S. Dept. of Agriculture.*)

one half the boll. A little later, with the production of spores, the spot becomes pink (Fig. 118). Mycelium enters the boll, arrests its growth if not full-sized, and causes a darkening and rotting of the parts within. Diseased bolls frequently become darkened and hardened throughout and never open; others crack, but the lint in the locks is weak and discolored, and does not become fluffy. In many instances a part of the locks open normally, apparently, but the lint and seed in these are, in most cases, infested with the disease-producing organism.

In main features, invasion of the bolls by other fungi follows the course of events seen in the case of anthracnose. Frequently the infection follows through lesions of bacterial blight which may be seen as water-soaked, green margins, surrounding the colored fungus mycelium in the centers of the spots. Most of the fungi responsible for seedling blight are capable of attacking the bolls. Exceptions are the soil-borne, non-spore-forming *Sclerotium bataticola* and *Rhizoctonia solani* (except when the bolls touch the ground). Attacks of the bolls by species of *Fusarium* show pink to white mycelium and lint discoloration. The lesions resemble anthracnose boll spots, in that at certain stages the spots are covered with pink spores, however the spots are not slimy as in anthracnose, and the spores are lighter in color.

The rot due to *Aspergillus niger* begins as a soft pinkish spot either on the side of the boll or somewhere near its base. (See the colored illustration of this and the *Rhizopus* rot in Shapovalov, Journal Agr. Res. 35: 307, 1927.) As the lesion increases in size, the color of the older decayed area turns from pink to brown. Within the boll the same pink to purplish and red-brown invaded tissues will be seen. The fructification of the fungus begins in relatively early stages of decay, and the dark spores give the diseased bolls a "smutty" appearance. The fungus is capable of destroying all parts of the boll, the capsule, the lint, and the seeds, or the bolls may open only partially, the affected portions remaining closed. The black masses of the *Aspergillus* spores may be seen in abundance both on the inside and the outside of the bolls.

The *Rhizopus nigricans* boll rot lacks the pink discoloration characteristic of the *Aspergillus* and *Fusarium* decays. The affected portions of the capsule are olive-green until the decayed parts dry up, at which time they become darker. The *Rhizopus* spore masses are not quite so dense as those of *Aspergillus niger*, and they form a dark gray or blue-gray, rather than a sooty-black powdery film over the boll.

In the case of the rot due to *Diplodia gossypina*, the boll takes on a black appearance and becomes papillate with the very numerous pycnidia; the spores develop rapidly and on coming out of the pycnidia form a smutty coating over the bolls.   The boll dries out rapidly and becomes more or less brittle.   The fungus grows into the lint and seed and destroys them, turning the entire contents of the boll into a black, hard mass.   These black masses are very seldom picked, and if they are, they are worthless, as the lint is weak and is torn to pieces in the gin.   The kernels of the seeds are usually destroyed and the seed will not germinate.   The diseased bolls dry up on the plant and do not fall off, so that it is very easy to find them in the field after all the cotton has been picked, or even in the following spring.

Other fungi which do not attack healthy bolls, participate in discoloring the lint.   In particular, a species of *Alternaria* causes a blue staining of lint, as shown by Owen.   Doubtless numerous organisms may have a similar effect if cotton is not picked promptly after the bolls open, judging by the number of species of fungi which attack cotton cloth (species of *Penicillium*, *Cladosporium*, *Aspergillus*, *Mucor*, *Chaetomium*, and *Epicoccum*).

Etiology.   A survey of cotton seedling and boll diseases in 1938 and 1939 including more than 15,000 culturings, indicates that the following organisms, listed in order of frequency, are chiefly involved:

Glomerella gossypii is an ascomycete, almost always found in the imperfect stage (*Colletotrichum gossypii*) with clear, one-celled, oblong conidia in flesh-colored acervuli (Fig. 119).

Fusarium moniliforme (with microconidia in chains) and other *Fusarium* species, have sickle-shaped macroconidia and ovoid microconidia in bright-colored spore masses (Fig. 119).

Rhizoctonia solani, already discussed in connection with potato black scurf, is usually seen as brown, coarse, sporeless mycelium with slight constrictions at the bases of right-angle branches (Fig. 119).

Sclerotium bataticola is a sporeless, black imperfect fungus with many tiny black sclerotia covering affected tissues.

Diplodia gossypina is an imperfect fungus in which the dark brown, two-celled conidia are produced in black, flask-shaped pycnidia.   These are under the surface of the epidermis of cotton, the spores exuding from the beak of the pycnidium, which bursts through the epidermis.   Under some conditions masses or strings of colorless, one-celled spores are produced (Fig. 119).

Alternaria (or *Macrosporium*) species, often called sooty molds, are common everywhere on decaying vegetation. The mycelium and spores are dark-colored, the spores being pear-shaped, in chains, and several-celled, the cross walls running both longitudinally and transversely (Fig. 119).

Rhizopus nigricans, the common bread mold, is easily recognized by its long, coarse, white hyphae and heads of black spores, at first enclosed in a sporangium, borne on the swollen end of the

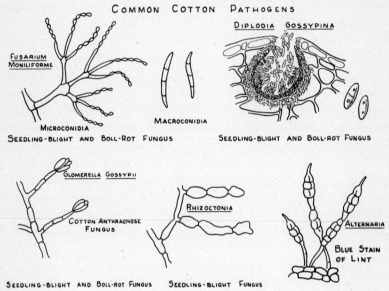

Figure 119. Mycological characteristics of fungi that cause cotton seedling blight and boll rots.

sporangiophore. The spores are small, spherical, and one-celled (Fig. 5).

In *Aspergillus niger* the tiny, chocolate-colored, spherical conidia are borne in chains on sterigmata arising from the swollen apex of the conidiophore. They are never surrounded by a sporangial wall.

Glomerella gossypii is generally conceded to be the most virulent of the cotton seedling and boll organisms. Its importance, however, also depends on its prevalence, and in the drier parts of the cotton belt it is so infrequently found that greater importance is attached to more prevalent but slightly less virulent organisms such as *Fusarium moniliforme* and *Rhizoctonia solani*. These two fungi rank next to *Glomerella* in virulence on seedlings, although *Rhizoctonia* and the similar *Sclerotium bataticola* rarely attack bolls unless these come in contact with soil. *Diplodia gossypina* is unable to attack unless the cotton tissues are first injured by insects or other causes, but there is no other fungus, not even the anthracnose organism, that attacks the boll with such vigor after it has once gained an entrance to the tissue. *Aspergillus* and *Rhizopus* require mechanical injury before the organisms can enter the bolls but thereafter also produce rapid and extensive decay.

With the exception of *Rhizoctonia solani* and *Sclerotium bataticola*, the seedling-blight fungi all form spores in abundance. These spores may be carried from one crop to the next in the fuzz of cotton seed from infected bolls or accidentally contaminated in picking and ginning. In many cases the seed are invaded and the organisms survive within the seed. Doubtless there is also considerable survival of these fungi in the soil as well, and overwintering in the soil is a regular feature of the life histories of *Rhizoctonia* and *Sclerotium* which are less commonly seed-borne. It should also be noted that a number of the cotton organisms are "weed" fungi that occur very widely as saprophytes (*Aspergillus, Penicillium, Alternaria*) or fungi that have wide host ranges (*Rhizoctonia, Sclerotium, Fusarium spp.*). None are obligate parasites of cotton. For this reason there would always be an abundance of inoculum in cotton soils even in the absence of seed infestation.

As the seed germinate and seedlings emerge, infection becomes active, the mycelium from germinated spores or from the soil invading the young roots and stems, killing many of the plants, stunting others. More or less root infection may persist throughout the life of the cotton plant. In the cases of the spore-bearing fungi, cycle after cycle of spore production will increase the disease in the field. In most cases these cycles are rather short, a matter of a few days.

The seasonal history from seedling stage to the stage of boll formation is not altogether clear in the drier states, where it is difficult to find stem and leaf infections during this period. It is quite likely that much of the infestation dies out during the hot and dry summer months, with only enough persisting in the soil to bring on new cycles of infection on the bolls during the cooler, moist fall months.

Most of the boll rot fungi are unable to enter the uninjured boll, and even *Glomerella* usually follows through small wounds.   Infections by *Phytomonas malvacearum* and insect punctures appear to be the commonest portals of entry of these fungi.   It is quite common to find a bacterial lesion surrounding an insect puncture, and carrying a secondary infection of *Fusarium*, *Aspergillus*, or *Rhizopus*.   Once having penetrated the boll, decay follows rapidly, and with the decay the production of myriads of spores which are borne by wind and insects to other bolls in successive cycles of infection so long as weather permits.   Many spores are also carried to the soil where they may develop saprophytic mycelium, or overwinter without germinating, in either case serving as sources for the next year's infections.

As the cotton is being picked and ginned the partly decayed bolls contaminate the healthy seed or yield internally infected seed on or in which the fungi may overwinter.

Epiphytology.   It is commonly held that seedling blight in cotton is most damaging when planting is followed by cool, wet weather.   While this is generally true, some of the seedling blight organisms can also be destructive under other conditions.   Ray and McLaughlin made a study of infection of cotton seedlings under a variety of conditions using several seedling-disease organisms. *Glomerella gossypii* retained its high order of virulence under standard, xerophytic, and variable conditions, also in alkaline soil. *Rhizoctonia solani* was more virulent than *Glomerella* in acid soil. Under conditions of excessive moisture both *Glomerella* and *R. solani* were strongly virulent, with the other organisms showing more virulence than under drier conditions.   It is commonly assumed that *R. solani* is most virulent under conditions of excessive moisture, however their data indicate that it may be just as severe under xerophytic conditions.

Stem and leaf infections and the boll rot phase of this disease complex are favored by humid weather, rank growth which retains moisture within the plant frame, and conditions favoring the cotton insects that initiate the boll infections.

Control.   A program of control of the seedling-blight and boll-rot complex is governed by several factors: the numerous organisms involved, the difficulty in distinguishing these without laboratory tests, the interaction of several organisms in the same field, the almost universal occurrence of certain of these organisms, and the survival of the organisms in and on seed as well as in soil.   Nevertheless much has been accomplished in warding off the more destructive effects of the complex, through seed treatments, crop management, and to a lesser extent other measures.

1. *Seed treatments.*   One of the early contributions to cotton seedling-disease control was Duggar and Cauthen's discovery in 1911 that cotton seed may be delinted with concentrated sulphuric acid with a killing of all surface-borne organisms, and numerous other advantages such as hastened germination, easier, more even planting, and lowered seeding rate.   This method, which has been further developed by Rolfs, Brown and Streets, Hancock, and Chester, has been recommended particularly in connection with the bacterial blight of cotton.   However, the acid treatment also destroys surface-borne fungi on the seed and thus contributes to control of the seedling-blight organisms insofar as they are carried in the lint of cotton seed.   Acid-treated seed, unless they are surface-treated with fungicidal solutions or dusts, carry no protection against soil-borne cotton seedling organisms, nor are they freed from internal infestation unless gravity-graded.

With the introduction of the organic mercury dusts for seed treatment in the early 1930's, it first became possible to launch a direct, broad, and effective campaign against seedling-disease and boll-rots.   Various dusts have been used, but those which are generally conceded to be most effective are ethyl mercury phosphate ("New Improved Ceresan") and ethyl mercury chloride ("2% Ceresan").   Those dusts not only kill surface-borne pathogens, but when in contact with moist soil they slowly give off a fungicidal vapor, which to some extent protects the seedling against soil-borne organisms.   The wide adoption of the dust treatments for cotton seed is brought out in Table 9.

In 1941 more than 10,000 tons of cotton seed were treated by commercial growers.   The improved stands and yields following treatments are due to control of seed- and soil-borne disease organisms, and the phenomenal adoption of seed dusting is an indication of the effectiveness of this control measure.

TABLE 9.—ADOPTION OF AND PROFIT FROM COTTON SEED TREATMENTS IN SEVERAL STATES

State	Year	Acres planted with dusted seed	Percentage of growers dusting seed	Increased stand from treatment	Profit from treatment
North Carolina	1935	7,000	0.8	No data	Average, $9.82 per acre
	1936	24,000	2.8		
	1937	200,000	23		
	1938	450,000	53		
	1939	600,000	70		
	1940	....	83*		
	1941	....	87*		
South Carolina	1935	4,000	0.3	No data	$2,000,000 in 2 years
	1939	510,000	42		
	1940	815,000	67*		
Georgia	1936	20,000	1	36%	No data
	1937	80,000	4	46%	
	1938	160,000	8	41%	
	1940	985,000	51*		
	1941	1,156,000	60*		
Virginia	1938	8,000	70*	28% (yield)	$11.95 per acre
	1939	19,300	60*		
	1940	24,000	75*		
	1941	25,800	80*		
Oklahoma	1939	89,000	5*	36% (4-year average)	$2,180,000 per year
	1942	1,430,000	80*		

* Acreage planted with dusted seed.

Seed dusting has its limitations. It will bring out the best in seed but it will not bring dead seed to life nor cure internally infected seed. When clean seed are grown under the most favorable conditions, little advantage is seen from dusting. When weather is exceedingly adverse to cotton, even treated seed will suffer from seedling blight and stands may fail. However, with average seed under average soil and weather conditions, the treatments show marked success in reducing seedling disease (Fig. 120). Some growers look upon the treatment as low-cost insurance against unfavorable conditions for seedling development; to others the advantage lies in being able to plant treated seed 2 to 3 weeks earlier than normal, with consequent less risk from the boll weevil and late-season drought.

The mercury dusts are not equally effective against all of the seedling-blight organisms. While they are quite efficient in killing surface-borne organisms, *Rhizoctonia solani* is more refractory to the

Figure 120. Seedling blight in cotton and its control by seed treatment. Seedlings from the same number of untreated (left) and treated (right) seed planted at the same time in soil infested with *Rhizoctonia*.

seed treatments and this is evidently an explanation why, under weather conditions particularly favorable for *Rhizoctonia*, even treated seed will suffer severely from seedling blight.

It has been seen that in general the boll-rots are caused by the same organisms as cause seedling-disease. A reduction in seedling disease reduces the amount of inoculum available for boll-rot later in the season, hence seed treatments have an indirect effect in reducing boll rot.

The details of seed dusting are described in a number of experiment station publications, and accordingly only an outline of the essential points is given here. The methods of acid delinting of cotton seed are described in connection with bacterial blight, on page 307.

Ethyl mercury chloride has been preferred in the past for dusting cotton seed, at the rate of 1½ oz. per bushel of seed. A recent report of the Cotton Disease Council of the American Phytopathological Society favors the phosphate at ½ oz. per bushel as more effective and cheaper. But it is difficult to distribute this small amount of dust evenly over a bushel of seed and work is under way in attempts to dilute the phosphate with an inert carrier, to facilitate coverage of the seed. Recent developments in this field also include the use of a tracer dye in the dust to aid recognition of dusted seed.

The dust is applied in a home-made, revolving-barrel type of treater (Fig. 28), turned about 25 revolutions, or in a power treater such as are installed in many gins. Treatment may be carried out at any time between crops. Cost of chemical for the treatment is about 6 cents per bushel of seed.

The dusts are poisonous. The operator should wear a gauze dust-mask and work out of doors, on the windward side of the treater. Hands and arms should be protected from contact with the dust. Treated seed should be marked "Poison" and stored out of reach of livestock. Cotton seed germinates well the second or third season after harvest, and if treated seed is left over after planting it should not be processed, but stored for next year's planting.

2. *Resistant varieties.* Considering the many organisms involved in seedling and boll disease, it is not surprising that relatively little progress has been made in controlling these troubles by the use of resistant varieties. Only in case of anthracnose boll-rot do we have a report that the varieties Toole, Dixie, Dillon, Cleveland, Russell, Express, Rowden, and Truitt are regarded as somewhat resistant, while the more susceptible varieties include Cook, Half and Half, Acala, Lone Star, Wilds, and Triumph. Edgerton has shown that the more "resistant" varieties are susceptible after inoculation, and hence may be disease-escaping because of their habits of growth, rather than truly resistant.

3. *Use of old seed.* The anthracnose organism dies out of cotton seed by the second season after harvest, and 2-year old seed, which germinate well, afford a simple and practical means of control of this

disease insofar as it is seed-borne. It is not known whether the other seed-borne organisms are controllable in this way.

4. *Cultural measures.* Excessively early planting should be avoided especially in tight soils. In rich bottom soils care should be taken to space the plants widely enough to prevent accumulation of moist air in the dense foliage, favoring boll rot. Running over the old stalks with a stalk cutter and turning them under thoroughly by fall plowing is helpful, because the anthracnose fungus and probably other seedling and boll pathogens live a much shorter time when buried in the soil. Under the Agricultural Administration Act cotton farmers are advised not to plant more than one fourth of their acreage in cotton. This permits rotating in a 2 to 4 year cycle. In spite of the wide host ranges and general prevalence of the cotton seedling and boll organisms, rotation will help in decreasing the losses from these and other soil-borne cotton pathogens, and apart from the agronomic value of the practice, pathological considerations point to the soundness of rotation as a routine practice in cotton management.

5. *Clean seed.* Even though cotton seed is to be treated, attempts should be made to increase the effectiveness of the treatment by securing seed from fields that were relatively free from boll-rot the previous year and by avoiding internally infected seed.

6. *Quarantines.* In certain of the cotton states, cottonseed quarantines are in force, in order to protect farmers from anthracnose, with other diseases. In some of these states the boll-rot phase of anthracnose is rarely present in serious amounts, and except in very unusual seasons or localities appears incapable of establishing itself even if introduced. However anthracnose-laden seed is subject to seedling-disease throughout the Cotton Belt, and the anthracnose quarantines may be of value in preventing seedling losses from this cause.

CORN ROOT, STALK, AND EAR ROTS.

Corn, like cotton, is subject throughout its life to a complex disease problem, in this case involving root decay, stalk rot, and ear rots on the stalk and in storage. Several different fungi take part in this. The Plant Disease Reporter indicates very extensive losses in the United States corn crop from these rots. In the 20 year period 1918–1937, the crop suffered an average loss of 6.3 per cent or slightly more than 150 million bushels per year from this cause.   About one half of the loss was due to ear rots and about one fourth each to stalk and root rots.   These troubles are epiphytotic in certain years such as 1917 and 1926.   During those years over 80 per cent of all cars of corn were placed in grade 3 or poorer (over 4 per cent ear rot), and about 60 per cent of the cars graded 4 or poorer (over 6 per cent ear rot).   In 1936, a quarter of a billion bushels or one sixth of the national crop was sacrificed to these decays.

The most important stalk, root, and ear rot fungi are given below, together with the essential features of their symptomatology and etiology:

Diplodia zeae is an imperfect fungus producing 2-celled, olive-brown conidia in black, sunken, beaked pycnidia, similar to those of *D. gossypina* seen in Fig. 119.   It produces dry rot in corn ears, seedling blight, and rotting of roots and stalks.   It is most common in the northern part of the corn belt, while in the Southwest it is replaced by a related, long-spored species, *Diplodia macrospora*. Seedlings are destroyed by *D. zeae* with a brown, dry decay.   The stalks are invaded with a resulting dark brown decay of the inner tissues, often followed by lodging.   The fungus passes out the shank into the ear where the effect varies from slight discoloration of the kernels to complete rotting of the entire ear.   Pycnidia may be found late in the season on the ears or less commonly on the stalks.

Gibberella zeae, the ascomycete causing scab of cereals, has been discussed (pages 106–110).   It is an ear rot fungus of leading importance.   Recall that its imperfect stage is a *Fusarium*.   Other species of *Fusarium*, especially *F. moniliforme*, together with the scab organism produce a variety of pink ear rots, and also are involved in stalk and root rots and seedling disease.   The *Fusarium* stages of all of these are distinguished by their white or bright colored mycelium freely covered with banana-shaped macroconidia and oval or cylindrical microconidia (Fig. 119).   Instead of extending outward from the shank the pink ear rots either work downward from the ear tip or, as in *F. moniliforme*, affect individual kernels at random.   Affected ears are discolored pink, reddish, or brown, and may be slightly injured or completely destroyed.   The perithecia of *G. zeae* appear on the overwintered corn residue.

Basisporium gallarum is a hyphomycete with single black, globose conidia on stalks.   It causes cob rot and an inconspicuous shredding of the inner stalk tissues.   The shank and cob are the primary points of attack with rotting and shredding, producing dull-colored, poorly filled, chaffy ears.   Spores arise on the infected parts.

Pythium arrhenomanes, which will be discussed more fully in connection with sorghum root and stalk rots, is also damaging to corn, producing a soft root decay, especially in seedlings.   It does not attack stalks and ears directly but its effects are seen in a stunting of the above-ground parts.

Minor ear rots are produced by species of *Rhizopus*, *Aspergillus*, and *Penicillium*, ubiquitous weed fungi that are not aggressive pathogens under field conditions but are occasionally destructive to stored corn.   They may be recognized in the crib as conspicuous green, blue, yellow, or black molds.

Although each of the stalk, root, and ear rot fungi has its own etiological peculiarities, they may be considered together because of similarities in life histories and control measures, and because very often no attempt is made to distinguish them in grading practice.

The principal sources of inoculum are infested seed and soil. The seed from partly rotted ears may be internally infected or may be surface-laden with ear rot spores.   When such seed are planted the pathogens are in a suitable position to initiate seedling infection. Likewise the soil yielding an infested crop is likely to be heavily contaminated with spores and mycelium of the ear rot fungi, all of which can live as soil saprophytes in the debris from corn crops. Certain of the ear rot fungi initiate infection by ascospores formed in perithecia on the overwintered crop residue.

Under suitable moisture and temperature conditions, the pathogens advance into the young seedlings producing damping-off. Sporulation on the dead parts and advancing mycelium in the soil serve for plant-to-plant spread.   In injured but surviving seedlings the root infections pass up into the stalk, producing stalk rot (Fig. 121), and thence out the shanks to the ears or the pathogens may attack the ears directly from the tip, aided at times by earworm infestation. During moist seasons many cycles of sporulation may occur until extensive ear decay results. When the ears are harvested, those infections that are already present may advance, and new infections may occur in the crib especially in corn that has not been thoroughly cured and stored in a dry place.

Control. The essential features of a program to reduce losses from the root, stalk, and ear rot fungi include the field selection of disease-free ears, careful curing and storage of the main crop and especially of the seed ears, seed corn treatment guided or controlled by seed germination tests, rotation of corn land with early plowing of corn crop residue, and cultural practices to encourage a vigorous crop. In the extensive corn breeding programs of Iowa and other states, attention is being given to root, stalk, and ear rot resistance in inbred lines and hybrids and the newer varieties are continually showing more resistance.

Figure 121. Hill of corn killed by *Diplodia* stalk rot. The plant at the right is cut open to show rot in the pith. (*Courtesy of B. Koehler, Ill. Agr. Exp. Sta.*)

Field selection of seed ears gives a much better opportunity to obtain disease-free ears than crib selection, because slight infections, resulting in a droopy shank might be unnoticed in the harvested ear. Field selection also gives opportunity to select for other desired characters at the same time: yield, smut-resistance, insect-resistance, drought-resistance, earliness, and habit.

Drying should be at about 100°F. on racks or hangers with good ventilation, and should begin immediately after harvest and continue until the moisture content is not greater than 12 to 14 per cent. The seed ears should then be stored in a place where they will be protected from humidity, high temperatures, mice, and insects.

Germination tests should be made of 10 kernels from each of 100 ears of the seed lot. If 3 or more kernels from any ear are defective or infected, every ear should be tested using a numbering system that identifies the kernels from each ear, and discarding all ears yielding infected kernels.   A germinator consisting of a flat of wet sand covered with cloth may be used, and good results are also obtained from a "rag doll" tester, made by rolling kernels in a wet cloth and placing in a 2-quart, closed fruit jar.   The good ears are then shelled separately into a sieve with hand picking of any defective kernels.   The tip of the ear is broken off and discarded before shelling.

Seed treatment is most necessary when germination tests have revealed seed infestation with ear rot fungi, but is so easy and inexpensive and serves as such a good insurance against damping-off that it is recommended as a routine practice.   A proof of the popularity of corn seed treatment among farmers is seen in the fact that 95 per cent of the seed corn for the great Iowa crop is dust-treated each year.   The dusts most commonly used for seed corn are "Semesan Jr." (ethyl mercuric phosphate), "Barbak C" (mercuric phenyl cyanamide plus cadmium oxide), and "Merko" (metallic mercury).   All are used according to the manufacturer's directions, at the rate of 2 oz. per bushel of seed, conveniently applied with one of the home-made seed treaters illustrated in Fig. 28.   All are poisonous and precautions should be observed against breathing the dust or feeding dusted corn to livestock.

SORGHUM ROOT AND STALK ROTS.

Sorghum suffers from a root and stalk rot complex analogous to that of corn but largely due to different organisms, perhaps because the two crops are commonly grown under quite dissimilar moisture conditions.

The first direct attack on this problem was the study in Kansas of a Milo root decay known as the "Milo disease," which was first noticed about 1926 in western Kansas, Oklahoma and Texas, and which proved to be very destructive in the dry-land areas.   When fields become fully infested it is impossible to grow a crop of susceptible sorghums on the land.   Although figures on the crop losses from this disease are not available, observers agree that it is a very destructive disease where it occurs.

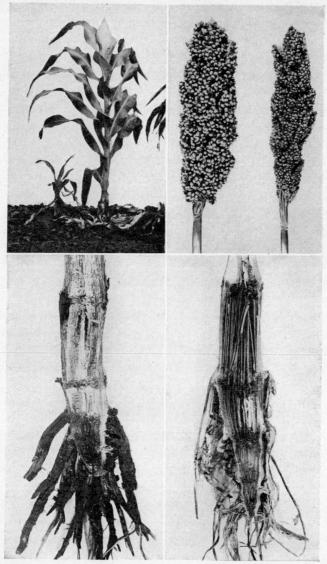

Figure 122. Root and stalk rots of sorghum. Left, *Pythium* root rot or Milo disease; above, diseased and dead plants beside healthy resistant selection; below, features of the stalk decay, in particular the discolored zone at the crown. Right, *Sclerotium bataticola* root and stalk rot; above, head from a diseased plant in comparison with a normal head (left); below, stringy dark stalk rot and decayed roots many of which are but papery shells.

The symptoms first appear when sorghum plants are 8 to 12 inches high or 30 to 35 days after planting. Growth is retarded as the leaves roll and die back from the tips. Eventually the plants die without heading, or in less severe attacks produce dwarfed heads. There is no abnormal tillering. This blighting is due to a progressive soft, brown or red decay of the roots which may begin when the plants are no more than 3 inches high. A dark red discoloration of the tissue at the base of the crown is characteristic, but there is no primary decay of the crown or stalk (Fig. 122).

The disease is caused by a phycomycete, *Pythium arrhenomanes* which attacks sorghums, corn, sugarcane, and a few other members of the grass family. The varieties of sorghum differ greatly in their susceptibility to the disease. It is principally a disease of Milo, the other sorghum types, such as the Kafirs, Feteritas, and Sorgos being resistant. Many of the Milos are very susceptible, including strains of Dwarf Yellow Milo, Double Dwarf Yellow Milo, Early Yellow Milo, Early White Milo, Day Milo, Sooner Milo, Pygmy Milo, Wheatland, Beaver, Desert Bishop, Darso, and certain hybrids with Milo or Darso as one parent. Selections which are resistant to the disease have been made from Dwarf Yellow Milo, Beaver, Day Milo, and Wheatland.

Pythium arrhenomanes is a soil-dwelling fungus that spreads during moist weather by means of swimming spores, and also forms thick-walled resting spores which enable it to survive in the soil as much as four years. Infested plant refuse, infested soil, and water leachings are common vehicles of spread. There is no indication that the disease is transmitted through the seed. The fungus can be found down to 24 inches soil depth. Since Milo is commonly grown under semi-arid conditions, the "Milo disease" is essentially a dry-land trouble, in spite of the fact that it is caused by a fungus of a group normally found in moist habitats. It develops well at 18 to 20 per cent moisture-holding capacity of the soil, which is favorable for sorghum growth. The fungus grows at temperatures between 32° and 95°F. with maximum growth between 77° and 86°, although the greatest injury to the sorghum plants occurs below this optimum, i.e. between 61° and 77°F. Resistant varieties maintain their resistance over a considerable range of temperatures and soil moisture percentages. Soil amendments and fertilizers do not consistently prevent Milo plants from becoming diseased when grown in infested soil.

The only satisfactory control for *Pythium* root rot, once the disease is established, is the use of resistant varieties of Milo. Agronomically desirable resistant strains of Dwarf Yellow Milo are available on a commercial basis, and are being widely distributed in the Southwest and in California. Considerable progress has been made in combining *Pythium* resistance and chinch-bug resistance in agronomically satisfactory sorghums, and varieties with these improvements are rapidly becoming available. It must be pointed out, however, that the *Pythium* resistant Milos are for the most part highly susceptible to the other stalk and root rots described below, and these diseases must be clearly distinguished in a program of control by the use of resistant varieties.

Since 1935, there have been a number of brief reports of a serious stalk-rot disease of sorghum in Texas, Oklahoma, Kansas, and Nebraska. The disease complex has been variously termed "weak-neck," "charcoal rot," and "root and stalk rot." In 1939 the sorghum plantings at the Federal Dry Land Experiment Station at Lawton, Oklahoma suffered severely from the seedling blight phase of the disease complex or later from lodging and stalk rot. The complex is poorly understood, but is under intensive study at the present time.

The disease consists principally of a root-rot which may attack sorghum at any stage of development. Under favorable conditions the seedlings are attacked soon after emergence. The young shoots die back as the root system rapidly decays. The stand loss may be virtually complete over rather extensive plantings. Plants which survive are usually injured and fail to develop normally, remain stunted, or fail to head. Attacks of older stands much resemble the *Pythium* root rot. Progressive decay of the feeding roots produces weak plants that do not head, or in which the heads are small or sterile (Fig. 122). The rot often advances up into the first few nodes of the stalk, causing a reddish-black pith-rot, the entire central core, except for stringy remains of the conducting vessels, being rotted away. This pith decay may lead to extensive lodging, the fields resembling the effects of heavy hail. In the roots, and especially in the rotted pith are often found quantities of tiny black granules, the sclerotia or resting bodies of one of the principal parasites involved.

This disease complex is caused by soil borne fungi including *Sclerotium bataticola* and one or more species of *Pythium*. Infection experiments have proven the virulence of *Sclerotium bataticola* and shown that it is capable of destroying young seedlings and injuring older plants under controlled conditions. The *Fusaria* which are often isolated from affected plants are not pathogenic in infection tests.

Sclerotium bataticola is a soil-borne fungus which is very prevalent in warm soils. It can attack the roots of many kinds of crop plants, including such varied hosts as sweet potatoes, corn, lima beans, cotton, cowpeas, beans, watermelons, peppers, gourds, chrysanthemums, and strawberries. Ordinarily the fungus has no air-borne spore stage, and spreads directly from plant to plant in the soil, or through such agencies as crop debris, surface water, and transported soil. The small black sclerotia are resistant resting bodies and serve to carry the fungus over unseasonable periods. The fungus is not an obligate parasite; it can flourish on decaying crop debris as well as on living plants.

Exact data are not yet available on the relation of this disease to the environment In one location, the stalk-rot phase has appeared for three consecutive seasons in experiment station plantings during both abnormally wet and dry seasons. In another, the seedling blight was very destructive in 1939, a relatively dry season. In both cases mentioned the soils were fertile, well suited to sorghum production. Observations on one farm showed a marked difference in the disease on limed and unlimed soils, the unlimed plots being badly lodged from *Sclerotium* stalk rot, while the limed plots were relatively free from the trouble. However on another farm the reverse condition was noted, perhaps because different pathogens were involved in these two cases of stalk rot. No correlation between temperature and prevalence of the disease has been noted. Dunlap has offered the suggestion that this may be a case of a fungus or fungi ordinarily of little economic importance, becoming an important factor in crop loss under certain weather and soil conditions. However its regular appearance during recent years suggests that the disease is tolerant of a considerable variety of environmental backgrounds.

This disease is regarded as a serious limiting factor in sorghum production, epiphytotic in numerous localities and capable of becoming very destructive. The concensus of opinion at a sorghum conference in 1940 was that the disease is a cause for real alarm, and justifies energetic endeavors toward its control. Little can be suggested for the control of this disease at the present time. The wide host ranges and general prevalence of *Sclerotium bataticola* and the other fungi concerned do not lead to the probability of rotation as an effective control measure. The promising results with liming are worthy of further testing. Seed treatments with organic mercury dusts are probably of little or no value against *Sclerotium bataticola*, but would be expected to be helpful against some of the other agents of seedling disease.

The outbreaks at experiment stations afforded excellent opportunities to observe varietal resistance, since large parts of the plantings consisted of segregating hybrid sorghums from experiments on breeding for resistance to chinch bugs and to the *Pythium* root rot. Some of the genetic lines were completely destroyed; in others a few individuals survived without serious injury although completely surrounded by dead or dying plants; in still other cases entire rows of certain hybrid lines developed normally although adjacent rows were wiped out. These observations indicate that resistance to the complex exists in grain sorghums and that it is heritable. There is reason to believe that this disease complex may ultimately be controlled through the selection and development of resistant sorghums. It is of more than passing interest to note that there appears to be no correlation between resistance to this disease complex and resistance to the *Pythium* root rot, since *Pythium*-resistant milos have been found fully susceptible to the *Sclerotium bataticola* complex.

REFERENCES

1. Elliott, C. et al. Pythium root rot of Milo. Jour. Agr. Res. **54**: 797–834. 1937.
2. Hartley, C. Damping off in forest nurseries. U. S. Dept. Agr. Bull. 934. 1921.
3. Haskell, R. J. and H. D. Barker. Cottonseed treatment. U. S. Dept. Agr., Leaflet 198. 1940.
4. Holbert, J. R. et al. Corn root, stalk and ear rot diseases, and their control through seed selection and breeding. Ill. Agr. Exp. Sta. Bull. 255. 1924.

5. Horsfall, J. G.   Combating damping-off.   N. Y. Agr. Exp. Sta. Bull. 683.   1938.
6. Kadow, K. J. and H. W. Anderson.   Damping-off control; an evaluation of seed and soil treatments.   Ill. Agr. Exp. Sta. Bull. 439.   1937.
7. Miller, P. R. and R. Weindling.   (Surveys of cotton seedling and boll rot diseases, 1938–1941.)   U. S. Dept. Agr., Pl. Dis. Rep. **23**: 29–32, 210–214, 329–334; **24**: 260–263, 417–423; **25**: 378–380.   1939–1941.
8. Newhall, A. G.   The theory and practice of soil sterilization.   Agr. Eng. **16**: 65–70.   1935.
9. Porter, R. H. and D. V. Layton.   Dust treatments for seed corn diseases.   Iowa Ext. Serv. Cir. 221.   1936.
10. Weindling, R. et al.   Fungi associated with disease of cotton seedlings and bolls. with special consideration of *Glomerella gossypii*.   Phytopath. **31**: 158–167.

Chapter 10

DISEASES CAUSED BY BACTERIA

Bacteria are familiar causes of human diseases, such as typhoid fever, plague, tuberculosis, and gangrene infections. In 1881, Burrill in Illinois proved that fire blight of apple and pears is a bacterial disease. About 1900 Erwin F. Smith took up the study of bacterial diseases of plants, dedicated his life to it, and is responsible for much of our modern knowledge of these diseases. Bacterial diseases have been found affecting 150 genera of 50 families of flowering plants, and doubtless many more remain to be discovered.

Bacteriology. Plant-parasitic bacteria are all rods, with or without motility. No coccus or spirillum forms cause plant disease.

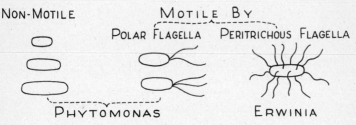

Figure 123. Genera of plant pathogenic bacteria.

The plant-parasitic forms were formerly classified by Migula, and again by Smith, their systems grouping the plant pathogens within the genera *Bacterium, Pseudomonas, Aplanobacter,* and *Bacillus.* A third system, that of Bergey et al., has now been accepted by international agreement and is used by all but occasional writers. According to the Bergey system of classification the plant-pathogenic bacteria are found within two genera, *Phytomonas* including short or long rod forms that are either non-motile or motile by polar flagella, and *Erwinia* including rod forms that are motile by flagella originating at random over the bacterial cell (peritrichous flagella) as illustrated in Fig. 123 This is the reason why, for example, the corn wilt bacterium may be found under any of three names:

Bacterium stewarti, *Aplanobacter stewarti*, or *Phytomonas stewarti*, only the last of which is in general use today.

The plant parasitic bacteria rarely form spores. They are nearly all Gram-negative, in contrast to many bacterial species that do not attack plants. Their resistance to crystal violet and related triphenylomethane dyes make these useful chemicals in isolating plant parasitic bacteria from bacterial mixtures, since such a dye kills most foreign organisms and leave the plant parasites unharmed. They are identified by their appearance, growth, and temperature relations, by their development and reactions in various nutrient media and in the presence of various chemicals, and by their parasitic tendencies, which are often highly specialized to one or few host species.

Pathology.

1. *Types of bacterial diseases.*
    a. Necrotic diseases in which the most pronounced effect is the killing of host tissues directly or indirectly through toxin formation or mechanical interference with water transport:
        a′. Vascular diseases in which invasion of the water-conducting system frequently leads to severe injury or death of the host plant. Examples: Corn wilt; alfalfa wilt; bacterial ring rot of potato.
        b′. Local infection diseases with progressive destruction of individual tissues: Examples: Leaf spots (Fig. 124) as in bean blight and angular leaf spots of cotton or tobacco: rots as in soft rot of vegetables; cankers as in fireblight of apple and pear. Powerful toxins secreted by the bacteria may be responsible for the necrotic host reaction, as in wildfire of tobacco.
    b. Hyperplastic diseases, in which overgrowth is the outstanding symptom:
        Examples: Crown gall of nursery stock; fasciation of sweet peas.
2. *Period of susceptibility.* Plants are often attacked in the succulent seedling stage, but in the soft rot and wilt diseases,

mature tissues are attacked. In vascular diseases, the infection often occurs in an early stage of host development and progresses with the growth of the host until the vascular bundles for a long distance from the original point of infection are filled with a continuous mass of bacterial slime. Examples: Corn wilt; banana wilt.

3. *Predisposition of the host.* Infection appears to be favored by juiciness or succulence of the tissues. High nitrogen fertilization and ample water supply are usually conducive to bacterial diseases; a rare exception is bacterial blight of stone fruits which is controlled by applications of nitrogen.

Figure 124. Typical necrotic bacterial diseases are the bacterial leaf spot of geranium (left) and that of ivy (right). (*Courtesy of P. P. Pirone, N. J. Agr. Exp. Sta.*)

Spread of bacterial diseases is ordinarily favored by shade, warm temperatures, excessive rain accompanied by high winds, wet soil, and dew. Total rainfall in itself is not decisive, and in regions where the annual rainfall is not great but in which the infrequent rains are often torrential and accompanied by high winds, which spread the bacteria over a wide area, these diseases are often very destructive. The infrequent heavy rains of dry areas may also produce a water-soaked condition in the plant tissues which is now known to greatly increase the susceptibility of plants toward bacterial disease. Once the plants are infected, spread over or through the plant is less dependent on abundant moisture.

4. *How infection occurs.* The bacteria usually enter the host plant through natural openings (stomata, nectaries, water-

pores), wounds (insect punctures, bruises), or delicate tissues (root hairs, growing tips of root or shoot). Tomato or tobacco plants with entire root systems will survive in bacteria-infested soils that are deadly to plants that have been root-pruned.

5. *Incubation period.* As in animal disease, the period between infection and appearance of symptoms may be short (1–2 days in soft rot; 10 days in cotton blight; 1–2 months in corn wilt) or very long (2 years in crown gall of orange).

6. *Recovery.* In woody perennials, bacterial activity ceases in the dormant period although the bacteria are often carried over alive in such plants, to serve as a source of infection in the next growing season, e.g. in the cankers in fire blight of apple and pear. Bacterial diseases of succulent parenchyma are often seen only in early spring (fire-blight of apple and pear; lilac blight), or they disappear in tissues that are subjected to drought or other unfavorable conditions (bacterial blight of cotton). Spontaneous recovery is sometimes seen in tomato and sugar cane but the plants are not immune and may later succumb to a second, fatal attack.

7. *Variability of the bacteria.* True physiologic specialization has not been recognized in phytopathogenic bacteria; however bacteria have in some cases shown decreased or increased virulence with ageing, following certain physical or chemical treatments, or as a result of passing them through various susceptible and resistant or unnatural hosts.

8. *Means of dissemination.* Infected plants often show a gummy ooze or exudate consisting of millions of bacteria. These bacteria are spread from one plant to another by contact, running water, wind-driven rains, movement of soil, insects, birds, molluscs, and man. (Example: picking blight-infected beans when the vines are wet.) Dry wind is not important as a vector. The bacteria are spread from field to field or first introduced into a crop by infested or infected seed, tubers, or other propagating parts, plants, soil, manure, and insects. A reference of special interest to

entomology students is Chapter 6: "Insects and bacterial diseases," in Leach: "Insect transmission of plant diseases." In some cases insects serve to carry the bacteria from one season to another in their bodies (Examples: overwintering of potato blackleg bacteria in puparia of the seed-corn maggot; overwintering of the cucumber wilt bacillus in adult striped cucumber beetles; overwintering of the corn wilt bacterium in adult flea beetles). In most cases, however, the insects are merely agents of spread in the field. (Examples: honey-bees and fire blight of apple and pear; Colorado potato beetle and bacterial wilt of potato, tomato, and tobacco.) The bacteria may be carried incidentally on the insects' mouth parts or feet, or may have a symbiotic, internal relationship with the insect. Bacterial infection is often preceded by fungous, insect, or nematode injury, and less commonly, bacterial lesions may open the way for general destruction of the plant by fungi that are unable to penetrate the uninjured epidermis. (Example: fungous boll rot of cotton following bacterial boll spot.)

9. *Saprophytic life of bacteria.* All plant pathogenic bacteria are facultative parasites, i.e. they can develop as saprophytes on decaying organic matter or in culture media. In some cases their survival in the soil is a regular source of infection of new crops following diseased ones, but in most cases they do not survive in soil for long periods of years, as do some of the parasitic fungi, probably being overcome by competition with natural soil microorganisms.

10. *Physical and chemical resistance.* Not being spore-formers, the plant-parasitic bacteria are not highly resistant to physical and chemical agencies, and unlike most animal pathogens they are not generally adapted to blood temperatures for their best growth. Some grow at 0°C or near it, others grow above 38°C, but the majority develop best between these limits. They are commonly similar to *Escherichia coli*, the colon bacillus, in resistance to acids, alkalis, and other chemicals. In general they are destroyed by ordinary disinfestants such as carbolic acid, bichloride of mercury, alcohol, and formaldehyde. Recall their unusual

resistance to certain dyes and its importance in isolating phytopathogenic bacteria.

11. *Relation between bacteria and plant.* Three possible situations exist, with intergrades:
   a. No relationship,—true of most bacteria with respect to most plants.
   b. Violently or mildly parasitic.
   c. Mutualistic (symbiotic). Examples: Root nodule bacteria which fix free nitrogen in roots of legumes; *Ardisia*, a tropical greenhouse plant, which always contains pockets of bacteria, with no external symptoms beyond slight lightening of the veins, and in which the bacteria are necessary for normal seed germination.

12. *Action of bacteria.* Many produce substances that destroy cells in advance of the bacteria, on the dead remains of which the bacteria feed as saprophytes within the living host; acids are broken down; pectic enzymes are secreted that break down the middle lamella and cause cells to fall apart as in soft rot of carrot and other vegetables. Ordinarily bacteria live between the host cells (intercellular), not invading the host cells until these are almost dead.

13. *Reaction of the plant.* The symptoms of bacterial diseases include *necrosis* (killing of cells), and *hyperplasia* (excessive development as seen in, witches brooms, adventitious buds, and fasciations). Interference with normal growth may result in underdevelopment (*hypoplasia*) of the plants as a whole. There is often a loss of starch or failure to store starch. The most common symptom is local or general necrosis, often leading to death of the plant.

14. *Distribution and importance of bacterial diseases.*
   In the United States and Canada the greatest losses from bacterial diseases have been those of potato, fruit trees, tobacco, beans, and tomatoes.
   In California fireblight destroyed one-third of the orchard trees, a $10,000,000 loss in the 5 years preceding quarantines. In 3 years, half a million trees were lost in the San Joaquin valley. Losses in eastern states are

comparable. Tobacco and tomato cannot be grown in many southern fields on account of bacterial wilt. In the Southwest bacterial blight causes up to 50 per cent loss in beans annually, ranking with mosaic as the most serious disease of this crop. Bacterial blight (angular leaf spot) is the most destructive general disease of cotton, outranked only in certain localities by Texas root rot and wilt. Bacterial wilt is the most important cause of the early dying out of alfalfa stands which is arousing much concern at the present time. Recently canker, a bacterial disease of citrus fruits, has become so menacing that Congress has made numerous appropriations for its control and quarantines have been enacted against Florida oranges and lemons because of this disease. Bacterial soft rot occurs everywhere and is the principal cause of the decay of carrots, turnips, and many other vegetables and fruits in storage, often reaching 100 per cent loss in the stored crops. Many other cases could be cited.

In other countries. Java and Sumatra sustain enormous losses from bacterial diseases of tobacco. These are serious bacterial diseases of sugar cane wherever the crop is grown. In Holland the bacterial yellows disease of hyacinths promised to put an end to this important industry until control measures were devised. The culture of mangoes in South Africa has suffered heavy losses from bacterial disease, and in the potato-growing regions of northern Europe several bacterial diseases exact a regular and serious toll from growers of potatoes. Much of the world is relatively unexplored for bacterial diseases, and much may be expected of them in the future.

15. *Control methods.*

    a. *In seed-borne bacterial diseases.* These are frequently controlled by the use of seed from uninfested areas, or surface sterilization of seed with bichloride of mercury (1:1000 for 15 minutes) or copper sulphate (1:1000 for 20 minutes followed by milk of lime), or formalin (1:400 for 10 minutes), or bactericidal dusts (organic mercuries, zinc oxide, cuprous oxide, etc.). Surface disinfestation is not effective against internally seed-borne bacteria, as occur in the case of corn wilt.

b. *In vegetative propagation.* Selection of disease-free stock; disinfestation of tools with formalin 1:9; dipping of stock plant materials in a disinfestant as Semesan. Bel.

c. *In greenhouse and nursery.* Soil sterilization by heat or chemicals.

d. *In the field.* Two or three year rotation: complete destruction of crop debris; spraying with Bordeaux mixture or lime sulphur in special cases; resistant varieties in special cases; insect control.

e. *Natural control.* Bacterial diseases vary greatly in severity from one season or location to another. Their occurrence and destructiveness is profoundly influenced by many environmental variables, among them temperature, soil moisture, air humidity, soil nutrients, wind, and others. Epiphytotic development of these diseases can only occur when all of a complex group of environmental factors permits, and in the lack of one or more of these requisites we see operating a type of natural disease control so highly effective that we can look upon an epiphytotic as a relatively rare exception in nature, which does not often combine such constellations of favorable circumstances.

We find another type of natural control operating when plant pathogenic bacteria find themselves in competition with organisms of the soil flora. We have already seen that these bacteria do not remain alive for long periods in the soil but are crowded out or destroyed by the true soil saprophytes.

Some plant pathogenic bacteria have been shown in laboratory tests to be attacked and destroyed by a lytic principle, possibly a virus, known as bacteriophage. We know little of the rôle of bacteriophage in controlling bacterial diseases in nature; most of the bacteria isolated in pure culture are resistant to bacteriophage, which suggests a tolerant relationship of long standing rather than an aggressive destructiveness of bacteriophage in nature. The practical use of bacteriophage in plant disease control is unexplored.

Bacterial Necroses

FIREBLIGHT OF APPLE AND PEAR (*Erwinia amylovora*).

History, distribution, and importance. Fireblight has been known in America since the Revolutionary War. Originally an Eastern disease, it spread to the West coast about 1900 and now occurs as a destructive disease in all apple and pear growing sections of America. It has been the most important limiting factor in pome fruit production in California. Annual United States losses (1930–1937) include from one to nine million bushels of apples, one-half million bushels of pears, and considerable additional losses in nursery stock and ornamental plants.

Host plants. Practically, pear is the most important host, followed by apple. Other members of the *Rosaceae* have been experimentally shown to be susceptible but on the majority of these the disease is rarely seen in nature They include: cherry, raspberry, blackberry, service berry, flowering quince, hawthorn, quince, loquat, strawberry, medlar, apricot, prune, plum, almond, rose, mountain ash, spiraea, California holly, and the evergreen, *Eriobotrya*.

The majority of cultivated apples and pears are susceptible, but vary considerably in degree of susceptibility. A few Asiatic pears are promising as resistant parents or as understocks.

Symptoms and signs. Various parts of the tree are attacked:

a. *Blossom blight*, the commonest symptom, is a killing of the blossoms, sometimes involving the entire tree, accompanied by bacterial ooze under moist conditions.
b. *Leaf blight* is a direct, partial, or complete killing of the leaves. Twig blight is also followed by secondary death of the leaves.
c. *Twig blight* is a killing back of the new shoots in the spring and summer involving both leaves and flowers. The blighted

twigs are often hooked back in a characteristic fashion (Fig. 125).

d. *Fruit blight* has the form of sunken, necrotic cankers, gradually involving the entire green fruit, accompanied by bacterial ooze in moist weather. Secondary blighting of the young fruits may follow killing of the twigs by twig blight.

Figure 125. Fireblight of pear. Affected shoot showing, at arrow, blackened necrotic lesion. Within a few days this entire shoot would be blackened and dead. (*Photo by Dept. of Plant Pathology, N. Y. Agr. Exp. Sta.*)

e. *Limb and trunk perennial cankers* (holdover cankers), are large sunken, necrotic lesions, maintaining the bacteria alive through summer, fall, and winter, exuding bacteria to initiate spring infections. The bacteria live in the living host tissues at the edges of the cankers.

The type of injury is determined by the season, the locality, the variety, and other factors.

Diagnosis is aided by the ready production of bacterial ooze from any of the above types of lesion under moist conditions, but ordinarily depends on the symptoms, which are not readily confused with those of any other pome-fruit disease. In doubtful cases the bacteria may be demonstrated microscopically.

Etiology. *Erwinia amylovora* is a rod, motile by peritrichous flagella. It does not form spores. It survives the winter only in the holdover cankers, not in the soil or dead plant remains, nor in the beehive, as some have claimed. In moist spring weather, the bacterial slime oozes out of the cankers and is carried to the new growth by splashing or wind-driven rain or by insects (Fig.

Figure 126. Fireblight of apple. Bacterial ooze from an overwintered canker. Splashing rains will wash the bacteria from this ooze to young shoots, thus initiating infection. (*Photo by Dept. of Plant Pathology, N. Y. Agr. Exp. Sta.*)

126). Primary infections are usually in the blossoms, followed by a rapid spread to open blossoms and shoots, aided particularly by visiting honeybees. Man is also a vector, carrying the bacteria on pruning tools. Infection is followed by a rapid necrotic breakdown of the parenchyma, with the bacteria intercellular, often in large pockets formed from disintegrated cells. In moist weather the bacteria ooze out to the surface, where further dissemination may lead to multitudes of secondary infections. The bacteria work

slowly down the twigs and into the branches. With the advent
of summer, they become less active, remaining alive in the woody
cankers, formed especially at the point where a smaller branch
joins a larger one.

Epiphytology. Fire-blight is favored by cloudy, humid
weather, and by driving rains. It is most serious in highly fertile
soils, rich in nitrogen. Old neglected fence row or windbreak trees
are often reservoirs of inoculum, serving each year as the source of
infection for nearby orchards.

Control. Many nostrums or worthless, patent-medicine type
"cures" have been advertised, but none proven of value.

In attempts at controlling fireblight full use should be made
of recommendations available from your state experiment station or
other reliable local sources. The recommendations suitable for
one section or orchard are often unsuitable for another.

1. Modify the susceptibility of the tree by avoiding excessive
   stimulation with nitrogen, or compensating for excessive
   nitrogen by application of potassium and phosphorus.
2. Follow a regular spray program for orchard insect control.
3. Avoid susceptible trees for windbreaks; take out and burn
   any non-bearing, neglected trees near the orchard.
4. During the regular winter pruning, cut out the holdover
   cankers. Repeat the pruning in the spring to detect any
   lesions that were missed before. Cut several inches below
   the lesions. Collect and burn the cuttings at once. In
   pruning, carry along a can of formeldehyde solution or
   Bordeaux mixture, and dip or wipe the tools frequently.
   Paint cut surfaces with Bordeaux paint or creosote. With
   large cankers, shave away the dead area and paint over with
   Bordeaux paint or creosote.
5. Other factors being equal, make use of resistant understocks
   in apple and pear propagation, or secure nursery trees that
   have been so propagated.
6. Recent practices worthy of trial but not generally in use as
   yet:
   a. Blossom spray; a weak application of Bordeaux mixture
      (1–3–50) applied just before the trees are in full bloom,

has proven beneficial in preventing infections of the blossoms and leaves.

b. Instead of cutting out large cankers, the cankers may be painted with a penetrating disinfectant. A zinc-chloride solution is used, prepared as follows: To one quart of hot water in an enamelled container add 3 oz. of concentrated hydrochloric acid and stir. In this mixture dissolve 9 lb. dry zinc chloride. When cool, mix with 7 pints of denatured alcohol. Store in tightly stoppered glass bottles. The material penetrates both bark and wood tissues and no bark should be removed from the cankers before treatment. Apply with a paint brush, covering the cankered area and the apparently healthy tissues for 5–6 inches beyond the evident margin of the canker.

BACTERIAL BLIGHT OF STONE FRUITS (*Phytomonas pruni*).

Bacterial blight, which is generally prevalent east of the Rocky Mountains, is one of the most destructive diseases of stone fruits. It occurs throughout the eastern half of the United States from New York and Michigan southward. The losses, which are due to devitalization of the tree, killing of twigs, and damage to the fruit range upward from 2 per cent on individual trees. In a favorable season the injury may range from 33 to 76 per cent on average trees or even 100 per cent in devitalized trees, and numberless orchards are heavily infested in such important stone fruit areas as Georgia, Illinois, and the Carolinas.

Bacterial blight produces several different types of injury in affected trees (Fig. 127). *On the leaves* the disease takes the form of numerous, brown, often angular-shaped dead spots. Later these dead areas have a tendency to fall out, leaving the leaves with an appearance as though they had been riddled by buckshot. Such "shotholing" may also be brought on by other causes and is not diagnostic of bacterial blight. *On the fruits* the disease appears as numerous, small, circular brown spots, which often crack, become star-shaped, or exude a gummy flux as the fruits mature. This lowers the grade of the fruit, and makes it especially susceptible to decay. Affected trees also show cankers *on the twigs*. These are dark, torn, open lesions about one half inch in length. They may girdle and destroy the twigs, and they serve as reservoirs to hold the parasite over the winter.

The etiology of this disease is much like that of fireblight. The bacteria overwinter in the stem cankers, from which they are disseminated to the new growth largely by splashing rain, or dew.

Bacterial blight is a difficult disease to control. Most sprays have little effect in preventing the disease, and this is also a hazard

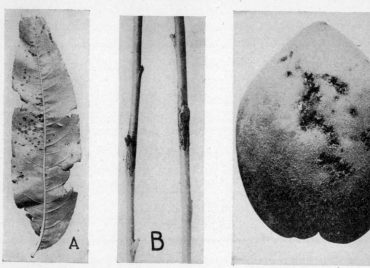

Figure 127. Bacterial blight of stone fruits. A, the angular lesions, at first water-soaked, later dead and dry, of blight on peach leaves; B, blight cankers on twigs; C, peach fruit showing several cracked lesions joined together to form an extensive injury. (*Photo by Bureau of Plant Industry, U. S. Dept. of Agriculture.*)

because stone fruits are highly susceptible to spray injury. Vigorous trees that are well fertilized with nitrogen do not suffer as badly as trees with less nitrogen, and it is a good plan to give affected trees an application of sodium nitrate or some other nitrogen-containing fertilizer. Annual pruning is not only a good horticultural practice but is also helpful in reducing bacterial blight, if an effort is made to prune out cankered and dead twigs during the winter. Very good results have recently been reported from Arkansas, using a zinc-lime spray. The spray consists of 4 lbs. of zinc sulfate and 4 lbs. of hydrated lime in 50 gallons of water. According to the reports this spray does not entirely eliminate the disease, but does check it very considerably. It is also said to stimulate the growth of leaves and give them a darker color.

BEAN BLIGHT (*Phytomonas phaseoli*).

Beans are attacked by several species of bacteria, most prevalent of which are those causing common blight, halo blight, and bacterial

Figure 128. Bacterial blight on bean leaves. Note the dead portions. Sometimes the injury is so extensive that growth of the plant is almost entirely stopped. (*Photo by the Bureau of Plant Industry, U. S. Dept. of Agriculture.*)

wilt. All are carried from one crop to another in association with the seed. Common and halo blights are of utmost importance in growing beans in the South, ranking second only to mosaic in producing the heavy or complete crop losses often encountered.

The same or similar bacteria also commonly affect peas, cowpeas, soybeans, and lima beans. On the leaves the bacteria cause extensive necrotic areas, exuding bacterial ooze (Fig. 128). Stems are attacked with necrotic zones which in some cases encircle the

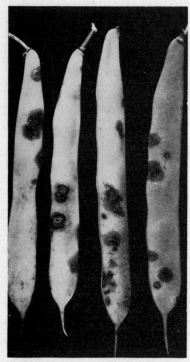

stems so that they break over. Affected pods first show small watersoaked areas which enlarge, dry out, and become brick red (Fig. 129). Seeds may be completely destroyed, or may be partially infected, and thus carry the disease from one crop to the next, and in addition the bacteria can over-winter in the soil. Spread from one plant or tissue to another is through the medium of splashing rain and dew, or through handling the vines when wet.

Control of the three prevalent bacterial diseases of beans consists mainly in the use of disease-free seed, preferably of blight-resistant bean varieties, and rotation of legumes. Blight is not of much importance west of the Rockies,

Figure 129. Bacterial blight on bean pods, showing reddish, water-soaked, irregularly-shaped, slightly sunken spots. The seed may be invaded and serve as a source of infection for the new crop. Blighted seed should never be planted. (*Photo by the Bureau of Plant Industry, U. S. Dept. of Agriculture.*)

and seed from Idaho and California is regularly free from infection. Locally grown seed is safe only if the field was inspected and found free of the disease the previous year. The bacteria are carried under the seed coat, and ordinary surface seed treatments are not effective in control, although success has been reported using very penetrating or volatile seed disinfestants, consisting of bichloride of mercury in ether or aniline dyes in a mixture of alcohol and acetic acid. Particular care should be taken to avoid picking beans when the vines are wet, as this spreads the bacteria so rapidly that the crop may be quickly destroyed. Spraying is of no value in controlling blight. Bean varieties resistant to common blight include Refugee 1000-1, Refugee Wax, Late Stringless Refugee, and White Imperial. Varieties resistant to halo blight are Refugee, Scotia, New Stringless Green Pod, and Tendergreen.

SOFT ROT OF VEGETABLES (*Erwinia carotovora*).

This is a rapid, soft, foul-smelling, wet decay of root crops, crucifers, cucurbits, solanaceous vegetables, onions, and flower bulbs. It occurs as a storage disease, and is the most frequent reason for failure of these crops to keep in storage. It may also be very destructive to cabbage, potatoes and other crops in the field. The bacteria are present in many soils; they enter primarily through wounds, and their destructiveness is dependent on high temperatures. Control requires thorough maturing and drying of crops before storage, storage in a cool, dry place, in thin layers, well aerated, avoidance of unnecessary bruising (as by pouring vegetables from one container to another, or throwing them into a container), and destruction of decayed vegetables to prevent the bacteria from returning to the field.

BACTERIAL DISEASES OF TOMATOES.

Bacterial spot, (*Phytomonas vesicatora*) a common and important loss factor in southern tomato culture, is recognized by the presence of small, black, scabby, roundish fruit spots, sometimes with a water-soaked border (Fig. 130). The spots do not penetrate deep into the pulp, but may be the points of entry of secondary decay organisms. On the leaves occur small circular watersoaked spots which become black and sunken. The leaves may be entirely destroyed. Elongated black lesions also occur on stems and petioles.

The organism overwinters principally on the seed, and possibly to a lesser extent in the soil. The standard control method is to soak tomato seed in a 1 : 3000 solution of bichloride of mercury for 10–15 minutes, then wash and dry. Supplementary control measures include selection of clean tomatoes for seed purposes, surface treatment of the tomato fruit with bichloride of mercury before extracting the seed, a three-year rotation, and complete destruction of diseased vines.

Two other bacterial diseases of the vascular type commonly affect tomatoes, bacterial canker (*Phytomonas michiganensis*), and bacterial wilt (*Phytomonas solanaceara*). Canker produces a wilting of the plant resembling the more common *Fusaurim* wilt. Dark, cracked streaks appear on the stems, and the phloem is discolored. The fruit spots are small, superficial, surrounded by a light halo, without a watersoaked border (Fig. 130). The organisms over-winter on and in the seed, and soil holdover is uncommon. Control depends chiefly on selection of seed from disease-free fields with mercury seed treatment as in bacterial spot. If seed-pulp is

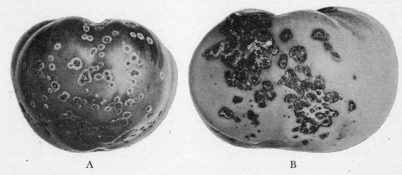

A   B

Figure 130. Bacterial diseases of tomatoes. A, bacterial canker, sometimes called "birdseye spot" on the fruit; B, bacterial spot. (*Photo by Purdue Univ. Agr. Exp. Sta.*)

allowed to ferment 3–6 days before extracting, the bacteria are killed. The disinfestation is due to accumulation of acetic and lactic acids which in pure form afford suitable seed treatment for controlling the disease. Rotation and sanitation should also be practiced.

Bacterial wilt produces an extensive browning of the vascular bundles, brown veins in the leaves and destruction of the pith, but no fruit lesions Suitable control measures include sterilization of the seed bed soil, preferably with steam, seed treatment with bichloride of mercury, spraying of young plants with Bordeaux mixture, and a rotation that avoids susceptible hosts. (For a complete list of these see Elliott: Manual of Bacterial Plant Pathogens, p. 204.)

BACTERIAL BLIGHT OF COTTON (*Phytomonas malvacearum*).

Bacterial blight (angular leaf-spot; black arm; bacterial boll rot) is the most common disease, and often the most serious general disease of cotton, occurring in nearly every field.

Hosts. Cultivated cotton, and the closely related Arizona wild cotton (*Thurberia thespesioides*) are the only natural hosts. Sea Island and Egyptian cottons are most susceptible; American upland cottons are intermediate; and Asiatic cottons are most resistant. No resistant varieties of American cottons are available.

History and distribution. Bacterial blight occurs wherever cotton is grown. It was first recognized in America in 1891 and the first extensive study was that of Rolfs in 1915. In the United States it is destructive from the Carolinas to the Southwest, and in irrigated areas in the western states. In other parts of the world, as in Egypt and the African Sudan, it is a factor of great importance in cotton production.

Economic importance. Bacterial blight is a major yield factor but since it is always present, losses are often disregarded. In the irrigated Nile Valley entire crops may be destroyed. In the Southwest up to 10 per cent of the crop is destroyed by blight. The losses are difficult to estimate because of the various ways in which the plant is affected, the disease producing poor stands, loss in vigor through destruction of leaf area, water loss through leaf lesions, stunting or killing by stem lesions, and boll decay. It is impractical to grow the long staple Sea Island cotton in the United States because of this disease.

Symptoms and signs. (Fig. 131). *Infected seed* may fail to germinate, with their content decomposed in bacterial slime; *sprouting seed* show a rapid yellow decay of the hypocotyl under the soil; *cotyledons* are affected with round watersoaked, then dead lesions; *leaf lesions*, often very numerous, are angular, water-soaked spots, later becoming dead, and with many infections the leaves shrivel and fall, *young leaves* often show extensive killing along the veins; *stem lesions* (black arm) are long black cankers, partly or completely girdling the stalk; *fruits* and *flowers* show extensive necrosis; and *boll-spots* are round, watersoaked, involving only the depth of the shuck, but often followed by the invasion of molds which discolor or destroy the lint. In the watersoaked stage the lesions exude droplets of slimy bacterial ooze, which later dries to form pale yellow scales on the lesions.

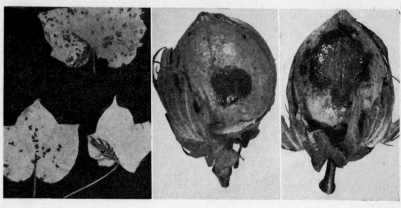

A   B   C

Figure 131. Bacterial blight of cotton. A: Angular leaf spots, and in the lower right corner, vein invasion such as occurs when leaves are very young at the time of infection. B and C: bolls showing early watersoaked stage and advanced stage of bacterial boll spot. In the latter case secondary fungous invasion has occurred.

Etiology. *Phytomonas malvacearum* is a short, motile rod, forming abundant yellow colonies in culture. It produces no spores, although gelatinous capsules occur around the cells. It over-winters mainly in the fuzz of seed from infected crops, and to a lesser extent within the seed and in the soil. As infested seed germinate, the fuzz draws across the emerging cotyledons, producing round primary infections. These exude bacteria which are carried to later-formed leaves and rapidly spread on the plants in 10-day cycles. Eventually lesions form in the bolls, and when seed from these are harvested, the lint is contaminated.

Further seed contamination may occur in ginning. Within the field, spread is effectuated by wind-driven rain, dew, ants and other insects crawling over the plants, and surface water.

Epiphytology. *P. malvacearum* flourishes under the high temperatures (84° to 95°F.) favoring cotton growth, and is most destructive in the succulent tissues of rapidly growing plants. Hard, splashing rains produce abundant spread of the bacteria, although a high total annual rainfall is not necessarily associated with epiphytotics. Periods of cool, moist weather retard the defoliation of

infected leaves, permitting the bacteria to grow down the petioles
and into the stems, producing black arm.   The most serious development of the disease occurs in acid soils and in soils high in nitrogen
or low in phosphorus.

Control.   Surface seed infestation can be counteracted by dusting the seed with organic mercury dusts or by delinting the seed

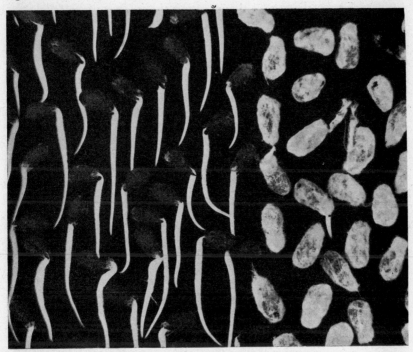

Figure 132.   When cotton seed are treated with concentrated sulphuric acid for
controlling bacterial blight and other surface seed borne diseases, the lint is removed
and the seed coat becomes more permeable to water.   Such seed (left) germinate
several days earlier than similar but untreated seed (right).   The saving in seed
required for planting more than pays for the treatment.

with concentrated sulphuric acid.   These treatments will largely
eliminate primary infections, substantially improving the crop but
not eradicating the disease entirely.   The few internally infected
seed are not affected by the seed treatments, but are largely removed
by skimming off floating seed in the wash water after acid delinting.
Seed treatments coupled with a 2 or 3 year rotation give the best
control at present available (Fig. 132).   The seed treatments are

also effective in destroying the anthracnose fungus and other seed-borne organisms. Delinted seed has the additional advantages of saving of 60 per cent of the seed by making it possible to plant with a corn plate, quicker germination, and more even stands, reducing losses from skips in the row, and reducing or eliminating the cost of chopping. The most valuable practice of all is delinting followed by flotation grading, and then dusting the seed.

In delinting cottonseed add ½ gallon of sulphuric acid (commercial, 66° Baumé) to 1 bushel of seed in a wooden tub. Stir until the lint is removed and the seeds form a black sticky mass. Quickly fill the tub with cold water, break up the seed mass, and pour into a second tub with a screened bottom. Rinse with several changes of water until no sour taste remains. Pour into a tight container, skim off and discard the floating seed, and spread the remaining seed out to dry. The work is simplified by a revolving-barrel treater, recently designed in Tennessee.

In dusting cottonseed use ethyl mercury phosphate dust ("New Improved Ceresan") at 1½ oz. per bushel of fuzzy seed or ½ oz. per bushel of delinted seed. With fuzzy seed, apply the dust in a rotating-barrel treater; with delinted seed the rotating barrel or any type of gravity seed duster may be used (Fig. 28).

Despite its pronounced advantages in improving the quality and behavior of cotton seed, delinting on the farm has never been popular with farmers, for a number of reasons, the dangers and disagreeable features of handling strong acid, and the problem of disposing of acid wash water ranking among these reasons. For many years equipment designed in Arizona for cottonseed delinting on a custom or large scale basis has been available. A few delinting plants were erected and operated in Arizona and neighboring states, but it was not until 1939 that means were devised for bringing this service to the entire Cotton Belt. At that time a commercial organization secured the patent rights for the Arizona equipment and is now engaged in erecting many delinting plants throughout the South. Considering the reduced planting rate permissible with delinted seed it is now possible for the cotton grower to secure through local seedsmen delinted, graded, and Ceresan-treated certified seed of locally adapted varieties at a planting-cost per acre no greater than the cost of planting ordinary gin-run untreated seed.

Spraying or dusting the crop with fungicides helps in controlling bacterial blight, but is too expensive to use except in small plots of valuable cotton for planting seed. Blight-resistant cotton varieties do not offer much value in controlling the disease at present, although the very susceptible Sea Island and Egyptian varieties should be avoided. Work is under way at a number of experiment stations in attempts to select blight resistant strains of standard varieties, but no such strains are yet commercially available.

BACTERIAL LEAF DISEASES OF CEREALS.

Halo blight of oats (*Phytomonas coronafaciens*), bacterial blight of barley (*Phytomonas translucens*), and three bacterial leaf diseases of sorghums, leaf spot (*Phytomonas holci*), streak (*Phytomonas holcicola*), and stripe (*Phytomonas andropogoni*) are common diseases of these crops, sometimes resulting in such extensive leaf damage that the grain or fodder yield is seriously impaired. All are caused by bacteria which frequently ooze out of the dying leaf areas in droplets that dry to form scales or crusts. The differential symptoms are:

Halo blight of oats. Gray or brown leaf spots, at first oval, later streak-like with dying back of leaf tips; spots often surrounded by a pale halo; bacterial exudate absent.

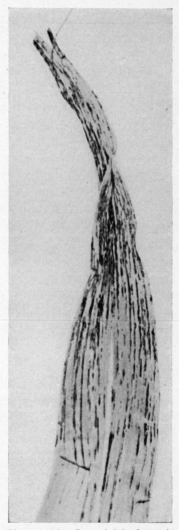

Figure 133. Bacterial leaf streak of sorghum.

Sorghum leaf spot. Round or oval spots, first watersoaked, then dry, parchment like, with a reddish border; no bacterial exudate.

Sorghum leaf streak. Narrow, watersoaked streaks, later drying, widening here and there with oval tan centers and narrow dark margins; bacterial exudate abundant (Fig. 133).

Sorghum leaf stripe. Brick-red or purplish or dark brown blotches, long and rather broad; no watersoaked stage and no tan centers, but uniform red discoloration; bacterial exudate present.

Bacterial blight of barley. Small watersoaked, translucent spots that become elongate, then dry, causing more or less extensive killing of leaf tissues or dieback of the leaf blades; bacterial exudate present.

Control.

1. Wherever possible select seed from fields that are free of these leaf diseases.
2. Mercury dust seed treatments will protect against the inoculum which is carried on seed surfaces.
3. Few data are available on overwintering of these diseases in soil, but it would be wise to practice a two or three year rotation in case of serious infestation.
4. Resistance to these diseases occurs in the following varieties:

    Bacterial blight of barley: Oderbrucker, Chevalier.

    Sorghum stripe: Sudan grass, Proso, German millet, Dwarf Early sumac, Hovey, Black Amber, Folgers Early, Early Rose, Sugar Drip, Orange, Gray Kafir, Texas Gooseneck, Guineacorn, Durra, and Shallu.

    Sorghum streak: a number of the kafirs, Kaoliang, Leoti Red Sorgo, Early White Milo, Buff Durra, Pierce Kafirita, and a Red Amber × Feterita selection.

    Sorghum leaf spot and halo blight of oats: no resistant varieties reported.

Bacterial Wilts

BACTERIAL WILT (STEWART'S DISEASE) OF CORN (*Phytomonas stewarti*).

Formerly bacterial wilt was primarily recognized as a disease of sweet corn, especially the earlier sweeter varieties. Field corns have proven more resistant. Recently, however, the wilt problem has been largely solved in sweet corn by the general adoption of

Golden Cross Bantam and other wilt-resistant hybrids (see Frontis-piece), while since 1932 increasing injury has been seen in field corn. Wilt is a vascular disease, i.e. the bacteria invade the con-ductive tissues wilting and killing affected plants. In some years it becomes epiphytotic with heavy losses.

Symptoms. Seedlings may be killed, or wilted and stunted. In larger plants, the leaves show watersoaked stripes which soon become yellow, then brown, dry out and crack (Fig. 135). The

Figure 134. Golden Bantam sweet corn heavily infected with bacterial wilt, showing some leaves with streaks, others wilted and top wilted, and the plants stunted. (*Photo by the Bureau of Plant Industry, U. S. Dept. of Agriculture.*)

plant wilts and may die at any stage of development (Fig. 134). If the stem is cut across, the vascular bundles appear dark, and exude drops of bacterial ooze (Fig. 136). In plants which form ears the kernels may be both externally and internally infested with bacteria. Affected fields are uneven, with many stunted or dead plants among the healthy ones.

Etiology. The bacteria survive the winter primarily in the seed, or in hibernating adult flea beetles (*Chaetocnema pulicularia*) infected the previous season. The primary infections usually result from the feeding of these beetles on the new crop or as infected seedlings from infected seed, but in some cases they may come from the soil. In the field the disease is spread mainly by insects, particularly the southern corn root worm and flea beetles.

Epiphytology. The bacteria are adapted to warm temperatures, 86°F. being optimal for their growth, and the disease is most

Figure 135. Golden Bantam sweet corn leaves showing three stages in the development of wilt leaf-lesions following insect feeding injuries. (*Photo by the Bureau of Plant Industry, U. S. Dept. of Agriculture.*)

destructive in the hotter parts of the season. Succulent plants, stimulated by rich soil and ample water are more susceptible than plants in less favorable soil. Epiphytotics usually follow mild winters which permit extensive overwintering of infected flea beetles, and a series of such winters has a cumulative effect in increasing wilt severity. This relationship between mild winters and consequent wilt epiphytotics is so regular that during the past

6 years it has been possible to make accurate predictions of future outbreaks, based on a study of winter temperatures, in time to adjust the planting program so as to avoid extensive losses during the epiphytotic years. Such predictions assume that the seed to be planted is not harboring the wilt pathogen.

Figure 136. Sections of stalks of Golden Bantam sweet corn showing droplets of bacterial ooze (arrows) on the cut ends of the vascular bundles. (*Photo by the Bureau of Plant Industry, U. S. Dept. of Agriculture.*)

Control.

1. Use resistant varieties. The most widely grown sweet corn, Golden Cross Bantam is resistant, and the resistant sweet corns also include Marcross 13.6 and Whipcross C 6.2. Ordinary Golden Bantam is very susceptible. The following dent and flint corns have been reported as highly resistant: Funk 176A, Golden Glow, Golden King Yellow Dent, Iowa Hybrids 931, 939, and 942, Krug, Leaming, Murdock, Silver King White Dent, Wisconsin Hybrid (A × hy), and Kutias.
2. Seed treatments, as with organic mercury dusts or bichloride of mercury are sometimes recommended, however their value, except in protecting uninfested corn areas, is questionable as regards wilt. The seed treatments are not effective against internally borne bacteria in the seed, and according to recent studies the seed is responsible for only a negligible part of spring infections in any case.

3. Dry pasteurizing of seed (140° to 158°F.) for 1 hour destroys external and internal infestation, but is not generally recommended nor practiced.

4. In the control program attention should be given to the annual forecasts with control programs utilizing resistant varieties and worked out on the basis of these forecasts.

ALFALFA WILT (*Phytomonas insidiosa*).

Not long ago, alfalfa stands lasted 20 years or more before they became unprofitable. Today five-year old alfalfa fields are often so poor that they must be replanted or used for other crops. The principal cause for this is bacterial wilt, a vascular disease that has only been known since 1925. During that time it has become widespread in most alfalfa-growing areas of the United States, and has come to rank as the most important disease of this crop. Alfalfa and white sweet clover are the only susceptible crops.

Symptoms. Wilt appears in alfalfa fields the second season after planting, or later, spreading outward from spots. Attacked plants are stunted, sometimes with an excessive number of weak stems (Fig. 137). The leaves roll upward, turn yellowish, or die. Wilting is not a common symptom. The tap root, near the crown especially, shows a wet, pale yellow zone under the bark, and the bark easily separates from the wood at this zone. The bacteria are readily demonstrated in the yellowed vascular tissues.

Etiology and epiphytology. *Phytomonas insidiosa* is a non-motile, rod-shaped organism, that produces bluish colonies on lactose nutrient agar. It forms no spores. It persists in infested soil, which is the principal source of primary infection. It is not considered to be carried in seed. Infection is favored by wounds made by cultivation when the plants are wet, or by insects or winter injury. The bacteria are spread by means of soil movement, infested hay, surface water, and mowing machines. Mowing when the plants are wet is especially dangerous. The bacteria develop best at 74°F. with no growth above 82° to 88°F. The disease is most prevalent in well-watered, highly productive alfalfa, although it may be found to a destructive extent both in moist areas and in semi-arid regions.

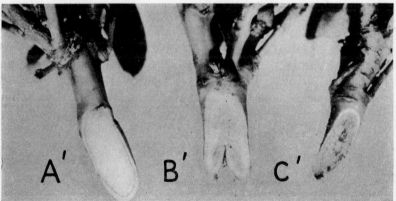

Figure 137. Bacterial wilt of alfalfa. A, healthy plant; B, plant showing moderate wilt symptoms; C, plant suffering from a severe wilt attack. A', B', and C' show sections of the taproots of each of these plants, bringing out the vascular discoloration that is characteristic of this disease. (*Photo by Bureau of Plant Industry, U. S. Dept. of Agriculture.*)

Control. The following practices are desirable:

1. Before reseeding infested fields with alfalfa, destroy all alfalfa plants and allow sufficient time for old roots to decay.
2. Sow alfalfa on fields that will not receive drainage from infested fields.
3. Sow certified seed of winter-hardy varieties of known sources. The winter-hardy varieties, Hardistan, and Orestan and to a lesser extent Ladak and Cossack are somewhat resistant to wilt, and in infested fields may out-yield the common varieties, although in wilt-free locations the common varieties are likely to be superior.
4. Cut alfalfa when the plants are dry.
5. If an infested field has been cut, wipe the mower with formaldehyde solution (1 part in 120 parts of water) before cutting a healthy field.
6. Do not topdress alfalfa with manure from animals fed on wilt-infested hay.
7. Clovers (except white sweet clover) are not susceptible to wilt and may be used in old alfalfa soils, or to fill the spots in which alfalfa plants have died from wilt. Never replant such spots with alfalfa.
8. Avoid cutting for hay or close grazing late in the season as this weakens the plants and predisposes them to winter injury, which in turn favors bacterial wilt.

BACTERIAL WILT OF CUCURBITS (*Erwinia tracheiphila*).

Cucurbits suffer from two types of wilt diseases, *Fusarium* wilt (as the common watermelon wilt) and bacterial wilt. The latter is widespread, somewhat more destructive in the North than in the South, but not uncommon in southern fields and in greenhouses. Cucumber is most seriously attacked, followed in order by cantaloupe, squash, and watermelon.

Symptoms. A few leaves are seen to wilt, followed soon by wilting and drying of the whole plant (Fig. 138). Cross sections of the stems show white bacterial exudate oozing from the vascular ring. Suspected plants should also be examined for *Fusarium* wilt (dark ring under the bark) and work of the squash vine borer (tunnels in the stem bases).

Etiology and epiphytology.   The bacteria overwinter in the bodies of cucumber beetles, and these are the only means of spread in the field.   When introduced into suscepts the bacteria multiply, plug the vascular bundles, dissolve cell walls and form cavities of decay in the parenchyma.

Control.   Control is entirely directed at restriction of the beetles which are the agents of overwintering and dissemination. Early and repeated sprayings with calcium arsenate have been

Figure 138.   Bacterial wilt of muskmelon.   (*Courtesy of C. T. Gregory, Ind. Agr. Ext. Serv.*)

effective.   Bordeaux mixture is a fungicide primarily, but in this case it repels the beetles and is used for wilt-control on this account. The Bordeaux mixture may be combined with an arsenical and the two applied together, e.g. Bordeaux mixture plus lead arsenate, 4–5–50–2.   In the greenhouse the beetles may be controlled by fumigation.   When the disease first appears, pulling of affected vines, if thoroughly done, may give adequate control.

Bacterial Hyperplasias

CROWN GALL (*Phytomonas tumefaciens*).

Crown gall is principally a disease of young nursery trees, occurring naturally on pome fruits, stone fruits, small fruits, nut-bearing and broad-leaved shade trees, and as a minor trouble of alfalfa, cotton, some of the root-vegetables, and herbaceous ornamentals. At times it is quite destructive to sugar beets.   Because of a resemblance to a human disease it has been called a plant tumor.   It is widespread and common, and losses from crown gall are often serious in young fruit trees, not because the plants are killed, but because they are unfit for sale. It is one of the most important reasons for condemnation of nursery stock, exceeded only by root-knot in warm regions.

Symptoms. In their usual form the galls are rounded, with a rough surface, ranging up to several inches in diameter, occurring

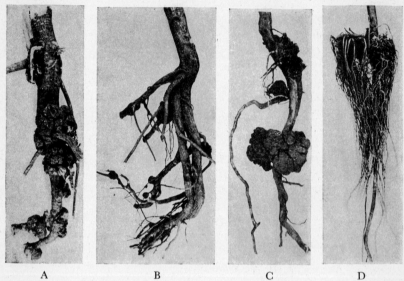

A   B   C   D

Figure 139. A, B, C, three cases of crown gall; D, hairy root.

chiefly at the soil line, but not uncommonly over the roots or above ground, especially at the graft union (Fig. 139). Internally the galls show irregular structure, with the tissue elements disarranged, as in burls, at first firm and white, but often later showing secondary decay. Hard and soft galls are distinguished, the latter decaying after a season of growth. Hard galls resembling crown gall are commonly knots of graft callus or wound over-growth. Other related types of disease include hairy root or broom root in which a large number of fine, weak roots replace the normal root system, and bur knot or wooly knot in which the gall is covered with "whiskers" of fine roots (Fig. 139). Hairy root is considered due to a distinct species of bacterium from that causing typical crown gall. Hairy root, bur knot, and wooly knot are indistinguishable in the field if the specimen is small.

Etiology. Crown gall is caused by *Phytomonas tumefaciens*, and hairy root by *P. rhizogenes.* Infection normally occurs on the grafting bench, the bacteria passing from diseased to healthy trees on the grafting tool, or carried inside, from the surface of infested roots, as the graft is made. Moreover many of our native soils are already infested with the crown gall organism, and healthy trees set in such soil readily contract the disease. There appears to be relatively little spread from tree to tree in the orchard.

In contrast to the necrotic bacterial diseases, the symptoms of crown gall are rather slow in appearing, the incubation period lasting from a few weeks to a year or more depending on weather, growth-rate of the host, and other factors. Despite the extensive studies of Erwin F. Smith on the disease, there still remain many controversial or poorly understood points. One of these is the question of the amount of damage sustained by galled plants. Although trees may at times suffer severely or even be killed by crown gall and its secondary consequences, there are numerous cases of spontaneous recovery in plants not affected on the trunk, or of heavily galled trees that have continued apparently normal growth and bearing for many years.

There are a number of features of crown gall of fundamental scientific interest. The basic cause of pathological growth in plants is probably not far different from that in man and other animals. Consequently, crown gall is being studied intensively in several laboratories in the hope that the results will contribute to a solution of certain problems including tumors and cancers. The production of galls is a process of stimulated, unorganized growth, somewhat analogous to the action of growth-promoting hormones. Galls closely resembling crown gall can be induced in plants by injecting them with growth-promoting substances although only at rather high concentrations. The bacteria in laboratory cultures are often associated with a bacteriophage, a lytic principle or virus that destroys the bacteria and may possibly contribute to the natural control of the crown gall organism.

Control of crown gall is largely a matter of sanitary practices in growing trees and shrubs. Planting stock or propagation wood should be selected for freedom from crown gall, and the efforts of state nursery inspectors aid in this.   Extreme care should be used in grafting, to avoid transmission of the disease from one plant to another.   Grafts should be well fitted and bound.   It is a good practice to dip graft understocks in a disinfestant solution such as bichloride of mercury (1:1000) followed by washing, copper sulphate (½ to 1 lb. in 26 gallons of water soaking for 1 hour) or Semesan Bel.   Finished grafts should not be treated with disinfestant chemicals as this will prevent suitable decay of the graft wrapping and may lead to girdling of the tree.   Infested soil should not be used for susceptible stock without one or two intervening years in a non-susceptible crop.   Mechanical wounds to the young trees or bushes should be avoided insofar as this is possible.   Other things being equal the varieties of fruits which show some resistance to crown gall in a given locality should be given preference to the more susceptible ones in that locality.   Heald lists the following varieties as crown gall resistant:

Grapes: Concord, Catawba, Delaware, and other American varieties in contrast to European varieties.

Apples: Variable in different localities; Jonathan is reported as less susceptible than Wealthy.

Stone fruits: Italian prune, German Prune, Damson, cherries, especially Mazzard (for understocks for the other stone fruits).

Nut trees: California black walnut (useful as understocks for other compatible nut trees).

Miscellaneous: Loquat, silk oak, avocado, olive.

It has been repeatedly observed that varieties behaving as resistant in one locality may prove susceptible in another, and the foregoing lists must be accepted only with that reservation.   Hildebrand found, in a series of hairy-root infection tests made in Kansas during two years, that the apple varieties Arkansas, Beauty, Early Harvest, Hopa, McIntosh, Rome Beauty, and York Imperial showed considerably less susceptibility than many other standard varieties; however, the results of one year's experiment did not always agree with those of the second year, as in the varieties Gano I (Black Ben) and Winesap which showed low infection in 1930 and very high susceptibility in 1931 experiments.

REFERENCES

1. Dunegan, J. C.   The bacterial spot disease of the peach and other stone fruits.
   U. S. Dept. Agr. Tech. Bull. 273.   1932.
2. Elliott, C.   Corn wilt.   U. S. Dept. Agr. Farm. Bull. 1878.   1941.
3. Elliott, C.   Manual of bacterial plant pathogens.   Williams and Wilkins Co.,
   Baltimore.   1930.   (Includes extensive bibliographies of all bacterial diseases
   treated.)
4. Gardner, W. W. and J. B. Kendrick.   Bacterial spot of tomato.   Jour. Agr. Res.
   21: 123–156, 1921 and Phytopath. 13: 307–315.   1923.
5. Heald, F. D.   Fire blight and Crown gall and hairy root.   In Manual of Plant
   Diseases, pp. 342–375.   McGraw-Hill Book Co., New York.   1933.
6. Hildebrand, E. M.   Fire blight and its control.   N. Y. (Cornell) Ext. Serv. Bull.
   405.   1939.
7. Jones, F. R.   Bacterial wilt of alfalfa and its control.   U. S. Dept. Agr. Cir. 573.
   1940.
8. Rand, F. V. and E. M. A. Enlows.   Bacterial wilt of cucurbits.   U. S. Dept. Agr.
   Bull. 828.   1920.
9. Rolfs, F. M.   Angular leaf-spot of cotton.   So. Car. Agr. Exp. Sta. Bull. 184.
   1915.
10. Smith, E. F.   An introduction to bacterial diseases of plants.   W. B. Saunders Co.,
    Philadelphia.   1920.
11. Smith, E. F.   Bacteria in relation to plant diseases.   Carnegie Inst., Washington.
    1905, 1911, 1914.
12. Zaumeyer, W. J.   The bacterial blight of beans caused by Bacterium phaseoli.
    U. S. Dept. Agr., Tech. Bull. 186.   1930.

Chapter 11

DISEASES CAUSED BY VIRUSES

Significance of Virus Diseases

Among the most interesting and elusive of plant pathogens are the viruses, mysterious entities too small to be seen with the microscope or to be retained by bacteria-holding filters, yet contagious, transmissible from one host organism to another, and capable of causing some of the most puzzling and destructive diseases not only of plants but also of animals and man.

The list of virus diseases is an imposing one. It includes infantile paralysis, sleeping sickness, smallpox, typhus and trench and yellow fevers, a whole group of children's diseases, the common cold and even warts. In domesticated and wild animals viruses cause, among other diseases, foot and mouth disease, infectious anaemia, swine fever, rabies, distemper, and sleeping sickness of horses, which in a single season wiped out one-third of all the horses in an epizootic area. It is not improbable that certain forms of human cancer may also be caused by viruses.

Best known of the plant virus diseases is the group of mosaics in which normally green leaves become variegated with yellow. Of these one of the more notorious is tobacco mosaic, on the average the most destructive disease of tobacco in the North Carolina area and elsewhere. In 18 years the production of sugar in Louisiana dropped from 400,000 tons to about 50,000 tons, as sugar cane mosaic gained a throttling grip on the industry, although the adoption of mosaic-resistant cane varieties has now raised production nearly back to the former high level. Likewise the beet-sugar industry has suffered extensive losses from the virus disease curlytop, which in 1925 caused the abandonment of 10,000 acres of beet culture in California alone. The potato has been accused of harboring more than 50 viruses. They undoubtedly constitute the gravest problem in modern potato pathology. And many other species of plants display mosaic diseases, among them such diverse crops as cucumbers, alfalfa, peas, and wheat.   In cotton a very serious virus disease, leaf curl is spreading in Southern Nigeria and India, a disease that is reducing yields by 100 lb. of lint or 312 lb. of seed cotton per acre.   This has fortunately not yet appeared in America.

While the mosaic diseases exert their influence to dwarf the plants and reduce their vitality, the group of yellows diseases of

Figure 140.   "Breaking," a virus disease of tulips, often enhances the beauty of the flowers.   Right: naturally occurring "broken" or mosaic Clara Butt tulip; left: healthy blossom of the same variety; center: another type of breaking obtained by inoculating the plant with cucumber mosaic virus.   (*Photo by Bureau of Plant Industry, U. S. Dept. of Agriculture.*)

plants are even more destructive, often killing the plants outright. This has become especially evident to growers of stone fruits, where the losses have frequently forced the growers out of production. These are diseases that are justifiably the subject of the strictest inspection and eradication programs.   To add to the already imposing list of peach viruses, peach mosaic has recently become the subject of strict quarantines in the southwestern states, while within the past few years the new "X-disease" of peaches has appeared at various locations in the United States to add another virus menace to the list.

A number of interesting and important viruses attack ornamental plants.   At times these diseases produce a variegation in the
leaves that is esteemed as enhancing the value of the ornamental
plants.   Among tulips, for example, "broken color" of the blossoms
(variegation) is regularly due to viruses, and such varieties as
"Sensation" and "Rembrandt" owe their distinctiveness to virus
infection (Fig. 140).   Indeed the tulip variety "Farncombe
Sanders" is merely the ordinary "Clara Butt" with a virus disease,
perpetuated in such cases by vegetative propagation.   Unfortunately these varieties that are ornamentally diseased may serve
as sources of infection for other varieties in which the effects of virus
disease are not at all desirable, so that we find undesired virus diseases playing an important part in the pathology of most of the
vegetatively-propagated ornamentals.

Even bacteria suffer from virus disease, here called bacteriophage, due to an infectious principle that spreads through bacterial
colonies dissolving the individual bacterial cells.

The wide host distribution and the scientific and practical
importance of virus diseases of plants are indicated in the fact that
some 5,000 papers and a few books had been written on the subject
by 1935, these papers dealing with virus diseases in more than 1,000
species of plants distributed through 450 genera of 90 families in
the plant kingdom.

Symptoms of Virus Diseases

A great variety of symptoms are seen in the various virus diseases.
A single virus when introduced into a number of different hosts may
produce a range of symptoms varying from none (masked or symptomless condition) through a variety of more or less striking reactions
up to extensive killing of tissues or entire plants.   Or, if individuals
of a single host species such as tobacco, are inoculated with the
different viruses to which this plant is susceptible, each different
virus produces a distinctive and characteristic reaction in the plant.
Virus symptoms of all types show a tendency to be most evident
under cool growing conditions, and to be less apparent or entirely
masked at high temperatures.   The leading types of virus symptoms
are:

1. Inhibition of pigment formation.

a. *Chlorophyll.* In the *mosaic* diseases, the chlorophyll in leaves formed subsequent to inoculation is lacking in certain leaf areas. These areas are usually patches scattered over the leaves in a random fashion (Fig. 141). When a leaf shows white or yellow areas in regular, geometrical designs, as large V-shaped areas between the veins, or only along the borders, the variegation is more likely due to a genetic defect than to a virus.

Figure 141. Cane fruit mosaic, showing various types of mottling and distortion on raspberry leaves. (*Photo by N. Y. (Geneva) Agr. Exp. Sta.*)

In parallel-veined plants the mosaic usually occurs as broken yellow streaks. In *ringspot* which is almost always due to viruses, the variegation has the form of yellowish rings against a green background. *Clearing of veins*, usually the first virus symptom seen after inoculation, is a transient pattern in which the veins are light against a dark background. The reverse of this condition, dark veins against a lighter background, sometimes occurs, in which case it is called *veinbanding*. In *yellows* diseases, entire leaves are uniformly yellowed (Fig. 142). The mosaic and ring patterns are easily distinguished from chlorosis due to unfavorable soil or growing conditions, as the latter is either uniform over the leaf, or begins at the leaf tips and margins and moves inward.

b. *Anthocyanin* and other blossom pigments may be inhibited as in the case of chlorophyll, giving the red-and-white and other variegations seen in many ornamental plants (Fig. 140).

2. **Reduced growth.** As a consequence of failure in chlorophyll formation, virus diseased plants commonly are reduced in size, 30 per cent or more reduction being not uncommon (Fig. 155). This takes the form of shorter internodes, smaller leaves and blossoms, and results in reduced yields.

3. **Distortions.** Leaves and flowers of affected plants are not only discolored, but often very irregular in shape, twisted or contorted abnormally narrowed (strap-shaped leaves), puckered, or covered with raised, blister-like areas due to greater growth of the green areas than of the chlorotic ones (Figs. 147, 151).

4. **Hypertrophy** or excessive growth is sometimes a characteristic of virus diseases.   It is seen in excessive branching characterizing such diseases as *witch's broom* of potatoes, in the production of little fin-like excrescences (*enations*) as in certain cases of tobacco and pea mosaic, and in excessive top growth without food storage in the roots, as in *giant hill* of potatoes, where affected hills may be the best looking in the field, but have few or no useable tubers.

5. **Abnormal growth form.** The habit of the plant may be markedly changed by virus disease. Examples are the rosette diseases of peanut, peach, and some other plants, in which the internodes are greatly shortened to produce a *rosette* habit in place of the normally elongated one, and *spindle tuber* of potato where the tops are abnormally stiff and erect, the leaves pointed upward, the tubers resembling sweet potatoes in shape (Fig. 142, 148).

6. **Necrosis** or killing of tissues due to viruses may be either local or general.   Roundish dead spots are produced on the leaves of certain plants (*local lesions*) when inoculated with viruses that do not become systemic.   In other cases the necrosis takes the form of dead rings with green centers

(*necrotic ringspot*, Fig. 145), *streaks* on stems (Fig. 150), or an oak-leaf-like outline within the leaf (*oak-leaf-pattern*). This last may be either chlorotic or necrotic. In severe cases the necrosis may become general, spreading to the growing point which is killed, soon resulting in death of the entire plant.

7. **Combinations of symptoms.** When a plant is infected with a virus disease it usually displays a combination of several of the symptoms described, for example, it may first show vein-clearing, followed by a general mosaic pattern, resulting in stunting, often accompanied by some form of distortion, and perhaps eventually exhibiting local or general necrosis.

8. **Internal symptoms.** While viruses, as such, cannot be seen with the microscope, examination of infected cells often brings out characteristic virus-disease symptoms. In addition to loss of pigments, reduced size of cells and cell elements, and occasional necrosis, certain of the viruses produce foreign bodies in the cells known as *X-bodies*. These are usually oval, spherical, or irregular in shape. It cannot be said whether they represent masses of virus or unusual byproducts of the host cell.

Figure 142. Peach yellows. The upright habit of growth, abnormal number of shoots, slender branches, and small narrow leaves are typical of the disease. (*Courtesy of L. O. Kunkel, Rockefeller Inst. for Med. Res.*)

Properties of Viruses

Although viruses cannot be seen, modern science has found means of determining their properties: they can be measured, counted, weighed, and many of their other characteristics can be determined.

1. **Infectiousness.** If virus is transferred from one susceptible plant to another by suitable means, the second plant becomes infected, shows symptoms of disease, and in turn is able to infect other plants. In studying a new suspected virus disease, it must first be proven that the disease is infectious. Viruses differ in their degree of infectiousness. Tobacco mosaic virus is an extreme case in that the juice from a mosaic diseased tobacco plant can be diluted with 1,000,000 parts of water, or one drop of virus juice in a barrel of water, and the diluted juice will still infect tobacco plants if rubbed on the leaves. Other viruses cannot be diluted to this extent and some cannot be diluted at all and still be infectious.

2. **Obligate parasitism.** All viruses, so far as is known, are dependent on living cells for their growth and reproduction; no virus multiplication occurs in lifeless media, although a virus, like a fungus spore, may retain inactive viability for considerable periods apart from the host. However, we only know viruses for their effects in producing disease. The world about us might be teeming with saprophytic viruses that we do not recognize because they cannot be seen and because they fail to produce some detected effect, such as disease, by which we might recognize them.

3. **Size.** Viruses may be measured by several means, one of the commonest of which is to force virus-containing plant juice through collodion filters of known pore size, which can be determined by physical means. If a series of these ultrafilters of graded pore sizes are used, the virus size can be estimated by noting the smallest pore size through which infectious juice can be drawn. While this method is subject to some errors (on account of virus particle shape or adsorption of particles to pore walls), it agrees fairly well with other methods of virus measurement in indicating that most viruses are from $\frac{1}{10}$ to $\frac{1}{1000}$ of a micron in diameter. The micron (μ), $\frac{1}{1000}$ millimeter, is the unit commonly

used in measuring fungus spores and bacteria. The unit
used in measuring viruses is $\frac{1}{1000}$ of a micron (1 milli-
micron = 1$\mu\mu$), and the virus sizes given above are thus 1 to
100 $\mu\mu$. The resolving power of the ordinary microscope is
about .5μ or 500 $\mu\mu$, and the smaller bacteria are about

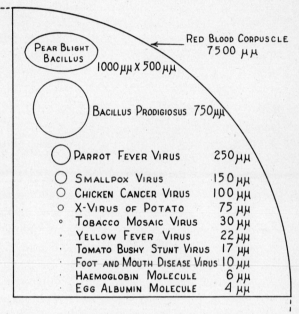

Figure 143. Scale illustrating the relative sizes of viruses and certain
other familiar types of small bodies.   Shape of the particle has not been considered, although it is known that some of these bodies are not spherical.   The
same relative proportions are seen if the blood corpuscle is compared to a 7½
foot cable spool as used for power and telephone lines, the pear-blight bacillus
to a football, tobacco mosaic virus to an English pea, and the egg albumin
molecule to a turnip or radish seed.

$1\mu \times .5\mu$ in size, or 10 times to 100 times the size of the
viruses. (Fig. 143.)

4. **Weight.** The weight of virus particles is determined,
   among other ways, by precipitating them in a high speed
   supercentrifuge.   Knowing the rate of sedimentation and
   the centrifugal force, it is possible to determine the particle
   weight, and this has been done for several viruses, the results
   usually being of the order of several millions (in terms

of molecular weights).   There is some question, however, whether the determinations refer to individual virus particles or to clusters or aggregates of virus units.

5. **Number.**   Bacteria can be counted by spreading them in a dilute layer over the surface of an agar plate and counting the bacterial colonies that develop on the plate.   Viruses in some cases can be counted in a similar fashion.   When the virus of tobacco mosaic is smeared on leaves of bean or of the wild tobacco, *Nicotiana glutinosa*, a little round local necrotic lesion appears in a few days at the site of each

Figure 144.   Local necrotic lesions of tobacco mosaic on *Nicotiana glutinosa*.   The figures give the dilutions of virus-containing tobacco juice, and the numbers of lesions shows how virus concentration may be estimated by "plating out" juice on leaves of this plant.   (*Courtesy of F. O. Holmes, Rockefeller Inst. for Med. Res.*)

infection (Fig. 144, 146).   The number of lesions bears a definite relation to the number of virus particles in the juice smeared on the leaf, and while this does not give us the absolute number of virus particles in the juice, it does give a means of titrating unknown virus concentrations against standard concentrations.   Much of the knowledge we have on the properties and nature of viruses depends on the use of the local lesion method of counting viruses.

6. **Transmission.**

a. *By mechanical means.*   The more highly infectious viruses such as those of tobacco, tomato, and cucumber mosaics, are readily transmitted by rubbing the juice of an infected plant onto the leaves of a healthy one.

So contagious are these viruses that merely to touch a diseased plant or to handle smoking tobacco (which commonly contains mosaic virus) and then to touch a healthy plant is sufficient to produce disease in the latter. In practice, transplanting and pruning plants are common means of virus spread. In experimental work, these viruses are sometimes transferred by pricking the leaves with needles wet with virus juice or by rubbing them with virus-wet gauze.

b. *By insects.* The majority of viruses are spread in nature by insects. In some cases the insect merely acts as the wet needle mentioned above; it feeds on a diseased plant, its proboscis is wet with the virus juice, and in its feeding on the healthy plant some of the virus is transmitted to the latter, mechanically.

But in many instances the insect is the only natural means by which the virus can pass from one plant to another. Here there is an obligate relationship between virus and insect. The insect feeds on a diseased plant, the virus passes into its digestive tract, and only after an incubation period of several days or weeks does the insect begin to transmit the virus to healthy plants. Thereafter it continues to transmit the virus to every plant on which it feeds, throughout its life. During the incubation period the virus appears to multiply in the insect's body, it passes about until it reaches the salivary glands, from which point, virus is supplied to healthy plants in the process of regurgitating saliva during feeding.

The virus-insect relationship is often very specific with those viruses that are transmitted in nature only by insects. The vectors involved are usually of groups with sucking mouth parts, especially Homoptera (aphids, leaf hoppers, plant hoppers, white flies). But not any insect with sucking mouth parts will suffice. Of all the insects feeding on peach trees, only the plum leaf hopper, *Macropsis trimaculata*, transmits peach yellows. Forty-eight other insects, including the most common sucking insects on peach, have been shown unable to transmit this virus, which is transmissible in no other way except by grafting.

In other cases the relationship between virus and insect may not be so specific, especially when the insect only acts as a mechanical, not a biological, agent of transmission.

c. *By vegetative propagation.*   Most viruses are not carried in the true seed from infected plants, but they pervade all other parts of the plant and are transmitted by any type of vegetative propagation.   Grafting and budding are common means of spreading infection in woody plants, and are also useful ways of experimentally transmitting those viruses that cannot be spread by mechanical means.   When a plant is normally propagated by vegetative parts, as in potatoes, sugar cane, bulb-plants, and ornamentals grown from cuttings, every vegetative descendant of a single virus-infected plant will in turn be infected.   This perhaps accounts for the particular importance of virus diseases in the plants that are vegetatively propagated.

d. *By seed.*   Though few viruses are transmitted in the true seed, some of the legume viruses, notably of the mosaics of bean and cowpea, are carried in this manner, and a few other cases outside the legume family have been noted.

7. **Host ranges.**   Among the plant viruses we find some with very extensive host ranges, as in the case of the beet curly-top virus that attacks 220 host species in 41 families of plants. Tobacco and cucumber mosaic viruses and aster yellows virus also attack many species often in widely separated families.   At the other extreme are such viruses as that of wheat mosaic, which is restricted to the wheats, barley, and rye, or corn mosaic that attacks only corn and sorghum. Many viruses have been recorded from only a single host species, but we must always deal with the possibility that virus diseases of two distinct plant species may be due to the

same virus. Usually, but not always, there is some degree of botanical kinship among the plant species susceptible to a given virus.

8. **Resistance to heat.** Plant viruses tolerate heating to various extents. On the one hand, tobacco mosaic virus, the most resistant of all, can stand 10 minutes of heating up to 92°C. before it is entirely destroyed. It easily stands the heating involved in the curing process. Spotted wilt virus of tomatoes and other plants is quite unstable. It is destroyed by heating for 10 minutes at 40°C. which is about blood temperature, or that of a moderately hot summer day. Indeed, if plants infected by this virus are placed in a hot greenhouse, they often lose the virus and recover. The other viruses that have been tested in this connection usually have heat tolerances between these extremes. Certain of the peach viruses can be removed from peach branches without injury to the peach tissues, by heating. This may have practical application in preventing virus spread by heat-treating propagation wood prior to use or shipment.

9. **Resistance to chemicals.** In a similar way we find different degrees of tolerance of chemicals among the viruses, with tobacco mosaic virus topping the list in its resistance. In general the viruses are quite sensitive to acids, alkalis, alcohol, and oxidizing agents. They are frequently quite resistant to decomposition by enzymes.

10. **Retention of infectivity in storage.** The mechanically transmissible viruses, the only ones in which a study of resistance is satisfactory, retain their infective power in extracted juice for varying lengths of time, from a few hours to many months or even years with tobacco mosaic virus if the juice is kept from decomposition. At refrigerator temperatures, or frozen solid, viruses remain viable for much longer periods than at room temperatures. Most viruses cannot stand dessication, but tobacco mosaic virus in dried leaves or juice dried on filter paper, remains infective for many years.

11. **Mutability.** Many viruses exist in the form of various distinct strains, differentiated according to their different

symptoms on one host plant or another. Indeed, some workers go so far as to feel that no two different field collections of a virus produce identical symptoms. In the case of tobacco mosaic virus, 50 or more strains have been distinguished. These agree for the most part in their physical and chemical properties and host ranges, but differ in their aggressiveness or in the symptoms produced on tobacco and other host plants. They include strains that produce no symptoms or very slight ones, strains that produce a moderate amount of mottling (mosaic) or distortion or both, strains that produce brilliant yellow or white mottling, strains that produce enations, and strains that result in moderate or extreme necrosis and death. Some remain localized in the infected leaf, others move slowly or rapidly to the growing point of the plant and become systemic. A similar situation exists in cucumber mosaic virus and that of tobacco ringspot. These strains either may occur in nature or they may be isolated in the laboratory as by heat treatments of ordinary strains or by transferring virus from localized, atypical spots in plants that otherwise show normal virus symptoms. This variation in viruses leads to great difficulties in virus recognition and classification.

12. **Serological reactions.** If a virus-containing juice is injected into the body of a rabbit, the rabbit's blood comes to contain antibodies that will give precipitation reactions with the virus juice. The reactions are specific, i.e. the antibodies formed by inoculation of tobacco mosaic virus, precipitate juices that contain various strains of tobacco mosaic virus but not other viruses, such as cucumber or potato mosaics. This affords a useful laboratory reagent for identifying unknown viruses and determining the relationships of viruses.

13. **Acquired immunity.** Just as a person who recovers from smallpox is thereafter immune from that virus disease, so it frequently happens that virus-diseased plants recover, display no further symptoms, and are immune from further disease caused by same virus, although they are still sus-

ceptible to other viruses. (Fig. 145.) The recovered plants and their vegetative progeny still contain the virus in a symptomless form, they are disease "carriers" like notorious "Typhoid Mary," and their juice will produce typical symptoms in inoculated plants. Because the acquired

Figure 145. Recovery from a plant virus. The plant at the left, after having experienced a severe case of tobacco ringspot is recovering. New growth appears normal and will continue to do so in plants propagated by cuttings from the new growth. The recovered tissue still contains ringspot virus, and is immune from further display of symptoms by this virus. The plant at the right is an uninoculated control. (*Courtesy of W. C. Price, Rockefeller Inst. for Med. Res.*)

immunity reaction is specifically directed against the virus of the original infection, or its strains, the reaction is useful in determining virus relationships. Thus if a plant recovers from tobacco ringspot and proves to be immune from unknown virus A but susceptible to unknown virus B, we have evidence that A is a strain of the ringspot virus, while

B is a distinct virus type. Similarly, a plant may be infected with a very mild strain of virus and thereafter prove immune from the severe strains of the same virus encountered in nature, analogous to smallpox vaccination with cowpox virus (Fig. 146). Whether or not mass immunization can be used to protect plants from virus

Figure 146.   Protective inoculation of a plant virus.   The left half of the left leaf and the lower half of the right leaf of *Nicotiana sylvestris* were each rubbed with juice containing tobacco mosaic virus.   Five days later the entire surface of both leaves was rubbed with juice containing tobacco aucuba mosaic virus.   Aucuba mosaic lesions developed only on the halves that had not been protected by a previous inoculation of the non-necrotic virus.   (*Courtesy of L. O. Kunkel, Rockefeller Inst. for Med. Res.*)

diseases on a practical scale, remains to be seen, but there may be some possibility of this in vegetatively propagated plants like potato where the immunizing virus would only need be introduced in the original breeding stock, or in mechanically transmissible viruses of plants like tomato and tobacco that are handled in transplanting, during which operation they could receive the immunizing dose from the operator's hands, kept wet in virus juice.

Nomenclature of Viruses

Prior to 1927, viruses were referred to by attaching the common name of the host to that of the principal symptom produced, as tobacco mosaic virus, peach yellows virus, or potato spindle-tuber virus. In that year J. Johnson proposed a system of numbering viruses, as tobacco virus 1, tomato virus 3, etc., a method that was further modified by Smith in England who substituted the latin generic name for the common name of the usual host, as *Nicotiana* virus 1, *Prunus* virus 2, etc. This was followed by suggestions on using a latin system of binomial nomenclature for viruses, similar to that used for animals and plants, a proposal that was carried out extensively by Holmes who, in 1939, published a book assigning latin binomials to large numbers of viruses. Here tobacco mosaic virus becomes *Marmor tabaci*, the genus *Marmor* including the mosaics, cotton leaf curl virus is *Ruga gossypii*, etc. The various virus genera are grouped into ten families and larger groups, all plant viruses falling within the *Phytophagi*. While Holmes' system is criticized in certain details by some of the present-day virus workers, there is likelihood that at least in modified form it will form the basis for future virus nomenclature, as pathologists gradually familiarize themselves with the binomials.

Nature of Viruses

Ever since they were first recognized, the nature of the viruses has been a challenge, and many theories have been advanced in attempts to answer the question: What is a virus? In the earlier days when potato degeneration, now known to be due to an accumulation of viruses, was a problem, some of the European workers advanced the hypothesis that the "running-out" of potato varieties was due to unbalanced nutrition. Others believed that it was caused by excessively long continued vegetative propagation and the absence of stimulation from sexual reproduction. At the end of the nineteenth century when the contagious nature of viruses was recognized, they were considered to be either filterable bacteria (Iwanowsky) or a "contagious living fluid" (Beyerinck). During the succeeding years up till 1935 the majority of workers held that viruses are living organisms, too small to be detected with the microscope, but in most other respects analogous to bacteria.   This view was based on no direct proof, but on many suggestive characteristics of the viruses: their biological relationships with insects and incubation periods in insect bodies, their mutability, their specialized plant-host relationships, their reproduction, and their susceptibility to heat and chemicals, which is comparable to that of living pathogens.   But not all virologists subscribed to this view. There were those like Vinson who maintained that viruses may be chemicals, analogous to enzymes, with the power of self-reproduction in living cells at the expense of cell materials.   There were others, like Nelson and Eckerson, who saw the amoeba-like x-bodies in virus-infected cells and concluded that these were protozoa, the causes of the virus diseases.   Duggar in 1923 advanced the ingenious theory that viruses are "wandering genes," or factors of cell inheritance, perhaps segments of chromosomes, that have the power to pass from cell to cell and in each new cell propagate themselves and produce, by a genetic-regulatory mechanism, the symptoms of virus disease.   Strange as this theory may seem, it has recently been revived by Gowan and Price who find that viruses and genes are remarkably alike in their reaction to x-rays.   Indeed we have always conceived of genes as fixed components of cells, but were it possible for genes to pass from one cell to another their results might well be akin to those we see in virus diseases.

In 1935, Stanley prepared from tobacco mosaic virus juice a crystalline protein which he and many others regard as the virus of tobacco mosaic in pure form.   Similar proteins have been prepared from other virus juices but are not obtained in all cases.   The question is not finally settled whether this material is in reality the virus or whether it may be a closely associated by-product of virus activity,—there are still some obstacles to be overcome before this view can be accepted without reserve.   The most recent studies on virus proteins, although involving highly elaborate methods of accumulating data and interpretation, deal more with the chemical nature of these proteins than with their pathology, which in the end has always been the criterion of viruses.

The question of whether viruses are living or lifeless goes back in the last analysis to a definition of life.   Formulate a workable definition of life and it is at once possible to say whether or not viruses fit the definition. But it is not possible to formulate such a definition. As we pass down to the simplest living organisms each of the attributes of higher living creatures becomes subject to exceptions. For example, there are bacteria that do not respire by burning oxygen and liberating carbon dioxide, and one by one the other criteria of life fail as we approach the lowest limits of acknowledged living things. Again, on the chemical side we find the most complex chemicals displaying properties ordinarily associated with life, as the autocatalytic enzymes with the power of self-reproduction.

Perhaps the view of Andrewes and other British workers comes closest to the truth: that there is no sharp line that divides the living from the non-living world. As we pass down the scale of life to the simplest living things, the iron and sulphur bacteria and the Rickettsia bodies that are too small to be seen with the ordinary microscope but are revealed by the ultra-microscope, we pass imperceptibly to the larger viruses, thence through to the smallest, as those of chicken cancer and bacteriophage, thence again imperceptibly into the most complex of chemicals, the self-reproducing enzymes with physiologic effects not unlike those of viruses, down through the growth promoting substances and proteins, into the world of lifeless matter. The biologist looking down his scale sees the viruses at the bottom and regards them as the simplest of living things; the chemist looks up his scale and sees the same viruses as the most complex of chemical substances. May not both be right, the viruses being only a connecting link that marks one step in a continuous and unbroken series from the one kingdom to the other?

VIRUS DISEASES OF POTATOES.

Although as many as 50 virus diseases of the Irish potato have been named, they represent probably not more than 12 to 20 distinct virus types, and of these only a few are of widespread importance. They may be characterized as follows:

Latent mosaic virus (*Marmor dubium* = X-virus of European workers = "healthy potato virus"). Although less common in other parts of the world, the latent mosaic virus occurs in practically every plant of some of the commercial potato varieties grown in America. In most potato varieties it produces no symptoms by itself, but when a second virus, in itself comparatively harmless, is added, the combination of the two viruses may produce serious disease. The latent mosaic virus is easily detected in potatoes by rubbing a little juice of an infected potato plant on the leaves of a pepper seedling, where it produces an extensive necrotic disease. The virus is very easily transmitted by mechanical methods. It ranks second to tobacco mosaic in infectiveness, and the virus juice may be diluted 1:10,000 and still produce infections. Its host range includes pepper, Jimson weed, henbane, tomato, tobacco, bittersweet, nightshade, amaranth, chrysanthemum, and veronica, The latent mosaic virus combines with tobacco mosaic virus to cause *double-virus streak*, a necrotic disease of tomatoes, and with the vein-banding virus of potato to produce the important *rugose mosaic* of this crop.

Veinbanding virus, (*Marmor cucumeris* var. *upsilon* = Y-virus of European workers) causes no symptoms in some potato varieties, and in other cases either a pale mottling or leaf-drop and a stem-streak. By itself it is not a major problem but in combination with the latent mosaic virus it produces *rugose mosaic*, one of the most destructive of the potato virus diseases. The veinbanding virus occurs widely in the United States and Europe. Its host range includes a number of the other Solanaceous plants and the cowpea, on which it produces characteristic red local lesions. It is easily transmitted by mechanical means, and also is carried by the aphid, *Myzus persicae*. The combination disease, rugose mosaic is a striking one (Fig. 147). The leaves are dwarfed, much wrinkled (rugose), and somewhat mottled, with a downward rolling of the leaf margins. There may be more or less necrosis of the stem tissues and of the veins. Affected plants are stunted and die prematurely so that tuber production is greatly reduced or even lacking.

Mild mosaic virus (*Marmor solani* = A-virus of European workers). The mild mosaic virus, which affects only potato and a few related *Solanaceae*, usually causes a very mild yellowish mottling of potato leaves with some crinkling or wrinkling of the leaf surfaces. Diseased plants are slightly to severely stunted, and die prematurely with yields reduced about one third. The disease is widespread in the United States and ranks among the major virus diseases of potato both because of its prevalence and because it may cause substantial losses that are largely unrecognized because

of the mild foliage symptoms.   The virus is mechanically transmissible but less easily than the viruses of latent mosaic and veinbanding.   In nature it is transmitted by two species of aphids.

Figure 147.   Rugose mosaic of potato.   (*Courtesy of J. M. Raeder, Idaho Agr. Exp. Sta.*)

Spindle tuber virus (*Acrogenus solani*).   This virus which
affects only the potato, is widespread in the United States and
Canada.   Affected plants are stiff, with upright, and small, dark
leaves.   The tubers are abnormally long, spindling, and tend to be
pointed especially at the stem end (Fig. 148).   In the Bliss Triumph

variety, the spindling shape is not so apparent. The tubers are small, often of a rounded conical form, bleached at one end, and with an excessive number of large, shallow eyes, rather evenly distributed over the surface. Yields are reduced 60 or 65 per cent. The virus is easily transmitted mechanically by leaf juice and by the seed-cutting knife, which is one of the chief means of spread of this virus. In the field it is also transmitted by aphids, grasshoppers, flea beetles, potato beetle larvae, and leaf beetles.

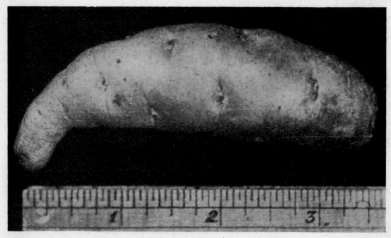

Figure 148. Spindle tuber of Irish potato, one of the few virus diseases that can be recognized in the tuber. Off-shaped tubers such as this should not be planted. (*Courtesy of C. D. Burke, Pa. Agr. Ext. Serv.*)

Leaf-roll virus (*Corium solani*). The leaf-roll virus, affects only potato and a few closely related *Solanaceae*. It is found wherever potatoes are grown and differs from all the preceeding viruses in that it cannot in nature be transmitted mechanically, but only through its insect vectors, three species of aphids, principally the peach aphis, *Myzus persicae*. In the insect, the virus has an incubation period of 24–48 hours. The leafroll virus causes one of the most destructive of the potato diseases. Affected plants are pale and dwarfed, their leaves thick and leathery, and rolled upward (Fig. 149). In some varieties the leaflets are reddened or purplish. Tubers are small and few, and as the infestation may reach 25 per cent or more in the field, the losses are heavy. In comparatively recent infections of some varieties of potatoes, the cut tubers show a network of brown strands, especially near the surface and stem end of the tuber. This is *net-necrosis*, one of the few easily recognized tuber symptoms of potato virus diseases in stocks that have not had

Figure 149. Potato leaf roll. (*Courtesy of J. M. Raeder, Idaho Agr. Exp. Sta.*)

the disease for over a year. It must be distinguished from a similar condition due to freezing.

Other potato viruses. There are a large number of other viruses affecting potato in local areas or in less severe fashion than the foregoing. Among them may be mentioned the witches' broom virus that causes such excessive branching that the plant becomes a great mass of weak shoots, yellow-dwarf virus, that is very destructive locally in the Eastern states, completely destroying the plants, and calico and aucuba mosaic viruses that cause brilliant yellow and white mottling of the potato foliage.

Control of potato virus diseases. Except for a few minor differences the potato viruses are all susceptible to similar control measures, viz.:

1. *Use of virus-free seed-tubers.* All potato viruses are carried in the tubers, usually without tuber symptoms that would enable the grower to detect virus diseased tubers. The best assurance in protecting against these diseases is to use certified potatoes for planting, because the fields producing certified potatoes have been inspected for virus diseases, and any considerable amount of these diseases in the field disqualify it for certification.

   In production of certified potatoes, the foundation stock is obtained by *tuber-indexing* or *hill-indexing.* An eye from each potato or a tuber from each hill is planted early or in the greenhouse. If the resulting plant shows virus symptoms the potatoes from that hill are discarded. After planting, the potato seed plot is inspected frequently and any hills showing virus-disease symptoms are destroyed. This "*rogueing*" of diseased hills is aided by the *tuber-unit method* of planting, in which the seed pieces from each potato are planted consecutively in the row, the end of the unit of four hills being marked by a missed hill or stake. Whenever a virus-diseased hill is found, the unit of four hills is destroyed. The procedure followed in Nebraska in the production of certified seed is representative: The first year's plants are raised from indexed tubers; this crop is multiplied the second year as a foundation seed plot, rogued as necessary; the third year the crop is planted by the certified seed grower in a tuber-unit seed plot; the fourth year's crop is then certified.

   Certified potatoes are available in several grades. All grades are equally free from virus diseases. They differ principally according to the size, shape, and appearance of the tubers, and their degree of infestation with scab and

Rhizoctonia, diseases that may be recognized on the tubers and controlled by seed treatment.

For southern growers it is usually impractical to produce their own seed tubers. In cooler climates this may be done, the home-grown tubers having all the advantages of certified seed-tubers provided that a relatively virus-free seed stock was originally used, and that the seed block is isolated, and thoroughly rogued several times during the season.

2. *Seed inspection.* Occasionally virus diseases can be detected in the tubers, as in spindle tuber and the net-necrosis phase of leafroll. Such tubers should be rejected. Because spindle tuber is so easily spread by the cutting knife, it is a good practice to dip the knife in alcohol or formaldehyde solution, or wipe it with a cloth wet with disinfestant at frequent intervals during the cutting.

3. *Field practices.* There is little that can be done in the commercial field once virus diseases have appeared. Sucking-insect control with contact insecticides is sometimes suggested to prevent field spread, but this has doubtful value except in seed plots. Rogueing in commercial fields is undesirable as this merely reduces yields without appreciable advantage. Rotation is of no importance in this connection, because potato viruses do not live over in soil. Weed control may have some value in reducing sources of infection, but hardly enough to justify more than the ordinary cultivation practices, except in the case of seed plots where Solanaceous weeds should be eliminated from adjacent fence rows.

4. *Resistant varieties.* Comparatively little has been accomplished thus far in breeding potatoes for virus-disease resistance. A noteworthy exception is the production of the strain S41956 which is immune to all tested strains of latent mosaic virus, and possesses two dominant genes, both necessary for resistance. While the latent mosaic virus in itself is not a serious problem, it combines with other viruses in producing destructive diseases, hence its elimination is desirable. The production of S41956 has another importance. It will be remembered that most commercial potatoes contain the latent mosaic virus. This makes it

difficult to study potato viruses experimentally, because the worker is usually dealing with virus mixtures rather than with pure viruses. By passing such mixtures through S41956, the latent mosaic element is "filtered out," giving a pure culture of the accompanying virus.

TOBACCO (TOMATO) MOSAIC (*Marmor tabaci*).

Best known of all viruses is the common mosaic virus of tobacco, which not only is a serious pathogen but also is the "guinea-pig" virus that has been of inestimable value in studies on the nature and properties of viruses in general.

History and distribution.   Tobacco mosaic virus occurs wherever susceptible plants will grow.   In America it is a major factor in tobacco production from Canada to Florida.   Moreover it is one of the oldest recognized viruses.   It was the first virus shown to be contagious (Mayer in Holland, 1886), the first to be filter-passing (Iwanowsky in Russia, 1892), the first to be extensively studied with regard to properties and strains, and the first to be prepared in crystalline form (Stanley, 1935).   The science of human and animal virology is much indebted to tobacco mosaic virus, for providing basic information on this group of pathogens.

Importance.   The losses in the nation's tobacco crop from mosaic range between 35 and 45 million pounds annually.   If, as often occurs, plants become infected at the time of transplanting, the yield is reduced 30 to 35 per cent and because of poorer quality as well as decreased yield, the value of the crop per acre is reduced more than 55 per cent.   If infection occurs a month later, the loss is nearly as great, and even late season infection (at topping time) significantly lowers the yield.   The losses in tomatoes are comparable.

Host plants.   Tobacco mosaic virus attacks 123 species of plants in 27 botanical families, but more than one third of the recorded host plants are in the *Solanaceae*.   All tested species of tobacco are susceptible.   Tobacco, tomato, pepper, and petunia are the most important economic hosts.

Symptoms.   The most common symptoms of tobacco mosaic are leaf mottling of light and dark green patches (Fig. 150), leaf distortion, with blister-like raised areas, and irregular or unnatural leaf shape, stunting of the entire plant, dwarfing, distortion, and variegation of the blossoms, production of mosaic suckers, and in some cases local or widespread necrosis. The symptoms vary with the virus strain and the host variety. Mild or symptomless strains have been isolated, as well as strains causing brilliant mottling or

A   B

Figure 150. Tobacco mosaic. A, mosaic tobacco leaf showing typical light and dark green mottling and crinkly distortion. Affected leaves are much smaller than normal ones of the same age. (*Courtesy of L. O. Kunkel, Rockefeller Inst. for Medical Research*). B, a severe strain of tobacco mosaic in tomato, showing yellow mottling, distortion, and necrosis of the leaflets, and necrotic streaking of the stem.

even death of the plant, although in general the disease is not a killing one. The symptoms are masked at high temperatures. If bean, *Nicotiana glutinosa*, or certain other plants are inoculated with the virus, primary infection takes the form of local necrotic spots from which the virus does not spread out into the growing point and other parts of the plant (Fig. 144). In tomatoes the fruit may be mottled, and severe strains of the virus cause dead streaks on the stems or general necrosis of the plant.   (Fig. 150.)

Etiology.   Tobacco mosaic virus is the most resistant and the most highly infectious of all viruses.   It withstands heating almost to boiling, is quite highly resistant to alcohol and other germicides, and retains infectivity in the dried state for many years.   The commonest original source of inoculum is smoking or chewing tobacco.   Workmen using tobacco contaminate their hands with the virus and infect tobacco or tomato plants handled in operations of transplanting, pruning, disbudding, tying, topping, artificial pollinating, or harvesting.   The virus is infective in high dilutions, up to 1:1,000,000, so that even a trace on the hands will serve to infect many plants.   The virus enters plants through scratches, abrasions, or broken hairs, due to handling or rubbing the leaves. In ordinary tobacco, no symptoms are seen on the inoculated leaf, but staining with iodine shows that there is disruption of the starch metabolism.   The virus rapidly multiplies and passes to the growing point, largely by way of the phloem vessels.   Here, in about 8 to 10 days after inoculation, are seen the first symptoms, a clearing-of-veins of the new leaves, and each succeeding leaf formed displays the characteristic mottling and distortion.   The virus spreads from one plant to another in the field or greenhouse either through the agency of man, handling diseased then healthy plants, or by means of several species of aphids.   There is no biological relationship with the insects, they merely act as mechanical transmitters.   The seed of diseased plants is not a source of infection.   In spite of the high infectivity of the virus, plants do not normally pick up the virus direct from soil, but they may get it indirectly from the hands of laborers who have handled soil that is contaminated with virus-infested plant refuse.

Control.   1. *Sanitation.*   In tobacco culture effective control is obtained by furnishing laborers with heat-sterilized smoking or chewing tobacco and requiring that they use no unsterilized tobacco.   Other important sanitary practices in growing tobacco and tomatoes include: washing the hands with soap, a good viricide, before handling plants; handling healthy plants in the early part of the day and reserving work that involves handling diseased plants for the last thing in the day's work; rogueing out and

destroying infected plants as they appear; burning of mosaic-
infested crop refuse; and avoiding unnecessary or excessive handling
of plants.   In the greenhouse there are many fine points of sanitation.   For example the doorknobs, faucets, pots, flats, and hose-
ends may become contaminated by handling with virus-smeared
hands, and thereafter serve as unsuspected sources of infestation.
The vibrating pollinator is particularly dangerous.   A combination
of routine sterilization of equipment and soil, devices for avoiding
contamination such as foot- or elbow-operated faucets and doors,
and above all vigorous vigilance in detecting and eliminating
dangerous practices will protect the greenhouse from mosaic.

2. *Breeding for resistance.* No mosaic resistant commercial
tomatoes are available. On the other hand recent work has
incorporated mosaic resistance into commercial tobacco and
peppers.   In tobacco, two sources of resistance have been used, the
variety Ambalema in which no symptoms appear and the virus has
a limited spread through the plant, and species in which the virus
forms a small local necrotic spot at the point of infection and does
not spread beyond this point (Fig. 144).   Holmes found that
although such a species, *Nicotiana glutinosa*, does not ordinarily
produce fertile hybrids with commercial tobacco, *N. tabacum*, a
fertile hybrid of this cross, known as *N. digluta* contained the *N.
glutinosa* gene for localizing the virus.   With repeated back crossing
of *N. digluta* with *N. tabacum*, Holmes has been able to produce
commercial-type tobaccos that contain the localizing gene, which
makes them for practical purposes essentially immune to the mosaic
disease.   Holmes has made a similar study of the pepper, transferring a localizing factor from the hot, small-fruited tabasco
pepper into the mild, large-fruited garden types of peppers.

PEACH MOSAIC (*Marmor persicae*).

History and distribution. Peach mosaic differs from the
foregoing virus diseases in that it is being controlled only by a state
and federal quarantine and eradication program.   The disease
first appeared in Texas in 1931 where it had apparently been present
for a few years previously.   The same year it was found in Colorado
although not identified as peach mosaic until 1934.   In 1933 it
appeared in California, in 1935 in Utah, in 1936 in New Mexico

and Arizona, and more recently in Oklahoma and Old Mexico. In each of the states it is localized in certain counties.

Importance. Peach mosaic is considered one of the most important of the virus diseases of tree fruits. Losses from mosaic are of two kinds, the low and poor quality or unmarketable yield from affected trees, and the losses from the regulatory program including condemnation and destruction of nursery stock and bearing trees as well as the cost of the quarantine, inspection, and eradication program. In a single county of Colorado over 30,000 new cases were found during a single year of inspection.

Host plants. Only stone fruits, species of *Prunus*, are affected by the peach mosaic virus, and symptoms are seen only in the peach. The plum, prune, apricot, and almond carry the virus without showing symptoms. No resistant varieties of peach have been reported.

Symptoms. Peach mosaic is not an easily identified disease because some of the symptoms are transient, and because other troubles than mosaic may produce symptoms resembling those of mosaic. Certain branches may display symptoms while other branches of the same tree appear healthy. In affected trees, the new spring growth shows shortened internodes, and later short and long internodes may occur at intervals on the same branch. The blossoms of certain varieties, as Carmen, Chilow, and Early Wheeler, are variegated as a result of the disease, while those of some other varieties, notably Elberta and Belle, are unaffected. Foliation in the spring may be retarded (Fig. 151). The new leaves are variegated or mottled with light green or yellow patches and are crinkly or distorted. As the season progresses the mottling may no longer be evident. Affected areas of the leaves may drop out in midsummer. The fruits are typically small, irregular in shape, bumpy especially on the crease side, with a protruding tip, and are often late in ripening. There is no constant discoloration, and the flesh is more or less normal. Seen from a distance, affected trees are thin, with bunches or clusters of leaves rather than evenly green. Any one of these symptoms may be duplicated or resembled due to other causes than mosaic, hence the need for a careful study of suspected trees, or better, the opinion of a specialist.

Figure 151. Peach mosaic. Above, affected tree in early spring; note the retarded foliation as compared with healthy trees in the background. Below, symptoms of mosaic mottling, stunted development, and distortion in leaves of affected trees; compare with healthy leaf at right. (*Courtesy of E. W. Bodine, Col. Agr. Exp. Sta.*)

Etiology. Relatively little is known of the virus that causes peach mosaic. It cannot be transmitted mechanically, and its rapid natural spread suggests that a highly efficient insect vector is responsible for its distribution. It can be transmitted by grafting and budding, which are means for its propagation and dissemination in the nursery stock trade. Unlike some of the other peach viruses, that of mosaic cannot be removed from peach tissues by heating without killing the tissues. After trees are inoculated there is an extended incubation period, sometimes a large part of the season or year, before symptoms appear. The occurrence of symptomless carriers, such as the Maynard plum, further obscures the etiology of the disease, and increases the difficulty of its eradication.

Control. The control of peach mosaic is purely a regulatory problem, the only direct approach being the detection and destruction of diseased trees in the nursery and orchard. The federal government maintains inspections for peach mosaic in states affected but leaves to the states the task of eradicating diseased trees and enforcing the restrictions on movement of trees from areas of infestation. Each of the various states involved has a uniform quarantine defining the areas of infestation and prohibiting movement of peach and plum trees or propagating wood from those areas. The laws are so strict that if a single infected tree is found in a nursery, the entire nursery is placed under quarantine.

The enforcement of the quarantines has at times been difficult, especially where small private orchards of bearing trees are involved. There is no provision for replacement of condemned trees, but in some states the organized nurserymen have supplied replacement trees *gratis*.

Although there is also some disagreement on the effectiveness and desirability of quarantines and eradication for control of peach mosaic, in some counties, notably in Colorado and Utah, the introduction of the mosaic quarantines appears to have halted an alarming increase in the disease, as in Mesa Co., Colorado, where the number of new cases dropped from 30,457 to 9,561 the year after eradication got under way, and to about 3,000 the second year. In celebration of this accomplishment the growers held a "peach mosaic banquet" dedicating themselves to continue the program to completion. Since the program has been operating some of the formerly infested counties have been declared mosaic-free and the quarantines have been lifted.

BEAN MOSAIC (*Marmor phaseoli*) and COWPEA MOSAIC (*Marmor vignae*).

These similar diseases are very destructive to their respective crops. Bean mosaic can cause 100 per cent losses in the crop, and cowpea mosaic will result in a 30 per cent or greater reduction of foliage and complete loss of the crop for seed purposes. In both cases the symptoms are similar: moderate to brilliant yellowish mottling (Fig. 152) with severe distortion of the leaves, marked stunting of the plants, with useable seed and pod production sharply reduced or inhibited. Contrary to the situation with other viruses, both these legume viruses are seed transmissible: in bean mosaic 30 to 50 per cent and in cowpea mosaic 5 per cent of the seed from infected plants transmit the disease. Very rapid spread from a few infected plants often to the entire crop occurs in the field. Both

Figure 152. Bean mosaic. The symptoms are dwarfing, distortion, and light green mottling of the leaves, resulting in poor yields.

viruses are transmitted by several species of aphids, and both are mechanically transmissible but with some difficulty, so that it appears that insects are the chief means of their field dissemination.

Control of bean mosaic depends on the use of seed from mosaic-free fields (certified seed) or growing of one of the new mosaic-resistant bean varieties of which there are several including white seeded and red seeded dry bean varieties and snap beans (Robust, Idaho Refugee, Wisconsin Refugee, Great Northern U.I. 81, U.I. 59, U.I. 123, Red Mexican U.I. 3, U.I. 34, U.I. 1, and U. S. 5 Mosaic Resistant).

There are no known varieties of cowpeas resistant to mosaic. Here control depends entirely on the use of seed from mosaic-free fields or certified seed. As the disease shows distinctly with a brilliant vein clearing on the cotyledonary leaves, it should be possible to clean mosaic out of valuable seed stocks by thorough rogueing just after the plants emerge from the soil.

WHEAT MOSAIC (*Marmor tritici*).

Importance.   Wheat mosaics have been reported in Kansas (5 counties), Nebraska, and Oklahoma as well as from several central and eastern states.   Once established the trouble often becomes very destructive.   The reports include a 40 acre field of mixed Turkey, Kanred, and James Fife wheat in Kansas that was completely destroyed in 1932, and two other Kansas fields in which the loss amounted to total failure, while Illinois growers have come to recognize mosaic as one of their most serious problems in that state. There is reason to believe that the disease is increasing in severity at the present time, and may very well become a major factor in production in other areas than the present infested localities east of the Mississippi river.

Symptoms.   There are several viruses affecting wheat, producing some combination of the following symptoms, usually most evident in the spring: mottling or variegation, the leaves showing a pattern of light and dark green or green and yellow patches or stripes (Fig. 153); rosette or stunting with excessive production of small tillers and lack of normal jointing; dead leaves at the base; rolling of the leaves as in wild garlic; and occasionally killing of the plants.   Attacked plants sometimes spontaneously recover.   The trouble often has a tendency to appear in well defined spots in the field, although in light attacks only single plants, here and there, may show the symptoms.

Etiology.   There are as many as seven distinct viruses involved in wheat mosaic, here grouped together for convenience in discussion.   Certain of them, while best known in winter wheat, also cause similar diseases in rye, barley, wheat grass, and possibly corn. They are of little consequence in spring wheats.   The wheat viruses of the eastern states appear to differ from those of the Great Plains, in that the eastern viruses are perpetuated from one crop to the next in the soil, while there is no positive evidence of this in the western viruses. Spread in the field is probably through the agency of insects, although data on this point are scanty. Volunteer grain or grasses may possibly serve for the oversummering of the viruses.

Figure 153. Yellow mosaic in Harvest Queen wheat. The four leaves at the left are from plants in the tiller-formation stage, the two at the right are from plants in the jointing stage. The lightest areas in these leaves were yellow or almost white. (*Photo by Bureau of Plant Industry, U. S. Dept. of Agriculture.*)

Control. Comparatively few data are available on which to base recommendations for the control of the wheat mosaics west of the Mississippi river. The eastern mosaics are readily controlled by resistant varieties of wheat many of which are available. In the West the disease is erratic in appearance, which hampers varietal resistance tests. In lack of specific control measures, it would be advisable to plant infested land with some cultivated crop other than wheat or rye for at least one year, and in localities where the disease is known to occur, to select seed from fields known to be free from the disease.   Observations on the varieties that fail to be attacked in the localities of infestation, will be a guide for future plantings.   Mosaic resistant soft red wheats under conditions east of the Mississippi include certain lots of Fulcaster and Fultz, Gladden, Forward, two selections of Jones Fife, Mediterranean, Poole, Red Rock, Red May, Red Wave, Trumbull, Shepherd, Prairie, Nabob, Wabash, Thorne, and Fulhio.   The more resistant hard red winter

Figure 154.   Curly top of sugar beets.   Natural infection, showing the inward curling of the leaves toward the midrib.   (*Courtesy of H. H. P. Severin, Cal. Agr. Exp. Sta.*)

wheats are Cooperatorka and Eagle Chief, with Oro and numerous other winter wheats partly resistant; however, such commonly used varieties as Kawvale, Turkey, Cheyenne, Tenmarq, Harvest Queen, and Clarkan are not resistant.

CURLY TOP OF SUGAR BEETS (*Chlorogenus eutetticola*).

   This virus has been a very serious menace to the sugar beet industry.   Typical symptoms of curly-top beets are seen in Figure 154.   It is also destructive on tomatoes, where the trouble is called western yellow blight.   Many other plants are susceptible.   The virus is confined to the western part of North America.   It is carried by the sugar beet leaf hopper, *Eutettix tenellus*, in which the virus has a 4–12 hour incubation period. Control is by use of newly developed resistant varieties of beets, timing of crops to be advanced before the leaf hoppers become abundant, and destroying the Russian thistle on which the leafhopper overwinters readily.

CUCURBIT MOSAIC (*Marmor cucumeris*).

This is a widespread typical mosaic disease of cucumber, squash, celery, spinach, tobacco, petunia, pepper, and many other species

A   B

Figure 155. Cucurbit mosaic. A, symptoms of distortion, chlorosis, and stunting in muskmelon; B, mosaic on the cucumber fruit, also known as "white pickle." (*Courtesy of C. T. Gregory, Ind. Agr. Ext. Service.*)

(Fig. 155). It overwinters on a number of species of weeds. The virus is easily transmitted mechanically and is also carried by aphids and cucumber beetles. It is controlled by cutting diseased plants at the base, to avoid spreading the disease by pulling them out, and fumigation or spraying to kill the aphid vectors.

REFERENCES

On the nature and properties of plant viruses.

1. Bawden, F. C. Plant viruses and virus diseases. Chronica Botanica Co., Leiden, Holland. 1939.
2. Smith, Kenneth M. Recent advances in the study of plant viruses. P. Blakiston's Son & Co. Inc., Philadelphia, Pa. 1933.

On the identification, host relationships, and control of plant viruses.

1. Holmes, Francis O. Handbook of phytopathogenic viruses. Burgess Publ. Co., Minneapolis, Minn. 1939.

2. Smith, Kenneth M.   A textbook of plant virus diseases.   P. Blakiston's Son & Co. Inc., Philadelphia, Pa.   1937.

On the chemistry of virus proteins.

1. Stanley, W. M.   The biochemistry of viruses.   Ann. Rev. Biochem. **9:** 545–570. 1940.

On the transmission of plant viruses.

1. Leach, J. G.   Insects and virus diseases.   *In* Insect transmission of plant diseases. McGraw-Hill Book Co., New York.   1940.

On specific virus diseases of plants.

Bibliographies are furnished in the works of Smith (1937) and Holmes (1940) cited above.

Chapter 12

DISEASES CAUSED BY PARASITIC SEED PLANTS AND ALGAE; EPIPHYTES

Parasitic Seed Plants

While the great majority of flowering plants are autophytes, manufacturing their foodstuffs by photosynthesis from carbon dioxide and the minerals and water that they secure from the soil, a few of them have other means of obtaining their nutritional essentials. Among the higher plants there are colorless ones that derive their sustenance saprophytically from dead organic matter, others that supplement their diet with artfully caught insects, as the sundew and pitcher plant. There are seed plants that derive benefit from mutualistic association with other organisms, as the nodule-bearing legumes, and finally there are those that steal part or all of their sustenance from other plants. It is with these last, the partially or entirely parasitic seed plants, that we are here concerned.

The parasitic seed plants are largely found in seven families: the mistletoe family (*Loranthaceae*) containing the leafy mistletoe of the southern states and the dwarf mistletoe of northern coniferous forests; the dodder family (*Cuscutaceae*), containing the dodders; the broomrape family (*Orobanchaceae*) with several genera of root parasites of which *Orobanche*, the broomrape, is most important; the figwort family (*Scrophulariaceae*), including the painted cup (*Castilleja*, a genus of root parasites); the *Santalaceae*, which includes several root parasites, among them the sandalwood tree, the shrub *Nestronia*, and the herbaceous bastard toadflax, *Comandra*; and three tropical families, the *Balanophoraceae*, and *Hydnoraceae*, chlorophyll-lacking root parasites, and the *Rafflesiaceae*, noted for the genus *Rafflesia* with enormous, flesh-colored, foul-smelling blossoms, the remainder of the plant consisting of mycelium-like feeding organs.

These seed-plant parasites differ in the extent and manner of their parasitism. They may be entirely dependent on a host, or

355

only partially so, and they may parasitize either stems or roots. With the exception of the broomrapes, which at times are destructive to tobacco, hemp, and clovers, the root parasites are not highly injurious to their hosts.   One of the root parasites, the sandalwood tree, is highly prized for its wood.   In contrast the stem parasites, mistletoe and dodder, are at times exceedingly injurious.

DODDER (*Cuscuta spp.*).

History and distribution.   There are about 100 species of dodder, some 54 of which are found in the United States.   They are known under various descriptive names, such as strangleweed, love vine, gold thread, pull-down, clover-silk, devil's hair, and others. The dodders are world wide in distribution but best known as pests in Europe and the United States.   Linnaeus recognized the dodder as a parasite, and undoubtedly its noxious effects had been observed for centuries previous.   Recent work on dodder has largely to do with the physiological and morphological relationship between dodder and its host, the control of the pest through seed legislation and cultural practices, and the development of ingenious means for freeing crop seed from dodder seed.

Importance.   Losses from dodder have been most serious in legumes, such as clovers and alfalfa, and in flax.   In parts of Europe, clover growing has been abandoned and flax production cut in half because of the destructiveness of dodder, but conditions in the United States seem to be less favorable to dodder injury. Nevertheless, there are frequent reports of serious local losses from dodder especially in alfalfa and clover seed producing states. These losses are aggravated by extremely strict legislation which in some states condemns seed with as little as one dodder seed in 10,000 crop seed.   Occasionally vegetables, ornamentals, young nursery stock, and even nursery trees may suffer appreciable losses from dodder.

Host plants.   The most important species of dodder found in the United States on economic plants are:

Small-seeded alfalfa dodder (*Cuscuta planiflora*), an introduced species from Europe that is established in the western states and particularly troublesome in alfalfa, although it occurs on other plants;

Field dodder (*Cuscuta arvensis*), a yellow-stemmed native species, widespread in the United States, an important contaminant of commercial seed, and destructive on many kinds of wild and cultivated plants beside legumes;

Clover dodder (*Cuscuta epithymum*), a reddish-stemmed introduced species found in various parts of the United States, particularly on clover and alfalfa, which, as it rarely sets seed in the United States, is most important the first year in crops from imported seed;

Large-seeded alfalfa dodder (*Cuscuta indecora*), a native, primarily western species, mainly on alfalfa and other legumes;

Common dodder (*Cuscuta gronovii*), a native species attacking many kinds of plants, wild and cultivated, including ornamentals and hedge plants; and

Chilean dodder (*Cuscuta racemosa chileana*), an introduced species the seeds of which are frequently found in red clover and alfalfa seed from South America; not considered serious.

The list of plants attacked by the various dodders is too long to recount; almost any species of dicotyledon may be found attacked. Among wild plants, the roadside ragweeds, and composites, such as sunflowers and *Eupatorium*, are common hosts of dodder.

Symptoms and signs. Dodder may be recognized from a distance as yellow or orange patches in otherwise green fields. The yellow mass is a dense tangle of thin, wiry stems overgrowing the normal vegetation. In advanced cases, the spot is in the form of a large yellow ring of dodder, 30 feet or more in diameter, surrounding a black, burned-over-appearing center where the host plants have been entirely destroyed.

On examining the dodder closely, tiny scales or rudimentary leaves are seen on the stems, and as the plant matures, dense clusters of tiny, pale blossoms appear (Fig. 156). These are found especially along the stems of the host plant. Large quantities of tiny gray or reddish-brown seed are produced, as many as 3,000 from a single plant. While the seed somewhat resemble those of the small-seeded legumes, they can be distinguished by the fact that they are roughened, with 3 flattened sides, and do not have a conspicuous scar.

Plants attacked by dodder show symptoms of starvation, stunting, and pallor, and soon they die. As the dodder is an obligate parasite it dies with the host unless new host plants are available. Ordinarily the dodder stems extend outward, grasping new hosts as the old ones fail, and thus steadily enlarging the spot of infestation.

Figure 156. Dodder on clover showing the habit of the parasite and its blossoms. Note the devitalized appearance of the clover plants in the center of the photograph. Soon they would die.   (*Photo by Bureau of Plant Industry, U. S. Dept. of Agriculture.*)

Etiology.   Although the dodder is a true seed plant, it exhibits remarkable adaptations to its parasitic mode of life.   The seed will mature even if the host is destroyed before the seed have normally matured.   They will retain their viability for several years.   In the spring the seed are adapted to germinate a little later than the host seed so that host plants are available to the dodder seedling when it appears.   In germination, the dodder seed sprouts to form a hair-like shoot (Fig. 157).   This anchors itself in the soil and the free end of the leafless seedling rotates until it comes in contact with a stem or other foreign object.   It then makes two or more coils about the foreign object.   If the latter is not a suitable host (e.g. a straw) the free end continues rotating, and when contact is made with a susceptible stem, there are formed on the inner, contact surfaces of the coils, little tooth-like swellings or haustoria, which force their

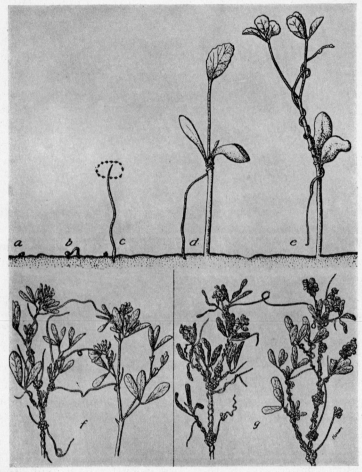

Figure 157. The life cycle of dodder.   a and b, germination of the seed; c, rotational movement in search of a host plant; d, e, feeding contact has been made and the dodder stem has lost contact with the soil; f, lateral spread of the dodder stems from plant to plant; g, blossoming and seed production of the parasite.   (*Photo by the Bureau of Plant Industry, U. S. Dept. of Agriculture.*)

way into the host stem, connect with the xylem and phloem elements of the stem, and begin using the water and food materials of the host plant.   The lower end of the dodder stem dies away, so that the parasite loses all contact with the soil.   If contact is not made with a suitable host, the seedling dodder stem may remain alive for several weeks, but then dies. Once the nutritive relation is established, the free ends of the dodder stems continue to make new host attachments until great masses of the parasite result. If the dodder stems are broken off and scattered, as in haying operations, the stem pieces may attach themselves to new hosts, thus acting as vegetative organs of reproduction.

Normally the dodder overwinters as seed, either in the soil, or mixed with crop seed. However, there are a few species, such as the clover dodder, that are perennial, and these may rarely produce seed. While the first introduction of dodder into a field is usually due to the use of contaminated seed, other means of infestation are dodder fragments on seed from hay, irrigation water, accidental spread by men or animals, and infested manure. The seeds will pass uninjured through the digestive tracts of animals, which increases the danger from this last source.

Epiphytology. The wide geographic distribution of dodder, its constant appearance year after year in the same fields, and its prevalence on roadside weeds under most unfavorable growing conditions, all attest the fact that dodder tolerates a wide range of environmental conditions. It has many hosts, and will flourish under almost any conditions that permit the host plants to develop. With its various adaptations for spread and survival, dodder can be regarded as a highly successful parasite under natural conditions, and this parasitic efficiency is further aided by man in local dissemination through agricultural operations and in long-distance spread by contaminated crop seed.

Control. 1. *Preventing introduction of dodder-infected seed.* As agricultural seed is the main original source of infestation, avoidance of dodder-infested seed, by regulation or by careful examination of seed, stands foremost among the control practices. It has been said that dodder has been more legislated against than any other weed, possibly excepting the Canada thistle. In parts of Europe it is unlawful to sell crop seed containing even a single seed of dodder. Federal law excludes from the United States all commercial seed containing one or more dodder seed per 5 gram sample. Many states have laws strictly regulating the sale of dodder-infested seed, and other states require a statement on the seed-sack label indicating the presence or amount of noxious weed seed, including dodder. Even with this supervision, however, a certain amount of dodder-infested seed is always to be found on the market. For this reason the buyer should examine his seed, especially that of small-seeded legumes, for the rough, flat-sided dodder seed, and if any doubt exists, the seed should be tested by the state seed laboratory for the presence of dodder. Seed, even with small amounts of dodder contamination should be rejected.

2. *Preventing introduction in hay and manure.* If hay and manure are secured locally, it will be possible to investigate the source, and reject them if there is danger of dodder contamination. It may be difficult to detect dodder in commercial hay, but the grower should be aware of the danger of dodder in such hay, and guard against introduction of the pest by this means.

3. *Cleaning dodder-infested seed.* If there is a marked difference in size between the dodder seed and the crop seed, the former may be removed by screening, as in the case of small-seeded dodder in clover or alfalfa seed. The recommended screen has 20 meshes to the inch, of No. 30 to 34 wire. In most cases it is not advisable to attempt to clean such seed if non-infested seed is available, and this is especially true of large-seeded dodder in small-seeded legumes.

The commercial seed industry has worked out efficient methods of cleaning dodder-infested crop seed, including an ingenious device by which crop seed are mixed with iron powder. Much of the powder sticks to the rough dodder seed which are then drawn out of the crop seed with magnets.

4. *Killing dodder in infested seed.* A method for killing dodder seed by dry heat, without injuring the crop seed, has been developed in Europe and appears promising, but as yet this has not been adopted in America.

5. *Selecting dodder-free sites for crop production.* It must be remembered that dodder is a common pest on weeds and other wild plants. Before breaking ground for a crop on native sod, the field should be examined for presence of dodder. If found, it should be eradicated by the means given below before the land is used for a susceptible crop.

6. *Eradicating dodder in cases of light infestation.* Where only a small amount of dodder is present in a field, mow the dodder areas

before seed are formed, allow the mowed plants to dry, or wet them with crude oil or kerosene and burn them, or burn them over with a blow torch, or feed the cut plants for hay, being careful not to distribute the pest in the process.   If the seed have formed, burn over the infested spots.   For a few weeks after, the burned spots should be repeatedly but lightly hoed, to allow buried seed to germinate and die.   The treated spots should be frequently examined to make sure that the eradication is complete.

Eradication of small spots of dodder by chemicals is sometimes practiced, but the chemicals recommended (iron sulphate, sulphuric acid, copper sulphate, salt, carbolic acid, sodium nitrate, potassium sulphate, calcium chlorate, and sodium chlorate) are rather expensive and disagreeable or sometimes dangerous to handle; hence, burning is preferable in most cases.

7. *Eradicating general infestations of dodder.*   Large areas of dodder in a field usually result from negligence in the past.   Where such infestations exist, the field should be mowed before seed are formed, and the hay fed to stock, preferably in the field.   The land may then be plowed and reseeded or closely grazed, to prevent formation of late seeds.   In early stages, close grazing alone, as by sheep, may suffice to prevent seeding of the dodder.

If the dodder has matured seed over large areas, the problem is very difficult, because the dodder seed will retain viability in the soil for five years or more, and clover or alfalfa cannot be used on the land for that period.   Soybeans, cowpeas, or velvet beans might be substituted, as these are rarely attacked by dodder.   In extreme cases the entire field may be mowed, allowed to dry, and then burned over.   This should be followed by fallowing for the remainder of the season, then beginning a 5-year rotation starting with a cultivated crop such as corn or sorghum, and then planting dodder-immune crops the remaining 4 years.   The heavily infested crop could be cut for hay, stacked, and fed in the field, but this leaves the danger of spread to other parts of the farm.   It goes without saying that a dodder-infested crop should not be harvested for seed.

MISTLETOE (*Phoradendron spp. and Arceuthobium spp.*).

History and distribution.   In America, two genera of mistletoes are found, the leafy mistletoes, species of *Phoradendron*, which are common in the southern states, and occur principally as parasites on angiosperm trees, and the dwarf mistletoes, species of *Arceuthobium* (= *Razoumofskya*) which are restricted to conifers, for the most part in northern forests.   There are about 80 species of *Phoradendron*, all in the Americas.   *Arceuthobium* comprises 5 species, and several physiologic forms, all found in the northern hemisphere, but lacking in Europe.   The classic mistletoe of Europe is *Viscum album* which consists of 3 physiologic forms, one occurring on hardwoods, one on fir, and one on pine and spruce.   While the mistletoes have been known for many centuries, their recognition as destructive parasites and the study of their pathology is comparatively recent, based largely on the extensive studies of Von Tubeuf in Europe (1923) and of Bray on the leafy mistletoe (1910) and Weir on the dwarf mistletoe (1915 ff.) in America.

Importance.   Under many conditions the mistletoes are relatively harmless, but in the southwestern states where tree growth is not vigorous, shade and forest trees may be seriously handicapped, and hackberrys and oaks are often killed by the pest, while incense cedar stands may be markedly retarded.   More serious damage is sustained by the northern softwoods from the dwarf mistletoes, which are rated next in importance to the wood rots as causes of loss in these forests.   Here the infestation results in heavy mortality or serious retardation of growth even in relatively young trees.   In addition, mistletoe-infested trees are predisposed to attack by bark beetles.   Even in cases where the tree growth is not seriously inhibited, the value of lumber from mistletoe-infested trees may be very low, due to wood faults produced by the mistletoe haustoria and to abnormal branching.   For example, in the Bitterroot and Missoula valleys of the Northwest there are great areas where the important Douglas fir is so badly injured by mistletoe that this tree is not even included in estimates of forest resources of these areas.

Host plants.   The great majority of tree species are subject to one or more of the mistletoe species.   The leafy mistletoes are found particularly on oak, elm, maple, sycamore, gumwood, mesquite, Bois d'arc, sugarberry, walnut, ash, poplar, willow, buckeye, incense cedar, and more rarely on fir, juniper, and cypress. The dwarf mistletoes are most serious on pines, firs, larch, hemlock, spruce, and tamarack.

Symptoms and signs. The mistletoe plant itself is an obvious and unmistakeable indication of infestation (Fig. 158). The plant of the leafy mistletoes is evergreen and rather large and dense, up to several feet in diameter, occurring on the upper branches of the host tree. In winter, these dense tufts of mistletoe can be recognized at long distances. Often the tree branch is swollen or distorted at the point of attachment of the mistletoe stem. The plant

is a yellowish or olive green, usually with broad, thick, leathery, oval leaves with spikes of inconspicuous, apetalous flowers and later berries, which are usually white with a sticky mesocarp.

A cross section of the host branch through the point of mistletoe attachment shows root-like feeding organs (haustoria) penetrating the wood to various depths. The haustoria consist largely of xylem vessels which are attached to the xylem elements of the host branch, enabling the mistletoe to make free use of the water and mineral salt supply of the host tree.

Figure 158. Heavy infestation of broadleaf mistletoe on sweet gum. Louisiana, 1932. (*Courtesy of A. F. Verrall.*)

Shoots of the dwarf mistletoe are in dense clusters but only a few inches long (Fig. 159). The leaves are reduced to inconspicuous scales, and the shoots are a dull yellowish or greenish brown in color. The sexes are separate. The blossoms are inconspicuous, in spikes, producing abundant sticky, fleshy berries. The attacked branch is usually swollen, and abnormal or excessive branching is often induced, so as to result in dense brooms, sometimes involving all or most of the tree. Haustoria extend into the wood as with the leafy mistletoes.

Heavily infested trees show symptoms of impaired vigor, with chlorosis, reduced size and number of leaves, dead or broken branches, and premature death.

Etiology and epiphytology.   The mistletoes are disseminated solely by their seeds.   Birds are the chief vectors involved, although washing of the seeds by rain aids in local spread, and in the case of the dwarf mistletoes the seeds are shot out violently to a maximum horizontal distance of 33 feet.   The adhesive substance on the seeds

Figure 159.   Dwarf mistletoe (*Arceuthobium campylopodium f. divaricatum*) on single-leaf piñon pine, California, showing immature flowers and fruits.   Little swelling of the limb is seen, although frequently the dwarf mistletoes produce large, muscle-like swellings.   (*Courtesy of L. S. Gill.*)

enables them to adhere to branches, and also favors their being deposited on branches by birds, in the act of wiping them off the bill.

The seeds germinate readily, the radicle forming a disk-shaped appressorium that adheres tightly to the bark, in the center of which a peg-like haustorium penetrates through to the cambium. Only relatively young, thin bark can be thus penetrated, and generally the haustorium makes use of lenticels or buds in its ingress. By modification of the meristematic tissues of the haustorium and those of the tree cambium, the newly developed xylem of the tree becomes continuous with that of the parasite, and the water and salts of the tree become available to the mistletoe.   This is perhaps favored by the fact that the mistletoes have a higher osmotic pressure of their cell sap than is true of their hosts, thus leading to a water exchange in favor of the parasite.   Branches of the haustorium also extend up and down and about the tree following the cambium layer, and here and there produce secondary haustoria. The haustoria do not penetrate into the wood, but as the tree grows and adds annual rings of wood, the haustorium elongates outward, thus becoming buried in the tree.   From the number of rings between the tip of the primary haustorium and the bark of the tree it is possible to tell the age of any mistletoe infection, and this may be very great, 60–70 years or more.   Two specimens have been reported 219 and 419 years old respectively.

In contrast to dodder, the mistletoes are hemi-parasites or partial parasites.   Although the host plant furnishes water and mineral salts, the mistletoe contains chlorophyll and manufactures its own food.   It has even been claimed in Europe that when a tree is defoliated, by insects for example, some of the food elaborated by the parasite is furnished to the tree.   Pollination of the mistletoe is accomplished by insects.

As well as being parasites, the mistletoes are in turn attacked by a number of insects and fungi, the latter including one or more species of rusts on the leafy mistletoes and a fungus (*Wallrothiella arceuthobii*) that destroys the immature fruits and sometimes kills the plants of the dwarf mistletoes.

Control.

1. *In ornamental and shade trees* affected by the leafy mistletoe the pest can be held in check by pruning out the parasitic growths as they appear.   For complete eradication it is necessary to cut off the affected branch several inches below the mistletoe, but a fairly satisfactory practice is merely to pull off the aerial portions of the parasite with a curved mistletoe hook, although this does not destroy the haustoria in the wood.   In

some cases there is opposition to mistletoe eradication because of traditional sentiment or desired decorative effect of the brooms.

2. *In forest trees* mistletoe, especially the dwarf mistletoe of northern forests, is not an easy problem to deal with. It is a problem associated with open, mature or overmature stands, and in the past it has been difficult to dispose of these stands. The best solution lies in felling affected trees, as this destroys the obligate parasite. Lumbering contracts should require the felling of all infested trees whether useful for lumber or not. In some cases this will require clean cutting, in which case measures must be taken to assure regeneration of the forest, as by delaying the cutting of a few seed trees until the new stand is established. Such cutting is best accomplished in late summer before the mistletoe fruits ripen, but when a good vegetative growth makes it easy to recognize affected trees. Particular attention should be given to avoid bringing mistletoe into uninfested regions on seedling trees, since many of the species are relatively restricted geographically. With the established fact of physiologic specialization within this group and the frequent observation that individual trees will be mistletoe-free although surrounded by heavily infested trees, there is reason to believe that selection of tree strains for mistletoe resistance offers good possibilities for the future.

Parasitic Algae

The algae, most of which are autophytic, are a group of very minor importance in pathology. Less than one per cent of Sorauer's extensive handbook on parasitic plant diseases is concerned with those caused by algae. Yet we find here at least one disease of considerable economic importance and several interesting instances of parasitism by algae in non-economic plants.

Two or more of the green algae, in particular *Cephaleuros virescens* (= *C. mycoidea*) and *C. parasitica* (= *C. coffeae* ?) cause serious injury in tea and coffee plantations, a disease known as red rust or orange rust. The former species also infects a number of other tropical or southern plants including citrus fruits, mango, jujube, persimmon, guava, acacia, pecan, magnolia, jasmine, fringe tree, privet, viburnum, and rhododendron. The disease may occasionally give trouble in greenhouses. It is spread by zoospores in drops of water. These enter through stomata and form mycelium-like chains of algal cells that grow through the host tissues producing extensive dead spots on the surface of which are borne reddish sporangiophores tipped with clusters of zoosporangia.

Epiphytes

A number of plants including flowering plants, fungi, lichens, and algae, customarily grow over the surfaces of other plants not parasitizing or deriving any benefit from the supporting plant except mechanical support. Occasionally these epiphytes may be harmful through shutting off light or gas exchange from the plant, breaking branches by their weight, or even strangling their supporting plant as in the strangler fig tree and the climbing bittersweet. Grapevines have been found responsible for suppression or even death of trees. The Spanish moss (*Tillandsia usneoides*), which resembles a lichen but in reality is a flowering plant of the pineapple family, at times has a repressing or killing effect on its supporting plants by excluding light and smothering. The smothering effect of the slime mold, *Spumaria alba*, was pointed out on page 250.

REFERENCES

1. Bray, W. L. The mistletoe pest in the Southwest. U. S. Dept. Agr., Bur. Pl. Indus. Bull. 166. 1910.
2. Gill, L. S. *Arceuthobium* in the United States. Conn. Acad. Arts & Sci. Trans. **32:** 111–245. 1935.
3. Hansen, A. A. Dodder. U. S. Dept. Agr. Farm. Bull. 1161. 1921.
4. Korstian, C. H. and W. H. Long. The western yellow pine mistletoe. U. S. Dept. Agr. Bull. 1112. 1922.
5. Ruehle, G. D. Algal leaf and fruit spot of guava. Phytopath. **31:** 95–96. 1941. (References to earlier papers on the disease in Florida.)
6. Stitt, R. E. Dodder control in annual lespedezas. Jour. Amer. Soc. Agron. **31:** 338–343. 1939.
7. Stitt, R. E. Yields of Korean lespedeza as affected by dodder. Jour. Amer. Soc. Agron. **32:** 969–971. 1940.
8. Weir, J. R. Mistletoe injury to conifers in the Northwest. U. S. Dept. Agr. Bull. 360. 1916.

Chapter 13

DISEASES CAUSED BY NEMATODES
OR EELWORMS

Many nematodes (eelworms or roundworms) are saprophytes in soil and water, others are predatory on one another, some are important intestinal parasites of higher animals, as the roundworms of horses and swine and the hookworm of man, a number are parasitic on plants including a few species that are causes of important diseases of economic crops. The most important plant parasitic genera are *Heterodera*, in which the adult female is pear-shaped, and several species of the family *Tylenchidae* with worm-like adult females. The plant-parasitic and free-living species are usually microscopic; the animal parasites include some forms that are larger, sometimes up to several inches in length.

ROOT KNOT (*Heterodera marioni*).

Distribution and importance. Root knot is a common and serious disease in all warmer climates and in greenhouses everywhere. Because of its wide host range it ranks as one of the most important diseases of agriculture. Few home vegetable gardens are free of the pest. The grower of nursery stock suffers most from the disease because even lightly infested stock cannot be sold, and is often a total loss. The pest is so widespread in the South that it almost invariably appears in plantings of susceptible crops after a few years of continuous cropping. In certain crops the loss is increased because root-knot predisposes the plants to injury by other diseases. Thus wilt-resistant varieties of cotton, tomato, and watermelon become susceptible to wilt if the root-knot organism is present.

Host plants. The root knot nematode attacks at least 1288 species of plants. The list of the more important plants attacked includes: alfalfa, beans, beets, cabbages, clover, cotton, most

369

TABLE 10.—REACTION OF NURSERY, ORCHARD, AND ORNAMENTAL PLANTS TO ROOT-KNOT†

Reported highly susceptible	Moderately resistant, or profitable even when infected		Resistant or escaping, or not reported as susceptible
Almond*	Agave	Iris	Apricot
Begonia	Aloe	Ivy, Ground	(most varieties)
Buddleia	Althaea	Larkspur	Avocado
Calendula	Alyssum	Lily	Azalea
(most varieties)	Apple*	Loganberry	Bittersweet
Carnation*	Arctotis	Loquat	Casuarina
Catalpa	Ash	Mango	Cherry*
Cherry*	Aster	Marguerite	(some varieties)
Chrysanthemum	Blackberry	Mesembryanthemum	Citrus
Cineraria	Bois d'arc	Mirabilis	Date
Clematis	Butternut	Narcissus	Dogwood
Coleus	Calendula*	Nasturtium	Euonymus
Cyclamen	(some varieties)	Nolana	Eustachys petraea
Dahlia*	Calla lily	Olive (?)	Evening primrose
Deutzia	Calliopsis	Opuntia	Feijea
Echevieria	Candytuft	Pear	Gaillardia
Elm	Cereus	Persimmon*	Heath family
Fig*	Chestnut	Phlox drummondi	Helianthemum
Gardenia	Cosmos	Poinsettia	Hippophaë
Goldenseal	Currant	Pomegranate	Holly
Gourd family	Dewberry	Privet, California*	Horse chestnut
Grape (European)*	Didiscus	Quince*	Jujube
Grape (American)*	Ferns	Raspberry	Lupine
Hibiscus	Forsythia	Royal Sweet Sultan	Marigold
Hollyhock	Geranium	Sweet William	Michaelmas Daisy
Hydrangea	Gladiolus	Tulip	Pandanus
Justicia	Gooseberry	Vinca (Periwinkle)	Peach*
Lobelia	Grape*	Wisteria	(some varieties)
Locust	(certain varieties)		Pistacio
Mulberry	Guava		Plum*
Nectarine*	Honeysuckle, Japanese		(some varieties)
Pansy			Rhododendron
Peach*			Rudbeckia
Pecan			Tamarisk
Peony			Zinnia

Reported highly susceptible (continued):
Petunia
Plum*
Rose*
Snapdragon
Sweet pea
Tuberose
Violet*
Walnut (Black, English, Persian)
Weigelia
Willow, Weeping

Root-knot Resistant Field Crops Which May be Used in Rotation Plans for Soil Enrichment and Root-knot Control

All grass and grain crops.
Cowpea, varieties Iron, Brabham, Monetta, Victor, Conch.
Soybean, varieties Laredo, Biloxi, O-too-tan (Laredo is most resistant of the three).
Velvet bean.
Peanut.
Bur and Southern Giant bur clover, *Melilotus indica*.
Crotolaria juncea and *C. spectabilis*.

* Some varieties are resistant.
† Compiled from reports of tests in various states. Offered as suggestions rather than unqualified recommendations, since in some cases these plants might react differently under other conditions than those originally used.

TABLE 11.—RESISTANCE OF VEGETABLES TO ROOT KNOT

Resistant vegetable varieties:

Beans—A resistant strain of Kentucky Wonder is available.

Beans—Alabama #1 and Alabama #2 are highly resistant.   Sure Crop Stringless Wax is slightly resistant.

Irish potato—There are some differences in susceptibility but none are really resistant, although Cobbler is less injured than Bliss Triumph or Green Mt.

Lettuce—Some resistant strains have been developed in Florida.

Lima beans—Hopi 155, 2000, 5987, 5988, and 5992 are less susceptible than other limas.

Sweet potato varieties—Big Stem Jersey, Gold Skin Jersey, Old Long Red, Red Jersey, Yellow Jersey, Yellow Belmont, and Yellow Jersey Vineless are reported resistant.

Tomatoes—Stone and Red Rock are more resistant than others.

Vegetables that are reported as affected but yielding a profitable crop even when attacked:

	Sweet potato varieties
Globe artichoke	Californian
Asparagus	Pumpkin Spanish
Cabbage	Southern Queen
Cauliflower	Triumph
Celery	Creola
Horse radish	Dixie Yam
Jerusalem artichoke	Early Carolina
Onion	Enormous
Parsnip	Golden Porto Rico
Radish	Improved Big Stem Jersey
Rhubarb	Japan Brown Sweet
Spinach	Little Stem Jersey
Turnip	New Gem
	Porto Rico

Vegetables that are not seriously injured but are not as resistant as the preceding list:

Broccoli	Garlic
Brussels sprouts	Leek
Chives	Rutabaga
Cress	

cowpeas, cucumbers, elm trees, muskmelons, okra, peach trees, peas, pecans, roses, most soy beans, spinach, strawberries, tomatoes, vetch, watermelons, and many other field, garden, ornamental, and fruit crops, as well as numerous weeds.   However, a number of important crops are resistant to the disease, and these may be used in rotations to starve out the worms.   The resistant crops include practically all grain and grass crops, cowpeas of the varieties Iron, Monetta, Brabham, Victor, and Conch, soybeans of the varieties Laredo, Biloxi, and O-too-tan, velvet beans, Acala cotton, peanuts, crotolaria, bur clover, some varieties of peaches, plums, apricots, and cherries, and numerous species of ornamental plants. The bush fruits are not highly susceptible. Susceptible legumes escape the disease if grown as winter crops, and susceptible vegetables can be safely grown as early spring crops before the nematodes are active. Many weeds are susceptible and are useful as indicators of root knot in the soil. The root-knot reactions of the more important ornamental, vegetable, and woody plants are given in tables 10 and 11.

Symptoms and signs. Affected plants exhibit symptoms of severe water deficiency, are stunted with wilting, yellowing, and ultimate death. The roots have many small and large swellings involving the entire thickness of the root in contrast to the beneficial legume nodules which are attached at the side of the root (Fig. 160). The only other swellings commonly found on roots are club root of the crucifer family (Fig. 114), which usually lacks the numerous small swellings, and crown gall of woody plants, with one or several large, woody knots at the side of stems or root, usually at the soil line (Fig. 139). Within the root-knots are pear-shaped, adult female nematodes, just visible to the unaided eye. In advanced stages the knots show extensive decay, caused by secondary fungi and bacteria attacking the weakened tissues.

Etiology. When mature the female nematode extrudes a jelly-like sack filled with about 400 eggs (Fig. 161). Within the older eggs, the worm-like larvae can be seen with the aid of a microscope. The larvae hatch, escape from the decaying knot, move about a short distance in the soil, and attack the root at a new point, imbedding themselves in the root tissues, and secreting a stimulating chemical which causes a new knot to form around the larva. Fertilization of the females may occur or may be omitted. Under optimum conditions the life history is completed in 25–30 days, but this is lengthened to as much as 80 days in cool climates. The nematode exhibits physiologic specialization, discussed on page 385.

Epiphytology. By their own efforts the nematodes move only very short distances,—not over a foot in a year. They are rapidly spread down furrows with surface or irrigation water. Any manner of moving soil will spread the nematodes across a field or from

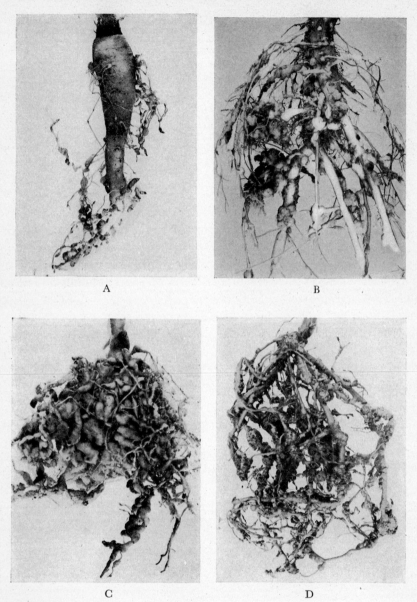

Figure 160.   Root knot.   A, on carrot; B, on mung bean.   C, on snapdragon; D, on peach.

HETERODERA MARIONI

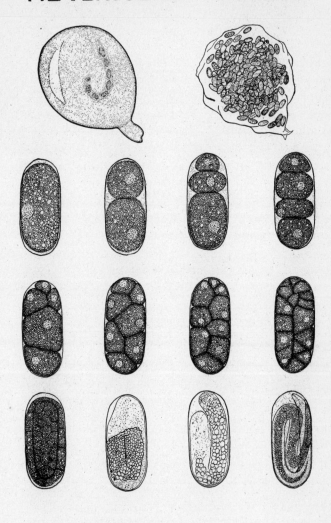

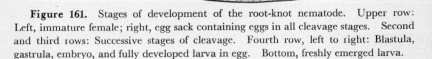

Figure 161. Stages of development of the root-knot nematode. Upper row: Left, immature female; right, egg sack containing eggs in all cleavage stages. Second and third rows: Successive stages of cleavage. Fourth row, left to right: Blastula, gastrula, embryo, and fully developed larva in egg. Bottom, freshly emerged larva.

one field to another, as on farm machinery, shoes, or hooves.   They are not carried in seed, but are often introduced into vegetable plantings on the roots of infected tomato, cabbage, strawberry, lettuce, and sweet potato plants, or on Irish potato tubers, and in the same way they can be introduced with diseased nursery stock.

High temperatures favor nematode development.   The worms are most prevalent in the southern states and in greenhouses, where the long period of warmth increases the number of generations.   In Oklahoma there are six or seven generations a year, in Florida twelve, and farther north only one or two.   The nematodes are most abundant in light sandy soils, which aid free movement. Their spread is favored by temporary water transport, but they are destroyed by prolonged flooding.   The worms and eggs are killed by temperatures of 118°F. in 30 minutes.

Control.   Control of root knot may be accomplished by different practices depending on how the crop is grown.   Except under greenhouse and seedbed conditions, complete and permanent eradication of the parasites is not practicable.   The most that can be accomplished is to reduce the worm population to a low level and keep it there.   Since we cannot wipe them out we must learn to live with them and keep the damage down to a point where no appreciable crop loss is incurred.   This may be done in the following ways.

1. *In field crops.*   Two or three years of resistant crops will largely starve out the root-knot worms, and make it possible to grow a susceptible crop for a year or possibly more.   Root-knot-resistant field crops have been mentioned, and the list is long enough to allow a liberal choice in planning a rotation program involving resistant cash and fodder crops or resistant soil-enrichment crops or both.   Ordinarily root-knot is not as serious in the field as in the garden, nursery, and orchard, and it only becomes troublesome when susceptible crops are grown year after year on the same land, when land becomes foul with susceptible weeds, or when susceptible legumes are planted between rows of other row crops. These practices should be avoided.

2. *In fruit orchards.*   In starting a new orchard, if possible, select land which has not been in susceptible crops or overgrown with weeds for a number of years.   The condition of the land, with reference to root knot, can be tested by examining the roots of susceptible weeds which may be present.   The common lamb's quarters and the wild lettuce are particularly good indicators of root knot.   Or some of the soil may be planted with seed of a susceptible crop such as okra, vetch, cowpeas, or tomatoes.   If these show no knots after 4 to 6 weeks, the soil can be considered relatively free from the parasite.   The young trees should be carefully inspected for root-knot before planting, and no knotted trees should be accepted or set out.   Insofar as possible, root-knot-resistant varieties and rootstocks should be used, and detailed lists of these are available at the state experiment stations.   Where a cover-crop is desired, it is best to use root-knot-resistant varieties (grass and grain family or the resistant legumes listed).   Where only a small part of the orchard is infested, the trees may be removed and destroyed, and the soil in their vicinity sterilized by one of the methods described below.   If the orchard is badly infested, production can continue if the trees are stimulated by liberal fertilization and cultivation, but in such cases it may be best to start a new orchard site with a view to abandoning the old site as soon as the new one is producing.

3. *In nurseries.*   Most of the suggestions above on controlling root knot in the orchard also apply to the nursery.   A considerable number of varieties of nursery stock and ornamentals are root-knot-resistant, and full use should be made of these in nurseries subject to this disease.   In case part of the nursery is infested it may be a good plan to return the land to corn or some other resistant field crop for 2 to 3 years before replanting with susceptible stock, and some of our nurserymen do this as a regular practice.   Most of the evergreens are resistant to root knot and may be successfully grown in infested land.   Arizona growers have indicated that clean bare fallow will starve out the worms in 2 to 3 years, but Florida workers report that this is injurious to the

soil. Chemical methods of soil disinfestation as described below can and should form a part of the routine in the greenhouse and beds, but it is doubtful if the expense is justified in the nursery except for special cases involving small areas of soil.

It has been found that heating at 118°F. for 30 minutes destroys the root knot parasite in infested roots, and some nursery stock can withstand this temperature without injury. Where nursery stock is only lightly infested with root knot (up to 5 per cent) the hot water treatment is permissible as a means of disinfesting stock. The treatment consists in immersing the roots in water for one-half hour, usually at 118°F. The work may be done in a vat, controlling the temperature by means of steam which bubbles through the water in the vat at a controlled rate. This temperature does not injure some types of ornamentals (black locust, peonies, and tuberoses), but growers are not advised to use the method on other plants except in an experimental way until definite data are available on the resistance of the various species to this temperature.

In their attempts to control root-knot, the nurseryman and the ultimate grower are aided by the conscientious efforts of the state nursery inspectors to keep badly infested stock out of the trade. Most states have no specific law on root-knot-infested stock, but interpret the clause on unsaleable nursery plants to include stock more than 5 per cent of which is obviously infested, while lighter infestations are heat-treated or culled over, depending on the degree of infestation.

4. *In commercial vegetable production.* The light, rich, well-watered soil of southern river bottoms, where important commercial vegetable production is carried on, is highly favorable for root-knot development and spread. Almost without exception, anywhere in the South, root-knot will soon become a limiting factor to production in such land if it is continuously cropped with susceptible vegetables. Control of root-knot becomes essential under these conditions, and it can best be accomplished by continuously practicing a well-planned rotation in which a root-knot susceptible crop

never follows a susceptible one without one or two years of resistant crops between.   Nearly all truck crops are highly susceptible to the disease.   For resistant crops in the rotation it is possible to use any crop of the grain and grass family, or any of the resistant legumes.   During the rotation the land should be kept free of weeds, as many common weeds are hosts of the root-knot worm.   In growing sweet potatoes and other crops which are first bedded, the bed-soil or sand should be free of the root-knot parasites, and in many cases it is worthwhile to make sure of this by sterilizing the bed soil with heat or chemicals as described below.   Infested sweet potato mother roots may be disinfested with heat at temperatures that destroy the nematodes without injuring the roots.

5. *In the home vegetable garden.*   Where a small plot on the farm is set aside for vegetable production for home use, root-knot frequently develops and may seriously lower the vegetable yield.   The best prevention under these conditions is to fence three adjacent plots with chicken wire and use them in a 3-year rotation consisting of vegetable garden, corn, and chicken yard (Fig. 162).   The chicken house may be set at one end with doors opening to any of the three plots. There should be no drainage from one plot to another.

6. *In ornamental plantings.*   Here above all an ounce of prevention is worth a pound of cure.   The soil for such plantings should be free of nematodes or disinfested before beginning to plant, and all new bedding stock carefully examined for root-knot before setting out.   Otherwise the disease may not only ruin the value of annual plants, but also spread to prized shrubs, roses, and other perennials.   Once these are infested there is very little that can be done to rid them of the disease.

Where root-knot is, or is likely to be, a trouble, the owner will do well to specialize on the more resistant ornamentals listed in table 10.

In ornamental plantings soil disinfestation may often be justified, since the areas are small and their value high. Heat in some form is the best means of freeing soil from the root-knot worms.   If steam is available it may be released under a large inverted pan, built for the purpose (Fig. 199), and a half-hour of such steaming is the best method for destroying the worms.   Boiling water is a fairly good soil disinfestant if applied liberally on loosened soil.

Where it is impractical to use heat, certain chemicals may be used for destroying the worms.   Of the many chemicals

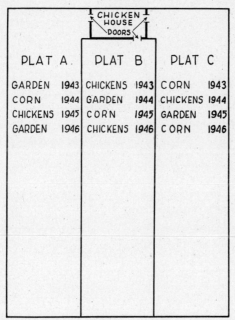

Figure 162.   Plan of a three-year rotation that can be used for controlling root knot in small home vegetable gardens.   (*After U. S. Dept. Agr., Bur. Pl. Indus., Farm. Bull. 1345.*)

which have been tried, the two that are most suitable are carbon disulphide and chloropicrin (tear gas).   The application of tear gas requires a special type of equipment, and for small plantings it would be best to have the treatment performed by a professional tree, landscape, or termite specialist. Few are equipped to do this work at the present time but the good results reported from the treatments justify the general availability of this service, and practicing specialists are beginning to look into the possibility of supplying this service to home owners.   Carbon disulphide for root-knot control has been found to be an efficient agent of soil disinfestation in a number of States.   The formula is: carbon disulphide, 3 gal. + rosin fish-oil soap, 1 quart (36 oz.) + water, 1 gal.   The soap and water are thoroughly mixed and then the carbon disulphide is added with stirring.   This is a concentrated emulsion which is diluted for use with 50 parts of water and applied at the rate of 1 gallon per square foot of soil.   The soil should be warm, loose, and moist.   Carbon disulphide is highly explosive.   The emulsion is less dangerous to handle but its vapor has been known to explode. The emulsion is injurious to living plants and should not be used near trees or shrubs.   The soil should be allowed to air out thoroughly before planting.

Both carbon disulphide and tear gas are fatal to plants and cannot be used closer than 3 feet from perennials without danger of killing them.   Formaldehyde, and certain other chemicals sometimes recommended for soil disinfestation are not as effective against the root-knot organism as heat, carbon disulphide, and tear gas.

7. *In the greenhouse and seedbeds.*   Root-knot is inevitably found in greenhouses where scrupulous attention has not been given to sanitation, and even under good greenhouse management it will occasionally be introduced.   It often becomes ruinous to gardenias, snapdragons, chrysanthemums, petunias, roses, and many other ornamentals and greenhouse vegetables. Under greenhouse conditions it is not difficult to control by following a rigorous practice of careful examination of introduced stock, and routine sterilization of soil, benches and pots with steam or an oven (Figs. 198, 199, 200).   Where valuable pot plants or bulbs are infected they can sometimes be saved by immersing the pots or bulbs in hot water at 118°F. for one-half hour, but this cannot be recommended as a general practice until more data have been obtained on the heat resistance of greenhouse plants.   One ingenious greenhouse operator has reported success in root-knot control by closing the empty greenhouse on a hot summer day, and turning on steam, which raises the temperature of the entire

house to a point that destroys the nematodes in the soil and on pots, flats, benches, and tools.   Further details on soil disinfestation are given in Chapter 20.

THE SUGAR BEET NEMATODE (*Heterodera schachtii*).

A major problem in many sections, especially Utah, Colorado, Idaho, and California, the nematode produces many more small roots than normal, with many dead rootlets.   No beets or only small ones are produced.   To the roots are attached flask-shaped females similar to those of root-knot (Fig. 163).   The only other crops affected in the United States are the crucifers.   Heavy applications of potash aid in control, but chief reliance is put on a 3 to 5 year rotation in infested patches or whole fields, with legumes, potatoes, or grains as popular rotation crops. This gives an effective control, but complete elimination of the nematode is not practical under field conditions. Figure 192 shows the destructiveness of this nematode.

WHEAT AND RYE NEMATODE
   (*Anguina tritici*).

This nematode produces no root swelling but infests stems and leaves making them rolled, twisted, and contorted (Fig. 164).   The worms pass up to the growing point, keeping pace with the developing plant, enter the young flowers, mature, copulate, the

Figure 163. Nematode infested sugar beet.   The small white bodies on the roots are female nematodes.   (*Photo by U. S. Dept. of Agriculture, Bur. Pl. Indus.*)

eggs are laid in the ovaries of the grain, and the adults die.   The infested ovary develops into a round, hard, dark gall filled with larvae.   When the galls are crushed in water the larvae are released and easily seen.   In stored galls the nematodes survive 9 years or more, but in nature alternate wet and dry periods in the absence of a susceptible host soon destroy them.   The parasite moves short distances from plant to plant but is introduced into new fields by infested seed.   Reinfestation of the new crop is from galls that are planted with the seed, or from nematodes that have lived between crops in the soil.   Wheat and rye are the only crops attacked, although other nematodes of less importance attack other grains

Figure 164.   Wheat seedlings attacked by nematodes.   Note the wrinkled leaves with curled edges and the emerging leaves tightly rolled.   (*Photo by the Bureau of Plant Industry, U. S. Dept. of Agriculture.*)

and grasses.   Losses are confined to the more eastern states, and the loss is small for the country as a whole, although on individual farms it may reach 70 per cent of the crop.

Control consists chiefly in the use of gall-free seed on uninfested soil.   Infested seed can be cleaned by immersing in a salt solution (40 lbs. in 25 gal. water), which causes the galls to float, while the good seed sinks.   The hot water treatment used for controlling loose smut in wheat (129°F. for 10 minutes) kills the nematodes in the galls.   If soil is infested the land should be used for oats, barley, corn, or other crops for two years before returning to wheat or rye. Wheat varieties vary in susceptibility to the nematode, some, such as Kanred, being resistant.

STEM AND BULB NEMATODE (*Ditylenchus dipsaci*).

This nematode infests over 100 species of plants.   It severely attacks strawberry, red clover, and alfalfa but is best known as a pest of ornamentals, including bulb plants, where the trouble is called "ring disease."   In such plants it is controlled by a hot-water disinfestation, e.g. 110°F. for ¾ hour or 1½ hours for large bulbs.

ROOT LESION NEMATODE (*Pratylenchus pratensis*).

In the past *Pratylenchus pratensis* has usually been referred to as the "meadow nematode."   The common name "root lesion nema-tode," proposed by Godfrey, is preferred, as the nematode is more cosmopolitan than the older term implies.   *P. pratensis*, like the root-knot and stem and bulb nematodes, affects many kinds of plants, at least one-hundred species including such varied economic hosts as strawberry, narcissus, coffee, cotton, alfalfa, tobacco, pineapples, potatoes, beets, various small grains, corn, turnips, cab-bage, and numerous legumes.   It is considered one of the most serious of the plant-parasitic nematodes, although it may often be overlooked because of the deficiency type of symptoms and because no obvious malformation of the roots is apparent.   Specific data on losses from this pest are not numerous but the reports include a case in Virginia in which 1300 bushels of Irish potatoes were affected, and accounts of serious losses in coffee, strawberries, chrysanthe-mums, cotton, and fruit trees.

The nematode attacks the feeding roots with the result that above-ground parts are deprived of water and exhibit symptoms of chronic water deficiency, wilting, yellowing, poor yield, sometimes culminating in death.   The appearance of the lesions varies with the host plant attacked but they are generally well-delimited necrotic spots that involve greater and greater masses of the root tissues (Fig. 165).   The male and female nematodes are wormlike and similar, about .5 mm. in length.   The larvae attack the root cortex forcing their way inward and through the peripheral tissues destroying the cells along the way.   Within the necrotic tissues may be found adults, larvae, and eggs.   Frequently the nematode lesions become invaded by secondary fungi or bacteria, which sometimes confuse the etiological conclusions.   In the case of affected cereal plants, the roots may be invaded without discoloration and the principal injury may be due to secondary organisms that follow infection by the root lesion nematode.   In cotton, susceptibility to wilt in normally wilt-resistant varieties has been ascribed to the influence of infection by the root lesion nematode.   Many features of the pathology of this pest are still poorly understood although there is no question of the importance and savageness of its attack.

Figure 165.   Lesions on pineapple roots produced by the root lesion nematode.   (*Courtesy of G. H. Godfrey, Texas Agr. Exp. Sta.*)

Similarly little specific information is available on control of the root lesion nematode.   In potatoes, emphasis is placed on the selection of healthy tubers for planting.   The treatments used for *Rhizoctonia* control (see page 104) are said to have some value against the nematode as well.   In coffee the eradication of diseased trees and replanting with some other crop is prescribed.   Infested coffee nursery stock can be disinfested by a hot water treatment (120°F. for 10 minutes).   The only recommendation for cereals is rotation with other crops and manuring.   In chrysanthemums, where failures occur due to heavy infestation with this nematode, highly effective control has been obtained by sterilizing the bedding soil with tear-gas (chloropicrin).

BUFFALO GRASS NEMATODE (*Anguina agrostis*).

There has been some trouble in the southern Great Plains with the nematode that enters the buds of buffalo grass, an important

range and soil-building grass, and causes a witches'-broom deforma-
tion.   A number of other genera are affected in Europe and North
America.   It is principally important in interfering with commercial seed production.   No control measures are known.

Nematodes: Some General Considerations

Physiologic specialization.   In nematodes, as in rusts, powdery mildews, and several other groups of plant pathogens, a
parasitic species may consist of several identical-appearing races or
strains.   Each race will attack certain plants within the host range
of the species and will avoid others.   The races are sometimes
highly specific.   Thus a strain of the stem and bulb nematode from
oats attacks only oats and cocksfoot (*Dactylis*) but no other of the
one hundred hosts of this nematode species.   A strain from
hyacinth would not attack narcissus, and that from narcissus would
not attack hyacinth.   Other strains are less particular; one from
potato attacks 53 species of plants.

Biological control.   "Mononchs" (species of the nematode
genus *Mononchus*) feed on other nematodes.   This is probably of
little importance as a practical control of parasitic nematodes,
since the Mononchs are not restricted to a diet of nematodes, but
also feed on rotifers and other soil organisms.   They, themselves,
are subject to a number of diseases caused by sporozoa and other
parasites which frequently destroy the Mononch colonies.   *Mononchus papillatus* vigorously attacks even large individuals of the sugar
beet nematode, sucking out the body contents.   From half-eaten
nematodes and other observations, Steiner and Heinly have concluded that *M. papillatus* kills the beet nematode mainly for pleasure,
after its appetite is satisfied with other food.

In another predatory nematode, *Dorylaimus*, one species has a
hollow spear.   It contacts its prey by accident, but at once orients
its head at right angles with the surface of its prey, makes a firm
contact with its lips, and then suddenly darts in its spear.   If
unsuccessful, it repeats the process.   Once it is in, it is held in
place by the heavy muscles of the oesophagus, where it sucks
rhythmically until the body wall collapses.   Nematodes of another
genus, *Aphelenchoides*, have still a different system.   A small *Aphelenchoides* will approach a large nematode, perhaps twice its length,

and quickly slip in and dart its mouth parts into its prey.   It may
remain attached or may be thrown off by the writhing of its prey,
but in a moment the large victim stretches out, paralyzed for several
hours by a quick-acting narcotic drug in the saliva of the attacker,
whereupon the latter feeds at its leisure.

Some fungi trap and kill nematodes by the aid of lasso-like
contraction loops with a trigger action (Fig. 166).   Practical use is
made of this in Hawaii where the root-knot nematode is a serious

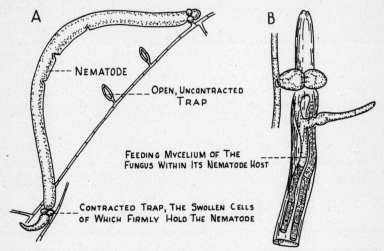

Figure 166. Parasitism of nematodes by the fungus *Dactylella bembicoides*. A, a
large nema trapped at both ends; its body was filled with fungous hyphae. B, details
of fungus trap, invading hyphae and an early stage of spore formation of the hyperparasitic fungus. (*After Couch.*)

pest of pineapple.   In 3 to 4 years of culture, much pineapple
waste accumulates.   This is plowed under at the rate of 100 to 150
tons per acre.   The organic matter stimulates the development of
the nematode-trapping fungus, and in a typical case the nematode
population dropped from 611 nematodes to 2 nematodes per
2500 gm. of soil, following the treatment.

REFERENCES

1. Filipjev, I. N.   Manual of agricultural helminthology.   E. J. Brill, Leiden, 1941.
2. Godfrey, G. H.   Root knot; its cause and control.   U. S. Dept. Agr., Farm. Bull.
   1345, 1923.
3. ———.   Effect of temperature and moisture on nematode root knot.   Jour. Agr.
   Res. **33:** 223–254.   1926.

4. Goodey, T.   Plant parasitic nematodes and the diseases they cause.   E. P. Dutton & Co., New York.   1933.

5. Leukel, R. W.   The nematode disease of wheat and rye.   U. S. Dept. Agr., Farm. Bull. 1607.   1929.

6. Thorne, G.   Control of sugar beet nematode by crop rotation.   U. S. Dept. Agr., Farm. Bull. 1514.   1926.

7. Tyler, J.   Plants reported resistant or tolerant to root knot nematode infestation. U. S. Dept. Agr., Misc. Publ. 406.   1941.

Chapter 14

PHYSIOGENIC DISEASES

For a plant to develop normally, it must not only be free from contagions of infectious disease and depredations of insects and other animals, but it must also be in a suitable environment. The soil must contain adequate supplies of water and mineral salts and must not contain excesses of water and mineral salts or of poisonous or toxic substances; the air about the plant must supply an adequate amount of oxygen and be free of toxic gases; the temperatures of air and soil must be favorable to growth and at no time reach excessively high or low levels; and the amount of light available must be adequate for normal growth and yet not excessive. For each plant at any time there is an *optimal* level of each of these environmental variables, at which level normal growth occurs. Departure from this optimum in either direction reduces development increasingly as the variable approaches the lowest level (*minimum*) or the highest level (*maximum*) at which the plant can survive. When a plant is in an environment in which one or more of these variables deviates significantly from the optimum, its health is impaired, and it is said to be suffering from *non-parasitic*, *abiotic*, or *physiogenic* diseases. A great many such diseases affect plants; rarely if ever is a plant in nature growing under fully optimal conditions. While physiogenic causes account for 70 per cent or more of all plant troubles, the amount of discussion devoted to these diseases in this book is very limited in proportion to their importance, since many of them are included in the subject matter of books and courses in plant physiology, field and horticultural crops, and soils.

I. Diseases Due to Unfavorable Soil Conditions

A. Lack of necessary chemical substances:

1. *Nitrogen shortage.* Affected plants may mature and produce fruit, but the leading symptoms are dwarfing, reduction in

shoot-length as compared with root-length, pale color of foliage, poor yield, and sometimes sterility.

Yellow-berry of wheat. The only symptoms are in the harvested grain. Instead of being translucent, the kernels have light yellowish spots affecting part or all of the grain. The grain is high in starch, but is low in test weight, specific gravity, and protein content, and may be penalized in price. Yellow berry is a very common degrading factor in wheat. The etiology of the disease is not well worked out, but the most important factor appears to be the N/K ratio in the soil. Yellow berry increases as soil potash and phosphorus increase, and is eliminated by applications of nitrates. It is best overcome by cropping and cultural practices that conserve and increase the soil nitrogen such as use of legumes in rotations, suitable green manure crops, summer fallowing, and applications of nitrogenous fertilizers.

2. *Phosphorus shortage.* The symptoms are areas of burning in the leaves, reduction in leaf size, and fading of the chlorophyll resulting in a bronzing or dull-green appearance of the leaves. Red or purple discoloration of the leaves is characteristic of those plants, e.g. tomato, but not tobacco, that have the enzymo-genetic equipment to produce anthocyanin pigments. In root crops, such as turnips and rutabagas, the roots may be dwarfed.

3. *Potassium shortage.* Lack of potassium is most evident in plants that store considerable quantities of carbohydrates. The symptoms include reduced photosynthesis, dwarfing of storage organs, weak terminal development with dieback in woody plants, yellowish, brownish, or whitish spots near the leaf margins and later more general, with blighting of the leaves and premature death, and decrease or inhibition of fruit or seed development.

Cotton "rust" is a common and serious trouble due to lack of potassium. The leaves first show a yellowish-white mottling, then yellow spots appear between the veins, these die at the center, brown specks appear around the leaf margin, this dries and curls, and finally the entire leaf is browned and drops prematurely. Many bolls fail to open, and the seed-cotton is hard to pick and of poor quality. Potash-deficient cotton plants are particularly susceptible to *Fusarium* wilt. Control consists in adding enough potash-containing fertilizer to eliminate the symptoms. A common recommendation is 4 per cent potash in a complete fertilizer, such as a 4–12–4 mixture used at a rate up to 200 pounds per acre.

Figure 167. Rosette, a common and destructive physiogenic disease of pecan trees, easily controllable by applying small amounts of zinc salts. The tufted appearance and numerous dead branches are characteristic.

4. *Shortage of minor elements.* Recent studies have shown that plants also require minute quantities of zinc, boron, manganese, and copper for normal development. The amounts required are very small, of the order of 10 pounds per acre. Lack of these elements produces characteristic and severe symptoms.

    a. *Zinc.* Pecan trees often suffer from "rosette," a zinc-deficiency disease in which the leaflets are narrow, crinkled, pale, then with dead or perforated areas giving the tree a rusty appearance. The internodes are shortened, giving a bunched or rosetted appearance to the foliage (Fig. 167). The twigs may die back. Affected trees may bear no nuts or only poor ones. "Money-maker" is the only important rosette-resistant variety. Affected trees may be quickly cured by applying zinc sulphate, preferably to the soil. The dosage is ½ to 1 pound per year of the tree's age or 1 to 2 pounds per inch of tree diameter, applied around the tree in early spring. Other methods of application include insertion of the dry zinc sulphate in holes bored in the trunk and spraying the trees in the early spring with 2 to 4 pounds of zinc sulphate per 100 gallons of water. Several applications are used. The soil applications give the most permanent results. Other zinc deficiency diseases of a similar type are apple and pear rosette, "mottle leaf" of citrus fruits, and "bronzing" of tung oil trees. Zinc deficiencies are commonly

Figure 168. Characteristics of alfalfa grown (1) with, and (2) without boron amendment in "yellows" (boron-deficient) soil. (*Courtesy of L. G. Willis, N. C. Agr. Exp. Sta.*)

encountered, not only in soils lacking this element but also in soils in which, because of alkalinity or other causes, the zinc present is not available to plants.

b. *Boron.* Boron deficiency has been a prominent subject of study in recent years, and many crops have been found to benefit by boron applications. Identification of the trouble depends both on plant symptoms and on chemical or spectroscopic analysis of soils.

Alfalfa yellows is a widespread boron-deficiency disease. The leaflets are pale to bright or bronzed with green midribs and in severe cases there is cessation of terminal growth. The leaf margins may dry and shrivel. The internodes are shortened and the entire plant stunted (Fig. 168). In the less severe cases the symptoms may show only at the first cutting   Control consists of applications of 5 to 30 pounds of borax per acre.   Larger doses must not be used as they may cause severe boron poisoning of the crop.

Figure 169. Brown heart of fodder beets, a serious disease due to boron deficiency. (*Reproduced with permission of R. W. G. Dennis from West of Scotland Agricultural College Research Bull. 5.*)

Other important boron deficiency diseases include:

Internal cork of apples (precocious ripening; dry fruits, with brown, spongy or corky spots in the flesh, accompanied by rosetting and dieback of the tree).

Brown-heart of turnips and beets (brownish, watery or punky core of dead cells in the center of the root as seen in Figure 169).

Dry rot of sugar beets (dry, spongy decay of the growing heart, ultimately destroying the entire root; adventitious leaves develop around the edge of the heart lesion; large numbers of small leaves with blackened, checked, and twisted petioles are characteristic).

Cracked stem of celery (brown mottling of leaves, brown stripes on stems, over which the epidermis breaks and curls back, browning and die-back of roots).

Many other crops show benefit from borax applications. including flax, cauliflower, radish, spinach, potatoes, tomatoes, tobacco, hops, carrots, cotton, asparagus, onion, and cereals.

c. *Manganese.* Gray speck of oats is due to manganese deficiency, and is especially prevalent in calcareous soils where manganese is not soluble. "It first appears as light green spots on the leaves, the areas enlarging and changing to buff or light brown color. The spots may be small or large, oblong to linear, depending on conditions and the variety of oats. In some cases the diseased plants are reduced in size." (Dickson.) Applications of manganese sulphate correct the condition. Manganese deficiency is also associated with a disease of sugar cane called Pahala blight, and with chlorosis as in various ornamentals.

d. *Magnesium.* Deficiency of magnesium produces chlorosis, stunting, and poor growth and fruiting in numerous crop plants. Among the magnesium deficiency diseases that have received attention are "sand-drown" of tobacco and cotton, a chlorotic condition found in plants grown on badly leached, sandy soils, bronzing of citrus trees, "yellow tip" of pine trees, chlorosis of corn, and mottling of the leaves of other cereals. The most usual means of correcting the deficiency is fertilization with dolomitic (magnesium-containing) limestone and manganese sulphate.

e. *Copper.* When crops are sprayed with Bordeaux mixture for control of fungous diseases, there is sometimes seen a marked improvement of the crop quite apart from the function of the spray in fungus control. This is now known to be due to the copper. Almost miraculous results have been seen following the use of copper on certain muck and peat soils. A specific copper-deficiency disease is die-back or exanthema of citrus trees. Here the leaves are first large and over-vigorous appearing, but soon the twigs begin to die back, or show very small yellowish, green leaves which soon fall. The dying twigs are covered with a reddish-brown gummy excrescence. The disease is controlled by soil treatment with $\frac{1}{4}$ to 2 pounds of copper sulphate per acre or by a copper spray.

B. Excess of soil chemicals. A feast may be as bad as a famine in the case of soil chemicals, and excesses of these chemicals are often associated with destructive physiogenic diseases, as seen in the following examples:

1. *Excessive nitrogen.* The principal symptoms of excessive nitrogen are overdevelopment of vegetative growth, delayed maturity, dropping of flower buds, sometimes dwarfing, chlorosis, and necrosis. These symptoms do not all appear together, and the appearance of one or more of them is dependent on the state of development of the plant and its external environment (temperature, water supply) and internal metabolism (protein-carbohydrate relations) at the time excessive nitrogen becomes available. The plants often show increased susceptibility to contagious diseases, such as those caused by rusts, powdery mildews, and bacteria. An example is *bud drop of roses, sweet peas, and tomatoes,* due to excessive nitrogen and increased if at the same time the temperature and moisture are unfavorable. *Niter poisoning of apple,* with marginal necrosis of the leaves is due to excessive soluble nitrates in clean cultivated orchards.

2. *Lime-induced chlorosis* is characteristic of plants growing in calcareous soils. The plants are sickly and dwarfed, with yellow foliage (Fig. 170). The injury is usually the indirect result of low hydrogen ion content which causes a chlorophyll failure by rendering iron, manganese, boron and zinc unavailable. The incidence of lime-induced chlorosis depends in part on the developmental stage at which roots make contact with calcareous pockets or layers in the soil. Remedial measures usually consist of addition of iron, manganese, boron, or zinc salts by sprays, injections, or soil treatments.

3. *Excessive acid.* Some plants are tolerant of acid soils or even prefer them, but with others, acid soils produce retarded growth, pallor, mottling, or general chlorosis. The roots are poorly developed and often decay. The injury in this case or in that of excessive alkalinity may be due directly

Figure 170. Chlorosis in grapefruit, resulting from a combination of zinc and manganese deficiencies, primarily the latter. (*Courtesy of A. F. Camp, Fla. Agr. Exp. Sta.*)

to the action of the excessive H^+ or OH^- ions or it may be indirect, due to the effect of these ions on the physical structure of soil or on the solubility of soil nutrients. Control consists in adding the amount of lime necessary for producing an optimum soil reaction for plant growth.

4. *Excessive alkali.* Excessive alkalinity results in poor stands, chlorosis, or death (Fig. 171). Crops differ in their alkali-resistance, some such as sugar beets being highly tolerant of alkaline and alkali soils. Where the value of the land war-

rants, the condition may be corrected by applications of gypsum (for "alkalis" consisting of NaCl, NA$_2$CO$_3$, etc.) or sulphur and by cultivation and mulching to retard evaporation and thus keep the alkali from rising to the soil surface.

5. *Oil well residues.* Chemicals released by oil well operations are often responsible for serious injury to nearby vegetation, and in such cases the lessee is financially responsible for such

Figure 171. An alkali spot in a grain field, distinguishable from a root rot spot (Fig. 73) by complete absence of plants, living or dead, within the spot, and increasing degrees of dwarfing as the edge of the spot is approached. (*Courtesy of H. J. Harper, Okla. Agr. Exp. Sta.*)

injury. In some court cases on oil waste injury, the oil companies may offer permanent damages, covering any plant injury that may arise in the future.

The principal chemicals involved are common salt, waste oil, and methane gas. The oil and salt may sterilize the soil for long periods of time, the gas causes sudden and extensive killing of trees and other vegetation, although some weeds are quite resistant to these chemicals. In the case of oil, the damage often results from shutting off the air from roots. Any type of commercial crop may be affected, but most legal cases concern fruit, nut, and timber trees.

Each case of oil-well injury is a problem in itself, often confused with drought or other types of plant injury, and research at the site of the trouble is usually necessary before proof of responsibility can be established.

Methods of avoiding this injury on the part of the lessee include the burning of waste gas, permitting salt and oil to run into dry holes, the use of slush pits, and frequent inspection of pipe lines. Slush pits may occasionally wash out or run over during rains, producing extensive damage.

6. *Toxic trace elements.* The minor elements that are necessary for normal plant development are often highly toxic to plants in doses only a little greater than the amounts required for best growth. *Boron injury* is often apparent when manure is treated with boron-containing larvicides to destroy maggots, and then used on crop land. Other sources of boron are commercial fertilizers, overdoses of borax for correcting boron deficiency, boron-containing irrigation water, and soils that are naturally oversupplied with boron. The principal symptoms of boron injury are retardation or inhibition of germination, stunting or death of plants leading to poor stands, bleaching or burning of leaves, premature ripening, and lowered yields. Control consists in avoiding the sources of boron listed above, and in leaching the soil. *Copper*, *aluminum*, and *thallium* in excess are also occasionally injurious to plants.

7. *Poisoning of soil by sprays.* In some leading orchard sections where applications of fungicides and insecticides, especially copper and arsenic, have been used abundantly over many years, it is being discovered that the soils around the trees are becoming so impregnated with these chemicals that it is almost impossible to grow cover crops around the trees. The problem is a new one and no satisfactory preventative has been worked out. Leaching by nature in a resting soil or by artificial means may be necessary if such soils are to continue productive.

C. Water deficiency. Many southern and western crops (cotton, trees, alfalfa) are regularly grown close to the minimal water requirement for survival, and far from the optimum seen for example in the seven-foot cotton of the Mississippi Delta. Their struggle for survival in the water-deficient soils of areas with low annual rainfall is further aggravated by enforced high transpiration rates due to high temperatures and dry air. In the periodic cycles of drought, they display symptoms of *chronic water deficiency*. The leaves are discolored, yellow, red, or brown, and may fall, and the plants are notably stunted. In root crops the roots are undersized, in cereals the grains are shrivelled, and in fruit crops the fruits are spotted, deformed, or shrivelled. In trees, chronic water deficiency predisposes the trees to attack by borers, which in turn pave the way for wood decay fungi, producing die-back or staghead, and death. The symptoms are often accompanied by excessive light and heat injury. While this condition is most characteristic of crops grown in the western Great Plains, it may be seen in any area of plant cultivation where occasional droughts occur,—indeed it may be most damaging in moist regions where cultivated species are least adapted to withstand the stress of unusual drought.

In *acute water deficiency* the principal symptom is sudden wilting without stunting or leaf discoloration, as occurs in transplanted plants, plants with sudden and serious root injury, or well-watered plants that are suddenly deprived of moisture. The various practices which reduce water deficiency include: mulching the soil by shallow cultivation or application of straw or leaf mulches, terracing and other practices that retard runoff, use of drought-resistant crops and varieties such as substitution of sorghum for corn, fallowing to accumulate subsoil moisture, heading back of plants in transplanting, and artificial supplying of water.

D. Excess of water and irregularity of water supply are responsible for a number of well-characterized plant diseases:

Sunscald of potatoes and many other crops is due to periods of high temperature following an excessive water supply. The tissues, accustomed to adequate water supply are suddenly deprived of water without opportunity to adapt themselves to a restricted supply, with resulting blighting or dying of large leaf areas.

Bursting of fruits and *hollow heart of potatoes* occur when the tissues have been growing slowly during a long dry period and

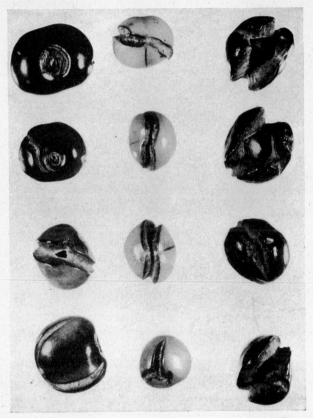

Figure 172. Cracking in Bing and Lambert cherries at different stages of development; due to rapid water absorption and limited ability of the fruit to expand. *(Courtesy of Leif Verner, Idaho Agr. Exp. Sta.)*

are unable to withstand the high osmotic pressures that develop with the advent of a sudden water excess. Bursting is a common and serious problem in stone fruits (Fig. 172) in areas with continental climates.

Intumescences and edema, as in tomatoes, cotton, and sunflowers, are blisters formed by cells that have burst from sudden water excess after dry periods. The leaves and fruits may be torn and ragged from this cause.

Blossom-end rot of tomatoes takes the form of a sunken, watery, then necrotic lesion at the blossom end of the fruit (Fig. 173). This is often followed by secondary bacterial or fungous infection, or in mild cases the affected area may cork over without further damage. The fruits ripen prematurely. Blossom-end rot may cause greater loss than any other tomato disease in areas subject to extreme variation in rainfall. It is associated

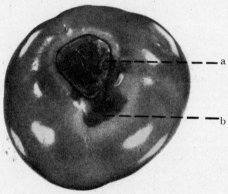

Figure 173. Blossom-end rot of tomato, a physiogenic disease associated with irregular water supply. Here the rot began as a soft, sunken lesion which later was checked, forming a well-defined corky spot ("a"); later, when conditions favoring blossom-end rot again occurred, the lesion extended outward as soft decay ("b").

with excessive water after dry periods and is increased or inhibited by salt concentrations in the soil. Control depends on the selection of the more resistant varieties and on mulching, watering, cultivating, and other devices to lessen extremes of water supply.

Alfalfa white spot is a local spotting of the leaf margins or entire blades. It is due to unbalanced water relations and occurs particularly when dry weather is followed by heavy rains.

Blasting of oats and sorghums, or failure to produce seed in an otherwise normal plant, appears to be associated with extremes of water excess or deficiency at blossoming time (Fig. 174). Since, in many crops, the water supply is uncontrollable, the only recourse is to plant the crops in two or more successive plantings, so that if one planting is affected the others may escape.

Figure 174. Blast of oats. On the two heads at the right, many spikelets are blasted; on the head at the left only a few blasted spikelets can be seen. (*Courtesy of Illinois Natural History Survey.*)

II. Diseases Due to Unfavorable Air Relationships

Plants require adequate oxygen and they are more susceptible to some of the poisonous gases in the air than are animals. Stress at either of these points produces physiogenic diseases.

A. Lack of oxygen (asphyxiation)

1. *Waterlogged soils.* Plants showing typical symptoms of chronic water deficiency are often found in heavily watered locations. The oxygen has been excluded from the water-logged soil, the roots are unable to respire properly, and as a

consequence lack the ability to take up water even though an abundance is present in the soil.   This condition is often found in ornamental plants that have been overwatered, and is the principal cause of dying of field crops in low places of a field.   Laying of concrete sidewalks may exclude oxygen from tree roots producing the same effect.   The remedy is drainage, lightening the soil with compost or sand, and avoidance of excessive artificial waterings and air exclusion by pavements.

2.   *Asphyxiation of fruits and vegetables in storage.*   When fruits and vegetables are stored in deep layers, poorly ventilated, they will often suffer from lack of oxygen or poisoning by carbon dioxide or other volatile products of metabolism.   Characteristic and serious storage diseases result.   The damage usually increases with increasing temperature, which raises the metabolic rate and increases the oxygen requirement.

Blackheart of potatoes. Affected tubers often appear normal externally, but on cutting show a black firm core in the center.   In advanced stages the black core extends out to the surface, showing as sunken cankers (Fig. 175).   In some cases the entire surface of the potato is moist, with a brown discoloration.   When the necrosis reaches the surface the tubers usually show rapid decay due to soft-rot bacteria or other secondary invaders.   Blackheart is brought on by the combination of poor aeration and high temperatures. Heavy losses occur in freight cars that are excessively heated to prevent freezing in transit.   Preventive measures include

Figure 175.   Potato black heart. Tuber showing dead tissue breaking through to the surface.   (*Courtesy of R. S. Kirby, Pa. Agr. Ext. Service.*)

storage in shallow layers, not in deep bins, leaving spaces between bins or ranks of sacks, and lowering the temperature of storage to 65°F. or lower if possible. It should never be higher than 95°F. Even without special refrigeration equipment, cool temperatures can be obtained by the use of insulated storage houses, preferable sunken in the ground, opened at night and closed during the hot part of the day, with fans for increasing circulation of the air. Potatoes should not be left in the soil after the vines die down, nor exposed to the sun for too long a time after digging.

Apple scald and internal browning are examples of asphyxiation injuries to fruits. Scald appears as a brown or black discoloration of the skin. It may be hard or soft, localized in sharply defined areas (as though the fruit had touched a hot

Figure 176. Apple scald, and its control by use of oiled wrappers. Yellow Newton apples photographed after 9 months of storage. Those on the left were in oiled wrappers; those on the right were unwrapped and show typical scald. (*Photo by Bureau of Plant Industry, U. S. Dept. of Agriculture.*)

stove), or general over the fruit, superficial or deep (Fig. 176). Affected fruits are soon decayed by secondary molds. The trouble is due to the accumulation of metabolic by-products (volatile esters, acetaldehyde, or ethylene) in poorly ventilated storage, rather than to lack of oxygen. It is greatest in immature fruit stored without adequate ventilation and at high humidity and temperature. Green and yellow varieties are more severely attacked than red ones. Control of scald and related troubles depends on: allowing fruit to mature and be well colored before picking; storage at once after this stage is reached; protection from sun and heat; storage as near to 32°F. as possible and at 80 to 85 per cent relative humidity; thorough ventilation of the storage compartment; avoidance of tight containers; and wrapping the fruits in oiled paper wrappers, or packing them in shredded oiled paper, or coating the apple skin with oil (Brogdexing process).

B. Poisonous gases. Plants may be poisoned by gases in doses so small that they are not injurious to animals and cannot be detected by smell. The chief sources of such gases are factory smoke, illuminating gas, and leakage of gases from refrigerating equipment. The most important toxic gases are sulphur dioxide from smoke, and ethylene from illuminating gas. The reaction of plants may be *acute*, with rapid bleaching of the chlorophyll and death, *chronic*, with a general depression of vital activities, retarded growth, failure to produce blossoms, fruits, or reserve food, early leaf fall, and ultimately death, or *invisible*, with no external symptoms but a reduced development detected only by measuring yield or by chemical analysis. Accurate diagnosis of gas injury is important, as the owners of gas-injured plants are legally entitled to compensation by firms responsible for leakage or liberation of the gas.

1. *Sulphur dioxide (sulphurous acid) injury.* Leaves of affected plants show sharply defined brown or red dead areas between the veins, often with a striking color contrast against the green leaf areas (Fig. 177). In coniferous trees the needles become wine red and fall. The injury resembles that from drought, frost, or sun-scald, but in these latter cases the dead areas are less sharply outlined. The average person cannot detect less than 3 parts per million of SO_2 by odor, but plants often react to lower concentrations, such as the oak tree (1.4 parts per million). Plant species vary in SO_2 susceptibility. The most susceptible ones include lupin, clover, bean, pea, alfalfa, and roses. Among the most resistant are beets, potatoes, iris, chicory, and vegetables of the cabbage

group. Grasses and cereals are intermediate in susceptibility (minimal toxic dose about 10 parts per million). *Diagnosis* of SO_2 depends on: (a) analysis of the SO_2 content of air by chemical methods and comparison with known toxic dosages; (b) analysis of leaves for sulphate or sulphite content; and (c) study of the behavior of indicator plants, the best of which include beans, knotweed (*Polygonum*), rhubarb, lupins, and grapes. *Prevention* of SO_2 injury depends on methods for

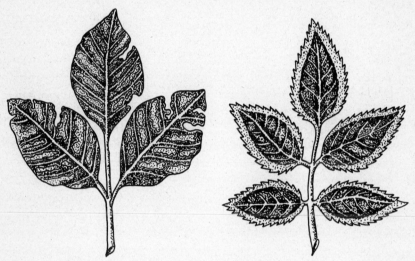

Figure 177. Injury by the gases in smoke. Left, on beech, the interveinal burning characteristic of sulphurous acid (sulphur dioxide); right, marginal burning such as results from hydrochloric acid or chlorine fumes. (*After Sorauer.*)

condensing or retaining smoke and gases in factories, methods for diffusing the gases over wide areas (high stacks, numerous small stacks, etc.), and the use of the more resistant plants in smoky areas.

2. *Illuminating gas (ethylene) injury.* The principal sources are leaky pipes with the primary effect on the plant through gas either in the soil, or in the air. The gas also contains carbon monoxide, but the ethylene is 5,000 times as poisonous to plants as the CO. In root poisoning the symptoms are those of general root failure, with water deficiency symptoms in the leaves plus specific types of curling of the stems and leaves in some plants. Illuminating gas in the air is not a

problem outdoors, but often becomes serious in greenhouses and dwellings, especially in winter when ventilation is poor and when the frozen soil permits lateral distribution of the gas for long distances from leaky mains. Carnations, for example, are very sensitive; $\frac{1}{2}$ part per million causes the buds to close, and 1 part per million prevents them from opening. The symptoms are retarded growth, yellowing and leaf fall in dicotyledons, curvatures in monocotyledons, rigor and loss of irritability, curving, even spirals of leaves and petioles. Dormant buds are stimulated to open. (Recall the use of ethylene in forcing potato tubers and woody plants out of dormancy.)

Diagnosis: In the past it was customary to use the etiolated sweet pea seedling as the standard test for ethylene, since this plant has a characteristic response to low concentrations of ethylene. Today the standard test plant is the tomato, which is easy to grow and handle, and which responds to .1 part per million of ethylene. This is 200 times as sensitive as the human nose, 60 to 100 times as sensitive as the canary (used in mines as a gas detector), and at least 50 times as sensitive as the best chemical test. The response of a 6 to 8 inch tomato plant is a downward bending of the leaves (epinasty). Other useful indicator plants are scarlet sage, mimosa, castor beans, *Bryophyllum*, and Jimson weeds. Greenhouse operators should keep a few tomato plants near possible gas sources as a routine practice. Control is limited to ventilation, and prompt repairs to leaky gas pipes. In lawsuits to recover property loss from leaky pipes, examination, tests, and testimony by a plant physiologist or plant pathologist are usually necessary.

3. *Hydrochloric acid and chlorine injury.* HCl and Cl gases from manufacturing processes are sometimes responsible for plant injury. The effect is a sharply outlined killing of leaf margins (Fig. 177), in contrast to the interveinal browning due to SO_2. In cases of smoke injury, the effect is often due to a mixture of SO_2, HCl, Cl, and other gases, with correspondingly complicated symptoms.

III. *Diseases Due to Unfavorable Temperatures*

A. Heat injury. The usual symptoms of heat injury are retarded growth, undersized plants, localized burns on leaves and stems, defoliation, premature ripening of fruits, and death. Passing from one part of the country to another, the effect of heat in dwarfing plants becomes noticeable; thus the lilac becomes almost a tree in the North and is often puny in the South, while the reverse is true of privet. Many northern crops, such as cauliflower and broccoli, can hardly be grown in the South because of a lack of extended cool periods. High temperatures are usually associated with high light intensity and drought, producing disease complexes rather than clear-cut cases of injury due to one of these factors. The direct effect of heat in killing tissues is obvious; less clear is the retarding effect of temperatures only a little above the optimum for growth of a crop. Two factors appear to be involved: (1) "denaturing" of plant proteins which can occur, although slowly at temperatures as moderate as 95°–104°F., and (2) alteration of the ratio, photosynthesis: respiration. Supra-optimal temperatures may decrease photosynthesis while at the same time increasing respiration, and if the latter becomes greater than the former, as it will at high temperatures, the plant will lose weight and live only by using up its reserves.

Heat cankers of seedlings. In bright sun the temperature at the soil line, where light is absorbed, may reach 150°F. on a summer day. This results in killing of the stem tissues at the soil line, most noticeable on the south sides of stems. It is most important in evergreen tree seedlings and in flax. In the case of tree seedlings it is avoided by sloping the seedlings to the south in transplanting, so that the needles shade the stem during the hottest part of the day. In flax, the preventive measures include drilling north and south rather than east and west, seeding early so that the plants pass through the seedling stage before the hot weather, and the poor agronomic practices of overseeding or allowing the stand to become weedy, in either case to induce shading of the plants.

Sunstroke is the outright killing of plants by excessive heat. It is a principal limiting factor in vegetable and flower production in the South. Nasturtiums, for example, regularly die in summer in the South, while in northern states they flourish throughout the summer.

Kelsey spot of plums is a localized injury of fruits due to temperatures above 100°F. The spots have a sharp margin, depressed, often waxy center, and purplish red color, with dead

Figure 178.   Kelsey spot of plums (heat injury).

flesh beneath, sometimes extending to the pit (Fig. 178). It is distinguished from sunburn, in that sunburned areas are diffuse in outline, show no depression, are brown, and occur only in fruits exposed to the sun, while shaded fruits may show Kelsey spot. The only control measure known is to grow a green cover crop, which will cool the orchard temperature as much as 4° to 6° in comparison with clean-cultivated orchards.

Tipburn of potatoes. In this common trouble the leaflets show yellow, then dead tips, the necrosis spreads down the margins and into the blade until the entire leaflet may be destroyed. It is most severe in older leaves and during hot periods accompanied by water shortage. It is distinguished from "hopper burn" due to feeding of the potato leaf hopper, although the two troubles often occur together and are controlled similarly (Fig. 179). Varieties of potatoes differ in their susceptibility to tipburn according to dates of maturity, but the chief measure of control against both tipburn and hopperburn is spraying the vines with Bordeaux mixture. This shades the leaves and thus reduces their temperature, kills young leaf hoppers, and repels the adults. In addition, cultivation and other means of retaining or providing moisture are advised.

Figure 179. Potato hopperburn showing dying and curling of the margins of the leaflets. Tipburn is indistinguishable in appearance from hopperburn, and both diseases are controlled by the same means. The holes are caused by flea beetles. (*Courtesy of P. E. Tilford, Ohio Agr. Exp. Sta.*)

B. Cold injury. As the temperature drops from the optimum, growth slows down, no more chlorophyll is formed, red pigments may develop, the tissues are partially dehydrated which gives them greater cold resistance, and with extremes of cold the tissues are frozen, the cells explode, and the plant is killed. Freezing injury is too obvious to warrant any prolonged discussion except in the following cases of interest because of their etiology or control.

1. *Frost injury of fruits.* The reproductive parts of blossoms are more sensitive to cold than the remainder of the plant, leading to the widespread and common sterility of fruit trees which suffer from late spring frost. The control measures used by citrus growers in protecting against frost might be

used to a much greater extent by growers of other tree and bush fruits. In many cases the late spring and early fall frosts do not reach more than a few degrees below the safe temperature. Various methods are used for raising the air temperature in the orchard or field this few degrees, such as the use of smudge fires (Fig. 180) or burning logs, especially on the north side of the field, patented orchard heaters, and

Figure 180. Protecting an orchard from frost by lard-pail oil heaters. At daybreak the first of two sets of heaters have burned dry and the second set are burning low. (*Reproduced from Farmers' Bulletin 1588 with permission of the U. S. Weather Bureau.*)

power fans or airplanes, flying low over the field to stir up the air and prevent it settling in cold pockets. Overhead irrigation or flooding with irrigation water will often save a crop. For frost-susceptible crops, elevated sites with southern exposure are safest from frost injury. In some crops, potash fertilizers are reported to increase cold resistance. The cost of such control measures is not excessive, considering that the entire crop may be saved by such measures, and that in the South particularly the losses from frost are very great, because the earliness of the season brings plants out of dormancy before the danger of late spring frost is past. A similar trouble is frequently encountered in wheat, where early maturing varieties may be sterilized by late frosts. This is one of the reasons for the waning popularity of Early Blackhull wheat in hard red winter wheat areas.

2. *Winter killing* due to abnormally low temperatures is especially serious in winter crops or perennials such as small grains, alfalfa, and strawberries. Many factors influence winter injury, such as species and variety of plant, provenience (geographic origin of seed), age (perennials), degree of dormancy or "hardening," kind, time, and degree of pruning, amount of last-year's crop, amount of heat and light during the growing season, especially late fall, physical characters of soil and subsoil, fertility and fertilizing practices, soil moisture and drainage, presence or absence of cover crops, and cultural practices such as time and manner of seeding. A control program must consider all of these variables and must be worked out in individual cases by starting with the hardier varieties and working out the other growing practices in ways that will reinforce this hardiness.

The Armistice-day freeze of 1940 which resulted in widespread injury to fruit trees, shrubs, and ornamental trees throughout Arkansas, Missouri, Kansas, and Oklahoma is a striking case of winter-killing. The freeze followed abruptly a period of warm Indian summer and the trees were not dormant at the time when the temperatures suddenly dropped from 85°F. to less than 17°F. within a few hours. The principal injury was to the inner bark of the lower parts of stems and trunks. Affected trees leaved out and blossomed as normal, but as soon as they began to draw heavily on the roots, the injury became evident, with sudden withering and dying of the foliage followed by death of part or all of the tree. The gumming or bleeding so often seen in branches of stone fruit trees is usually a result either of freeze injury or summer sun scald (Fig. 181).

3. *Winter injuries:*
Winter browning of evergreens. When, as often occurs, a cold winter is interrupted by a period of unseasonably warm weather in January or February, evergreens show extensive

browning of leaves. This is due to excessive evaporation from the leaves, under the influence of warmth, at a time when the roots in cold soil are unable to replace the water deficit. It is the common reason for browning of conifers

Figure 181. Gummosis of peach. The exudation of masses of sticky or amber-like gum, may be a result of borer attack or bacterial blight, but more commonly it follows winter injury or summer sun scald. The gum is normal sap, released by any agency that ruptures the bark.

Figure 182. Winter injury of rhododendron, due to excessive loss of water from the leaves during a warm spell in winter, when the cold soil does not permit replacement of the water lost by transpiration.

and magnolias in early spring (Fig. 182) and a similar phenomenon accounts for the browning of lawns in midsummer. Deciduous trees show an allied trouble, when the warm spell stimulates buds into precocious activity, followed by usual February and March freezes which destroy the unfolding shoots, thus inhibiting flowering and fruiting for

that year. An analogous situation is seen in conifers growing in rather cold climates which frequently show a golden
yellow appearance on the southern exposure. Evidently
one reason for this is that chlorophyll synthesis and chlorophyll photo-oxidation are differently affected by low temperatures, in this case the pigment being photo-oxidized
more rapidly than new chlorophyll is synthesized, hence the
yellowing.

4. *Cold injuries to harvested crops.* Stored fruits and vegetables
are changed, sometimes improved, in composition, color, and
flavor by moderate freezing, but are subject to much greater
mechanical injury if handled while frozen. Solid freezing is
followed by watery disintegration and usually the complete
loss of the crop. Potatoes for example turn sweet at 32–35°F.,
develop internal frost necrosis (browning) from 28–32° and
freeze solid below 28°. Control is a matter of providing heat
for protection in storage, and it should be noted that public
carriers are legally responsible for freezing of crops in transit
and must reimburse the shipper for crops destroyed in this
way.

IV. Diseases Due to Unfavorable Light Conditions

Plants vary in their light requirements, there are shade and sun
plants, but each has its optimal light requirement and suffers from
departures from this optimum.

A. Insufficient light. Plants grown in insufficient light are
etiolated. The internodes and petioles are abnormally elongated,
the leaves are reduced in size, the chlorophyll disappears, and
there is a suppression of reproductive function. Thus the
potato produces true seed regularly in the North where days are
longer during the summer, and can be made to set seed in the
South only if artificial light is supplied. The growth of etiolated
plants is succulent, the leaves are thin and wilt easily, the
plants are delayed in maturity, and show increased susceptibility
to certain contagious diseases. Etiolation is sometimes desirable
as a horticultural practice, as in the blanching of celery,
cauliflower, lettuce, and cabbage, or in the production of bulb

flowers, but in other cases lack of light may be a serious handicap, as in the case of lodging of cereals.

Lodging of cereals. Lodging or falling down previous to
harvest is common in some regions, and rare in others (Fig.
183). There is no one cause of lodging and any of the following
factors may be involved: excessive nitrogen, abundance of
moisture producing succulent growth, frost injury, attacks of

Figure 183. Lodging in wheat, primarily a light-deficiency disease, which
can be overcome by the use of stiff-strawed, lodging-resistant varieties, as Missouri
Early Premium, shown at the left of the photograph. (*Photo by Mo. Agr. Exp. Sta.*)

insects or diseases at the crown or foot or along the stems, and
mechanical breaking, as by hail, but the most important factor
of all in lodging is lack of light, due to overcrowding of the
plants and resulting in weak development of the bases of the
culms. Control of lodging depends on lowering the rate of
seeding to allow light penetration, cultural methods that avoid
nitrogen excess in the soil, and the use of lodging-resistant
varieties (Fig. 183). In any locality the adapted varieties of
cereals are likely to be more lodging-resistant than unadapted
varieties. Much attention is being given to selection for lodg-

ing-resistance in cereal breeding at the present time, and the results are very encouraging.

B. Excessive light. Although excessive light is usually associated with and complicated by excessive heat and water shortage, there are cases where the light alone is responsible for plant injury, as in the following case.

Scalding of bean, cowpea, and soybean leaves is common in regions characterized by a high proportion of days with brilliant sunshine, as in Oklahoma, Colorado, and Arizona. On cowpeas the trouble first appears as small red raised spots which enlarge to several millimeters in diameter or coalesce to form extensive blotches, with tan papery centers and a raised, bright red margin. Eventually the entire leaf will die, still retaining some green color, however. The petioles, stems, and sometimes the pods show dead lesions somewhat resembling those from bacterial blight. In beans and soybeans the disease is similar. In beans there is little loss to the seed crop, but in the soybean the disease may seriously lessen the value of the plant for green manure, cover, or forage. No direct control measures are known. The Biloxi soybean is less susceptible than other varieties, and in cases of serious prevalence, the most susceptible legumes should be replaced by those that show less scalding.

C. Photoperiodism. Plants are habituated to length of day, and there are short-day plants and long-day plants. To move a plant to a locality with a different day-length may mean an agricultural failure, as plants cannot thrive unless provided with the length of day to which they are habituated. This can be overcome in the greenhouse by artificial lighting or shading, but it is one of the many points to consider in attempting to introduce a new type of agriculture into any area.

REFERENCES

1. Eckstein, O. et al. Potash deficiency symptoms. Verlagsges. f. Ackerbau, Berlin. 1937.
2. Heald, F. D. Non-parasitic diseases. *In* "Manual of plant diseases," pp. 58–247. McGraw-Hill Book Co. 1933. (Treats numerous physiogenic diseases and includes references to many others. There is a comparable section in his later "Introduction to plant pathology" but abridged and lacking most of the references.)

3. McMurtrey, J. E.   Distinctive plant symptoms caused by deficiency of any one of the chemical elements essential for normal development.   Bot. Rev. **4**: 183–203. 1938.

4. Plagge, H. H. et al.   Functional diseases of the apple in storage.   Iowa Agr. Exp. Sta. Bull. **329**: 35–79.   1935.

5. Robbins, W. R.   Relation of nutrient salt concentration to growth of the tomato and to the incidence of blossom-end rot of the fruit.   Pl. Physiol. **12**: 21–50. 1937.

6. Sorauer, P. et al.   Manual of plant diseases.   Vol. 1, Nonparasitic diseases. (Translation by F. Dorrance from the third German edition.   The sixth German edition is more up-to-date but is not available in English.)   Record Press, Wilkes-Barré, Pa.   1914.

7. Willis, L. G.   Bibliography of references to the literature on the minor elements and their relation to plant and animal nutrition.   Ed. 3.   Chilean Nitrate Educ. Bur., New York.   1939–1941.

8. Wilson, J. D.   Environmental factors in relation to plant disease and injury: a bibliography.   Ohio Agr. Exp. Sta. Tech. Bull. 9.   1932.

9. Young, F. D.   Frost and the prevention of frost damage.   U. S. Dept. Agr. Farm. Bull. 1588 rev.   1940.

Chapter 15

THE METHODS OF STUDYING PLANT DISEASES

In meeting with a plant disease problem, two questions are uppermost: What is wrong? What can be done to correct it? The latter depends on the former; the plant pathologist like the physician must first make a diagnosis of the cause of disease before he can intelligently recommend control measures.

I. **Field observations.** A study of the disease as it occurs in field, forest, orchard, garden, nursery, or greenhouse will go far toward determining the cause of the disease. In making such a study the observer should give attention to many of the following questions:

1. Does the trouble occur on a single crop or is it widespread on vegetation in the vicinity? If the latter, it is most likely an environmental disturbance such as might be caused by drought, gas, or storms.

2. How is the trouble distributed through the field? Is it general over the field, as is usually true of air-borne diseases, or is it in well defined spots as is often true of soil-borne diseases? If the latter, are the spots at random or are they related to the topography of the land?

3. What loss is the trouble causing? If slight, in comparison with a normal crop, control measures may not be warranted.

4. What are the species and varieties affected and those nearby which are not affected?

5. What is the exact location of the field, and the name of the tenant or owner? A map of the distribution of the trouble in the field might be helpful.

6. What are the ecological features of the location: type and fertility of the soil, water supply, slope, exposure, shade, and condition of other vegetation?

7. Are there peculiar features or disturbances of the location, such as digging operations, underlying pipes, excavations, pavement, factory or oil well residues, etc.?

8. What is the history of this year's crop: time and manner of planting, fertilization, watering, pruning, control practices used, previous insect or disease attacks, cultivation?

9. What is the history of the land: has it been rotated; what other crops have been grown here in past years; how did they succeed; has this same crop in this or neighboring locations shown this trouble in previous years and to what extent?

10. What has been the weather record this year and in recent years past: moisture, hail, frosts, temperatures?

11. What was the source of seed or planting stock: where was it grown; was it certified or inspected; are the label or bill of sale and samples of the seed still available?

12. What is the exact nature of the symptoms and signs; are the symptoms systemic, as in cases of root rots, wilt, and many physiogenic diseases, or in the form of local lesions; are leaf lesions at the tips and edges, farthest from the veins, as in water deficiencies, or at random over the blade; how does the diseased plant differ from healthy ones in color, size, habit, degree of maturity; are there any signs pointing to the cause of the trouble, such as fungus fruiting bodies, mycelium, rhizomorphs, or sclerotia, molds, mildew, rust, or indications of insect work such as holes, eggs, chewed leaves, droppings, or "sawdust" (frass)?

From this study it may be possible to arrive at once at the cause of the trouble, and if not, the field study can often provide far more information than can be obtained from a laboratory sample.

II. **Plant disease surveys.** There are many reasons why it is desirable to know the distribution of plant diseases and the amount of damage they are doing in various crops and localities and from one season to another. We must have exact information on the destructiveness of diseases so that funds and energy allotted to plant disease research and extension work may be directed to the most vital problems. We must know the distribution of plant diseases to guide an efficient program of disease control by quarantines and other methods of disease exclusion.   We must be informed on the losses suffered by individual growers in order to determine whether the expense of control measures is justified.   Up-to-the-minute information on the progress of epiphytotics is useful in directing growers' practices in the immediate future, and reduces financial losses from low prices or speculation due to over-optimistic crop-yield predictions.   For these and other reasons it is indispensable that pathologists and growers be currently informed on the prevalence, distribution, and destructiveness of plant diseases.

This information is obtained by plant disease surveys.   Each state experiment station devotes a small portion of its resources toward securing such data on the leading crops grown.   From time to time, as epiphytotics or emergencies dictate, special extensive surveys of a single plant disease may be made.   The need for a national unification of plant disease survey activity became apparent at the time of the first world war and resulted in publication of the "Plant Disease Reporter," issued by the Division of Mycology and Plant Disease Survey of the U. S. Department of Agriculture.   This division guides and integrates surveys on disease problems of particular importance. The Plant Disease Reporter publishes bimonthly reports of the progress, distribution, and new occurrences of plant diseases, annual summaries of the disease situations in various crops, and of the losses from plant diseases in leading crops, and occasional supplements giving detailed information on epiphytotics and special surveys.

In a few cases the estimates of disease loss are based on accurate measurements.   For example, the dockage records of the federal grain inspectors give a fairly exact picture of the annual loss from bunt in wheat or ergot in rye.   But most of the estimates cannot be based on such accurate data but depend on the judgment of well informed plant pathologists, agronomists, and horticulturists.   In most states the final crop loss figures are averages of the estimates of several agricultural workers.   In the few cases where crude estimates can be compared with accurate measurements of crop loss, experience has shown that crop observers for the most part have leaned so far on the conservative side that the crop loss figures are much smaller than the losses actually realized.   This has been clearly shown in the case of leaf rust of wheat, for example, and the Plant Disease Reporter estimates of crop loss must be interpreted from this standpoint.

For a survey to be efficient it must be extensive, must present a typical cross-section of disease occurrence, and wherever possible measurements of some sort must be made the basis of estimates.   On pp. 31–32 are given the chart and table used in estimating stem rust losses, and aids such as these make for uniformity in the estimates of different observers.   Whenever a disease control demonstration is conducted, with comparable plots protected and unprotected, a measurable basis is supplied for future crop loss estimates.   Sulphur dusting of wheat and spraying of potatoes have both materially aided in arriving at accurate disease loss estimates in these crops.   In the smut diseases, where infected heads represent total loss, sample counts of the percentages of diseased heads give fairly accurate measures of smut losses.   The customary practice is to step well out into the field, select a representative spot, and starting at random in the row count 200–400 consecutive heads, recording the percentage of those smutted.   The same procedure is repeated several times in the field, and the results are averaged.

Occasionally, as in certain of the root rot diseases, the spots of diseased or dead plants are apparent in bold relief against adjacent healthy areas, and in such cases airplane surveying is practical and affords a means of fairly exact measurement of disease loss.   Figure 184 is an airplane photograph of a cotton field containing large root rot spots.   By using such a photograph and tracing the spots with a planimeter a fairly exact measure of the damage can be obtained.

In other cases it is very difficult even to approach an accurate guess at crop loss because of the varied injurious effects of the disease.   In the root, stalk, and ear rot complex of corn, for example, the loss involves many things, stand reduction from seedling blight, devitalization from root decay, reduced food and water transport from stalk and shank infection, lodging, and direct attack on the grain.   Actual count of diseased plants may be a poor index of loss because of the various degrees of injury in different plants.   Counts of dead plants are often misleading, because adjacent healthy plants may partly compensate for the loss in profiting by the additional space, light, and soil nutrients released by the dead plants.   Quality as well as quantity of the harvested crop must be considered in the loss estimate.   More-

Figure 184.   Aerial photograph of Texas root rot spots in a cotton field. Airplane surveying and the use of such photographs give fairly accurate measurements of disease damage in cases of those diseases that result in large well-defined spots of dead plants.   (*Photo by the Bureau of Plant Industry, U. S. Dept. of Agriculture.*)

over, the loss estimate is not based on harvest alone.   It includes cost of control practices even where no crop damage is sustained, and it must be corrected for certain savings as in reduced cost of harvesting a diseased or short crop, or compensation for the loss by use of a late-planted substitute crop.   When two or more diseases or other types of crop injury affect a crop simultaneously it becomes difficult or impossible to determine the proper proportion of each factor in the total loss.   These various considerations show us that in many cases it is very difficult to obtain accurate estimates of crop loss from plant disease. They should not leave us with the feeling that many disease loss estimates are valueless. In spite of these difficulties, the estimates have proven themselves very useful in the past, and as more detailed study is given to individual crops and their diseases the estimates tend to become increasingly accurate. An important phase of pathological research in the future concerns improved techniques for determining crop damage from plant disease.

III. **Collections.** It will often be necessary to make collections for laboratory study. The collected material should include the whole plant or several plants if they are small, and a generous supply of twigs, bark, wood, roots, and leaves if a tree or other large plant concerned. The plants should be affected but not yet dead. They should be typical of the trouble, not the worst affected ones in the field unless so indicated. One or more healthy plants should be included for comparison. If these are to be sent to a specialist, they should be wrapped in moist paper and shipped directly. In this case a letter describing the field observations should accompany the specimens. If for laboratory study by the collector, they should be kept moist and placed in a refrigerator until examination.

IV. **Preservation of specimens.** If extended microscopic study is intended or a long time must elapse before examination, it may be necessary to preserve the specimens in a preservative solution. For preserving small entire specimens, leaves, or fruits in natural color, the following solutions, devised by G. A. Vacha, are recommended:

1. *For green tissues.* Formula:

Fresh sulphurous acid*	142 c.c.
Ethyl alcohol	142 c.c.
Formaldehyde	3 c.c.
Oil of cloves	1 c.c.
Copper sulphate	1 gram
Acetyl-salicylic acid	1.5 grams
Water, sufficient to make	1000 c.c.

* Most economically prepared by bubbling SO_2 gas through water to saturation.

When the desired green color is attained (usually 3 to 5 days), discard the solution and replace with fresh solution, prepared in identically the same manner as the above but omitting the copper sulphate. The above solution may also be used for yellow colors in certain tissues, such as sunflowers, pears which lack the customary reddish blush, some varieties of peaches, yellow apples, etc.

2. *The following formula, found to be useful in the preservation of red colors, is known as Vacha's Formula 14A.*

Cobaltous nitrate....................................	15 grams
Stannic chloride.....................................	10 grams
Formaldehyde.......................................	25 c.c.
Water..	2000 c.c.

This is a color fixing solution, and it may be used for the preservation of some of the strawberry varieties, red peppers, and also Bliss Triumph potatoes and other red colors. The specimens are thoroughly washed in cold water, placed in a specimen jar, and submerged in the above solution. Keep in this solution for at least two weeks, and at the end of this time, discard and replace it with a holding solution, which is designated as Formula 14B. Formula 14B is made as follows:

Formaldehyde.......................................	10 c.c.
Ethyl alcohol.......................................	10 c.c.
Sulphurous acid.....................................	30 to 50 c.c.
Water..	1000 c.c.

3. *For preserving gross specimens where color is immaterial* either 5 per cent formalin or 70 per cent alcohol is commonly used. Very fragile materials, such as the telial horns of cedar rusts, are best prepared in the standard killing and fixing solution, F.A.A., given below.

4. *For preserving material for preparing microscopic sections* any of the common histological killing and fixing agents may be used, such as formalacetic alcohol (F.A.A.):

Formalin...	13 c.c.
Glacial acetic acid..................................	5 c.c.
Ethyl alcohol (50%).................................	200 c.c.

or Flemming's solution:

Distilled water......................................	60 c.c.
Chromic acid (1%)..................................	25 c.c.
Acetic acid (1%)...................................	10 c.c.
Osmic acid (2%)—Added just before use..............	5 c.c.

For further details on preparation of permanent slides see
the manuals on botanical microtechnique, such as Chamberlain's "Methods in Plant Histology" or Johansen's
"Plant Microtechnique."

5. *For dried specimens* the methods commonly used in botanical
herbaria are used, pressing, mounting, and using such
fumigation as may be necessary.

V. Laboratory examination of specimens. The first step in
identifying diseases in the laboratory is a careful examination
of specimens in a search for the less obvious or microscopic
symptoms and signs that will permit diagnosis. At first the
hand lens and low power, wide field microscope should be
used, then if necessary the compound microscope. The low-
power search may reveal such structures as fungus fruiting
bodies, spore masses, droplets of exuding bacteria, mycelial
mats, the bodies, skins, eggs, or frass of insects. For study
with the compound microscope it is usually necessary to prepare
a slide mount, although in cases where spores are delicately
attached and it is necessary to determine the method of spore
attachment it may be desirable to use the low power of the
compound microscope and focus directly on the specimen, under
a strong reflected light. Microscopic mounts may be made in
several ways:

1. *Scraping* with a scalpel or knife blade to remove spores or
epidermis which are then transferred to a drop on the slide.
2. *Teasing* the tissue apart with two needles in a drop on the
slide, often best accomplished under the low power microscope. Teasing is especially useful with bacterial diseases,
as when the tissues are torn apart the bacterial masses can
often be seen streaming out like smoke from a chimney.
3. *Sectioning* with a hand razor or razor blade to make thin,
transparent sections. The material if soft, is usually placed
in a slit in a stick of elder pith to hold it during the sectioning.
The razor and the pith are flooded with alcohol during
sectioning. The sections are floated out in a watch glass of
water, and under the low-power microscope good sections
are transferred with a needle point to a drop on the slide.

4. *Maceration* may be necessary with very hard tissues such as dead leaves or pine needles. The tissue is placed in a little water or potassium hydroxide solution and gently boiled for a few minutes before tearing or sectioning.

The fluid for mounting may be water, or commonly lactophenol solution (Ammann's fluid), to which a dye has been added, is used since this does not evaporate and gives a semi-permanent preparation. The formula for lactophenol is:

```
Distilled water........................................... 20 c.c.
Carbolic acid crystals (warmed until melted)............... 20 c.c.
Lactic acid................................................ 20 c.c.
Glycerine.................................................. 40 c.c.
```

A trace of safranin, acid fuchsin, eosin, cotton blue or other stain may be added.

Staining is desirable for bringing out mycelium and bacteria in plant tissues, and may be indispensible. Various stains are used for the purpose, and these are discussed in references on histological technique.

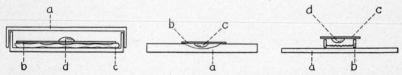

Figure 185. Three common methods of studying spore germination. Left *Petri dish mount:* a, petri dish; b, slide; c, wet filter paper; d, spore suspension. Center, *hollow ground slide:* a, hollow-ground slide; b, cover glass; c, spore suspension. Right, *Van Tieghem cell:* a, slide; b, Van Tieghem cell; c, cover glass; d, spore suspension.

In dealing with fungi it is often necessary to measure spores or other structures, in order to determine the species involved. Microscopic measuring is done with a micrometer eyepiece, which projects a measuring scale onto the microscopic field of vision. The marks on the scale are arbitrarily spaced, and to learn the value for each space it is first necessary to calibrate the eyepiece by examining a slide (slide micrometer) on which is a ruled scale, each space of which has a known value. The corresponding values for the eyepiece are then calculated, and thereafter spores or other structures can be measured in microns (1 micron = .001 millimeter).

Occasionally it is necessary to germinate spores for assistance in identifying fungi, for instance, to determine whether a given spore is a urediospore or a teliospore of a rust. This is done by placing a spore suspension in a saturated atmosphere. Tap water, rainwater, distilled water, and sugar solutions (1%) are all used for making suspensions. Some of the methods of preparing the germination chambers are shown in Figure 185.

VI. Identification of organisms. The first object of laboratory diagnosis of disease is to determine the cause of the disease, and if this is a fungus, bacterium, or nematode, to identify the organism. Space cannot be devoted here to a detailed account of classification and identification of these organisms; that is reserved for courses in mycology, bacteriology, and nematology. The following references and suggestions are given, however, for pursuing such study.

Fungus pathogens are diagnosed in part by their structure, and in part by their host relations. In groups where the host ranges are narrow, as in rusts and smuts, or where identification of the species is a research problem in itself, as with bacteria, it is pardonable to depend largely on the host relations in diagnosis, but final and absolute identification in critical cases, depends on a comparison of the organism with all known related species, regardless of host. Among the most useful reference works are:

For diagnosis of plant-parasitic fungus genera and in some cases species:

Stevens, F. L. The fungi which cause plant disease. Macmillan Co., New York. 1913. (Most useful but now out of print. The following revised edition is available but less complete.)

Stevens, F. L. Plant disease fungi. Macmillan Co., New York. 1925.

Clements, F. E. and C. L. Shear. The genera of fungi. H. W. Wilson Co., New York. 1931.

Sorauer, P. Handbuch der Pflanzenkrankheiten, II, III. Parey, Berlin. 1928–1932.

Engler, A. and K. Prantl. Die Natürlichen Pflanzenfamilien, Bd. 5–7. Leipzig. 1928–1938.

For determining what genera and species of fungi have been found on a given host:

Seymour, A. B.   Host index of the fungi of North America. Harvard University Press, Cambridge, Mass.   1929.

Anderson, P. et al.   Check list of diseases of economic plants in the United States.   U. S. Dept. Agr., Dept. Bull. 1366. 1926.   (Now being revised by F. Weiss and available as reprints from the Plant Disease Reporter, so far as issued.)

Check lists of local areas, such as Brown, C. C.   Contribution toward a host index to plant diseases in Oklahoma. Okla. Agr. Exp. Sta. Mimeogr. Circ. 33, rev., 1941; Hilborn, M. T.   List of causes of fungous and bacterial plant diseases in Maine to 1936 inclusive.   Pl. Dis. Rep. Supp. 105, 1938; Maneval, W. E.   A list of Missouri fungi with special reference to plant pathogens and wood destroying species.   Univ. of Mo. Studies *12* (3), 1937; Schade, A. L.   A preliminary list of the parasitic fungi of Idaho.   Pl. Dis. Rep. Supp. 95, 1936.

For diagnosis of rust fungi:

Arthur, J. C.   Manual of the rusts in United States and Canada.   Purdue Res. Found., Lafayette, Ind.   1934.

For diagnosis of smut fungi:

Clinton, G. L.   Ustilaginales.   No. Amer. Flora 7: 1–82, 1906.

For descriptions of all known fungus species:

Saccardo, P. A. et al.   Sylloge Fungorum.   Padera and Avellino,   1882–1931.   (Twenty-five volumes.   A research tool for final determinations as in describing new species of fungi.)

For diagnosis of plant-parasitic bacteria:

Elliott, C.   Manual of bacterial plant pathogens.   Williams and Wilkins Co., Baltimore, Md.   1930.

Bergey D. H. et al.   Bergey's manual of determinative bacteriology.   Ed.   4.   Williams and Wilkins Co., Baltimore, Md.   1934.

428 NATURE AND PREVENTION OF PLANT DISEASES

For diagnosis of plant viruses:

Holmes, F. O. Handbook of phytopathogenic viruses. Burgess Co., Minneapolis, Minn. 1939.

Smith, K. M. A textbook of plant virus diseases. Blakiston Co., New York, N. Y. 1937.

For diagnosis of plant parasitic nematodes:

Goodey, T. Plant parasitic nematodes. Dutton Co., 1933.

———. The nematode parasites of plants catalogued under their hosts. Imp. Bur. Agr. Parasit., St. Albans. 1940.

For diagnosis and literature of non-parasitic diseases:

Sorauer, P. Handbuch der Pflanzenkrankheiten. I. Ed. 6. Parey, Berlin. 1933–1934. (An English translation of the third edition of this is available: Sorauer, P. Manual of plant diseases, Vol. 1, Non-parasitic diseases, Transl. by F. Dorrance. Record Press, Wilkes-Barré, Pa. 1914.)

Wilson, J. O. Environmental factors in relation to plant disease and injury: a bibliography. Ohio Agr. Exp. Sta. Tech. Bull. 9. 1932.

VII. Investigating the causes of diseases. Assuming that a disease is under study and that an organism has been found associated with the disease symptoms, it is not always safe to conclude at once that the organism is the cause of the disease. It may be a secondary, saprophytic organism which has gained a foothold on tissues that were diseased from some other cause. It becomes necessary at this point to demonstrate that the organism found is or is not the primary cause of the disease.

A. *Koch's postulates.* In the case of contagious diseases, proof of the cause of disease follows the principles laid down by the bacteriologist Robert Koch for proving the causation of animal disease. Koch's rules of proof or postulates as applied to plant diseases are:

1. The organism must be found constantly associated with the observed symptoms.

2. It must be isolated and studied in pure culture, free from all other organisms.

3. Such pure cultures must be used to inoculate healthy susceptible plants and there produce the same disease as was first observed.

4. From these inoculated plants the fungus must be reisolated in pure culture and shown to be the same organism as was present in the original cultures.

It is not always possible to carry through Koch's postulates, since some organisms are obligate parasites and cannot be grown in artificial culture. In these cases (rusts, powdery mildews) the constant association of the organism with the symptoms is taken as proof of the causal relationship, while with virus diseases, infection experiments with juice of diseased plants, insects, or grafting are commonly used to demonstrate pathogenicity. Koch's rules of proof, while very helpful, do not give infallible evidence of the causation of disease in nature. It is sometimes possible to demonstrate infection and the recovery of the inoculated organism under experimental conditions so rarely encountered in nature that for practical purposes the inoculated plant can be considered resistant or immune, as seen in the case of tobacco wildfire. In dealing with environmental disease, proof of causation by a given environmental situation is obtained by reproducing that situation under controlled conditions and thereby producing the same symptoms as originally observed.

B. *Culture media*.

1. *Composition*.   Many kinds of nutrient materials are used in culturing pathogens. These are used in either liquid or solid form. Liquid media may be broths, or decoctions of plant and animal substances, or solutions of definite composition. Fruit or vegetable decoctions are prepared by adding 100 to 400 gms. of fresh or dry material (beans, peas, potatoes, onions, oatmeal, prunes, etc.) to 1000 cc. of water, boiling, filtering, and sterilizing. Sugar may be added, usually dextrose at the rate of 20 gm. per liter. Beef extract (3 gm. per liter) or peptone (10 gm. per liter) or both are added in preparing animal broths. For analytical work, bal-

anced salt solutions with sugar are used. It is then desirable to titrate the media to known pH values.

For some purposes it is desirable to use sterilized plant tissues as culture media. Stems, and cores of potatoes, carrots, and other vegetables are used for this purpose, merely washed, placed in tubes or flasks plugged with cotton, and sterilized.

Solid media are usually obtained by preparing a broth, decoction, or nutrient solution to each liter of which is added about 20 gm. of agar. Agar is the product of a Japanese seaweed. It has no nutrient value and has the property of congealing to form a stiff jelly at room temperatures, and melting at temperatures not high enough to injure most organisms. One of the commonest and best culture media for plant pathogens is potato-dextrose agar prepared as follows:

In 500 c.c. of distilled water dissolve 17 gm. of agar shreds or powder by very carefully boiling or steaming. Boil 400 gm. of diced potatoes in 500 c.c. of water and strain. Add the potato decoction to the agar solution, add enough water to make 1000 c.c., filter through cloth, and add 20 gm. of dextrose.

2. *Tubing and sterilizing.* Although agar may be sterilized and stored in flasks it is customary to pour it into test tubes before sterilizing. Devices are available which avoid smearing the mouth of the tube with agar, to prevent contaminations later on. The tubes are filled $\frac{1}{3}$ to $\frac{2}{5}$ full of the hot agar medium, plugged with a fairly tight roll of cotton, placed in wire baskets and sterilized.

Sterilization of nutrient media is usually by means of steam under pressure. Fifteen minutes at 15 pounds pressure suffices in most cases. Two common types of steam sterilizers are shown in Figure 186 and others can be seen in biological supply house catalogues. To diminish chemical changes, free steam is sometimes used. The autoclave serves for this purpose, with escape valve open and a gentle flow of steam, or the

Arnold steam sterilizer, designed for free steam sterilization can be used.   The procedure is to heat the medium
to 100 degrees C. for one hour on each of 3 successive
days.   Other methods of sterilization as by chemical
vapors or radiation are used in exceptional cases.

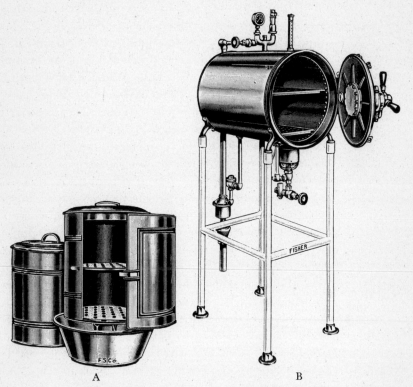

A   B

Figure 186.   Equipment for sterilization of culture media.   A,
Arnold free-steam sterilizer; B, autoclave.   (*Courtesy of The Fisher
Scientific Co.*)

After tubes of agar are removed from the sterilizer
they should be slanted at an angle of about 15 degrees
and allowed to harden.   They are then used at once
or stored in a refrigerator.   In many types of work the
hot agar is poured into round, flat, sterile petri dishes
and there allowed to harden.

C. *Isolation of organisms in pure culture.*
   1. *Tissue transfers.*   In dealing with objects such as fruit or
   vegetables decays or stem diseases, select a point at the

edge of the lesion, adjoining healthy tissue, surface sterilize the tissue by wiping with a cloth or cotton damp with alcohol (which may or may not be burned off), with a flamed knife or scalpel tear away the outer tissues exposing the inner lesion, grub out a small bit of the diseased tissue at the edge of the lesion with a freshly sterilized knife blade, and place on an agar slant or petri dish. With lesions on small tissues such as leaf spots or rootlet-decay, fragments of the lesions may be cut off with a sterile knife, dropped for a minute or two in calcium hypochlorite solution ("B-K" powder, 3% to 10% solution, filtered) and then transferred with a sterile needle to agar.

After a period of one to several days, fungus or bacterial growth will usually be apparent at the edge of the lesion. If a mixture of organisms is present, places on the plate can be selected where one organism has grown out more rapidly than others, and where a fragment of the growth can be picked off with a sterile needle and transferred to a fresh tube or plate.

2. *Dilution plates.* In dealing with bacteria or fungi that are producing an abundance of spores, pure cultures can be obtained by the dilution plate method. A suspension of spores or bacteria is made with a sterile needle in a drop of sterile water. Three tubes of agar are melted, then allowed to cool until they can be handled freely but in which the agar has not yet congealed. A sterile inoculating needle with the end in the form of a small loop is dipped into the suspension and a loopful of spores or bacteria transferred to one of the tubes. It is thoroughly mixed with the agar by stirring with the needle, then a loopful from this tube is transferred to a second tube, the process repeated, and a loopful from the second tube transferred to the third tube. The contents of each tube is then poured into a sterile petri dish and allowed to harden. By so diluting, the first dish will yield many colonies of the organism, the second tube fewer, and the third tube

still fewer.   Later, when the colonies have grown to such a size as to be readily seen, individual colonies can be transferred with a sterile needle from the dish to a fresh tube of agar, which then will contain a pure culture.

3. *Streaking spores or bacteria.*   A rapid method to secure pure cultures from bacterial or spore masses is to flame a needle, stab it into sterile agar to wet it, touch it to the spore or bacterial mass, then make a series of 6 to 8 streaks across a plate of agar.   Toward the end of the streaking most of the bacteria or spores have been rubbed off the needle, and colonies that develop from that area will often be pure.

4. *Mycelium transfer.*   If a fungus is producing an abundance of aerial mycelium, individual hyphae may be lifted off with a flamed needle and transferred to agar, and some of these are likely to grow into pure cultures.

5. *Monosporic cultures.*   A skilled operator, using a very fine glass needle or pipet under the microscope can pick out individual spores or bacteria and transfer them to agar.   Elaborate micro-manipulators can be used to facilitate this work.   The spores are first smeared in a thin suspension over a dish of very clear, filtered agar, from which they may be selected and transferred.

6. *Observing and storing cultures.*   Some fungi and bacteria will develop very rapidly on agar; others may require weeks to produce obvious growth.   Storage of cultures is generally either at room temperature or in a refrigerator.   To maintain cultures alive it is necessary to transfer them to fresh agar within periods of a few weeks to several months, depending on the species.   Growth of the organisms will vary greatly with the nature of the medium, the temperature of incubation and other environmental factors.

7. *Inducing sporulation.*   It may be necessary to induce the production of spores in order to identify a fungus in culture.   This is done by trying various expedients: changing the temperature, culturing on less nutritious

media of different pH levels, suddenly removing the food supply, or matching sexual strains. In inducing phycomycetes to produce zoospores, Klebs's technique may be used: grow the fungus in broth or vegetable decoction, then pour off the broth, wash the mycelium, and place in sterile water. Many fungi exist in sexual strains, and it is then necessary to combine the two sexes to induce sexual reproduction. This is done by inoculating a petri dish of agar with 2 or more cultures of the fungus from different sources in the hope that both sexes may be represented in the same dish, in which case sexual reproduction occurs at the meeting line of the two mycelial mats.

8. *Isolating organisms from mixtures.* Nature deals, not with pure cultures, but with mixtures of organisms. In attempting to isolate single organisms it is often difficult to separate the desired organism from its contaminants. If the desired one is producing spores or is a bacterium, the dilution plate method usually suffices. With phycomycetes it is advantageous to make tissue plantings on water agar, containing no nutrient. On this, the phycomycetes commonly develop more rapidly than their contaminants. A little lactic or acetic acid added to agar tends to inhibit bacterial contaminations without interfering with fungus growth. Most plant-pathogenic bacteria (Gram-negative) are unaffected by the dye gentian violet or crystal violet, while many of their common contaminating bacteria are killed by it. Consequently the addition of a little of this dye will often aid in freeing phytopathogenic bacteria from their bacterial contaminants.

D. *Inoculation of plants.*

1. *Inoculations in vitro.* A rapid and useful method for testing the pathogenicity of disease organisms is to perform the experiment in the laboratory under completely aseptic conditions. In testing damping-off organisms, large tubes or flasks of water agar are prepared, seed of the plant to be used are surface disin-

fested with 10 per cent calcium hypochlorite ("B-K" powder), and planted in the agar, and at once or after seed germination, fungus mycelium, spores, or bacteria are placed in the tube near the seed. Root infections can be readily watched through the glass. Similar methods may be used in cases where cut leaves or stems in water are inoculated in the laboratory.

2. *Inoculations in greenhouse or field.*

   a. *Methods of applying inoculum.* In some cases attempts are made to duplicate nature's methods of inoculating, but often more or less artificial means are used. Spores or bacteria in suspension may be sprayed on plants with an atomizer, or spores may be dusted on or allowed to fall naturally on moist plants. Mycelium may be placed on uninjured leaves or stems, or the tissues may be pricked, scratched or cut as the inoculum is applied. In grain rust inoculations it is common to rub off the bloom on the leaves with thumb and forefinger, then apply a suspension of spores with a spear-headed needle or spatula. In the case of seedling infection smuts and other surface seed-borne diseases, the spores are dusted on the seed before planting. With soil-borne diseases it is customary to infest the soil. A common method is to grow the pathogen on wheat, meal, or grain and sand, then crumble the medium and mix it with the soil, or simply to prepare a suspension of the organism and water the soil about the plant with this suspension.

   b. *Control system.* Each experiment must include plants that are uninoculated but in every other respect are treated as the inoculated plants, even to the extent of laying sterile agar on the control plants, or pricking and scratching them first as with the inoculated ones. Rigid attention must be given to the environment and many failures may be expected where the environmental requirements are not understood or met. With most types of inoculation experiments the infection court must be kept moist for 24 to 48 hours after inoculation as by placing plants in a moist chamber, on a base of wet sphagnum moss, by covering them with plugged lamp chimneys, wet tents, bell jars, or cans, or by binding the infection court with wet cotton or sphagnum. The temperature must be adapted to disease development. For example it is almost impossible to demonstrate infection with *Botrytis allii*, the cause of onion neck rot, at ordinary greenhouse temperatures, but very easy if the bulbs are placed in a cold storage compartment. Numerous other environmental factors such as light, vigor of the host plant, and fertility of the soil, will also play a part in determining the success or failure of infection experiments. Because it is often difficult to maintain all of the requisite conditions for infection, little value can usually be attached to negative results or failures to produce infection, while positive results must be qualified with the phrase "under the conditions of the experiment," with the realization that under other conditions negative results might be obtained.

c. *Precautions in infection tests.* Apart from attention to the requisites set forth above, an experiment must be managed so as to avoid complicating factors. Insects, other diseases than that under study, mice, rabbits, crows, and slugs should be excluded. In greenhouse tests it is customary to disinfest the soil with steam prior to inoculation unless there is a definite reason for not doing so, as in studying naturally infested soil or competition among the soil organisms. Seed disinfestation is often used to exclude seed-borne organisms as complicating factors. In some cases the plants are watered with boiled or distilled water to exclude water-borne contagion. Otherwise the greenhouse or field should be managed in a manner calculated to produce a normal healthy crop.

d. *Special inoculation methods for virus diseases.* Some
virus diseases may be transmitted by rubbing the
juice of an infected plant onto the leaves of a healthy
one; others can be transmitted only by specific
insects or by grafting. Sap transmission is accomplished by rubbing the virus juice gently across
leaves, or by stabbing the leaves with needle points
wet with virus juice. In refractory cases, the leaves
may first be sprinkled with an abrasive such as
carborundum. Tuber and bulb viruses are often
transmitted experimentally by cutting out a plug
of infected tissue with a cork borer and inserting it
in a borer hole in a healthy bulb or tuber. Grafting
is commonly used to demonstrate infectivity of those
viruses that are not sap-transmissible (e.g. the peach
viruses). In demonstrating transmission by insects
it is necessary to rear them in cages, to keep accurate
account of the viruliferous condition of each insect
or colony and to give proper attention to such
points as the length of feeding time required by the
insect to acquire the virus and the length of incubation period of the virus in the insect prior to its
ability to transmit the virus. Methods of counting
viruses, measuring viruses, preparing crystalline
virus proteins, and serological techniques with
viruses are described in manuals on virus diseases
or on phytopathological techniques, such as that of
Riker and Riker.

VIII. Studies on epiphytology.

A. *Seasonal development of disease.* Much may be learned of
the epiphytology of a disease by merely observing it
closely throughout the year, noting the prevalence and
condition of the pathogen at each season, and correlating
this information with the condition of the host and the
meteorological record. Often long and painstaking
searches are necessary to determine the condition of the
pathogen during dormant seasons, but they have been

well repaid in extension of our information on the annual cycles of cereal rusts, bacterial blight of stone fruits, peach leaf curl, and many other diseases. Many diseases are relatively unexplored in this connection, and a fruitful field of discovery lies ahead of the student who is willing to devote time and careful, persistent observation to this problem.

Searching for a pathogen in the dormant season is often akin to hunting for a needle in a haystack. To simplify this problem it is customary to gather fallen leaves, fruits, or other plant parts known to be infected during the growing season, enclose them in cheesecloth sacks, tie the sacks to labelled stakes, arrange the tissues in as natural position as possible, and examine them from time to time during the dormant season. A covered chicken-wire enclosure aids to protect the material from marauders. In this way it has been possible to discover the perfect stages of many imperfect fungi, to follow the changes that occur during saprogenesis, and to determine the exact details of the resumption of pathogenesis.

B. *Dissemination of diseases.* With strictly soil-borne diseases, much may be learned by staking out the outlines of spots of infestation and following the development and spread of the disease during one or several seasons. Important information on the breaking up of Texas root rot spots and its relation to antibiotic action in the soil has been gained in this way. Spread of diseases by water, wind-driven leaves, and insects, can be profitably studied by simple but painstaking means such as will readily suggest themselves. The dissemination of pathogens by wind has received much attention in connection with cereal rusts and downy mildews. A common procedure is to expose vasilene- or agar-covered microscope slides at various altitudes, sometimes from airplanes, and from examination of such slides, exposed at critical periods, much useful information has been obtained on the migration of pathogens, the resistance of spores to long periods of exposure in the air, and sources of infection. (Fig. 187.)

Figure 187.   Methods of exploring the upper air in studying the migration of fungus spores.   1: F. C. Meier, pioneer in this work (left) and E. B. McKinley examining improved Lindberg-Meier "sky hook"; 2: Testing equipment used in National Geographic Society flight for sampling the stratosphere for fungus spores; 3: Meier, demonstrating early method of exposing culture dish.   (*Courtesy of R. J. Haskell.*)

Devices to filter and concentrate spores from the air are sometimes used.

C. *Relation of disease to weather.* Studies on epiphytology must always be connected with the meteorological record. The minimal requirement is a continuous record of temperature, air humidity, and rainfall, together with data, if possible, on soil moisture, wind, and light. In this connection, study the graphic summary of meteorology in relation to cherry leaf spot reproduced in Figure 188 or better consult the original paper of Keitt. While the records of the U. S. Weather Bureau hold a wealth of useful data that may be correlated with studies on epiphytology, unless the point of observation is close to a weather station it may be necessary to set up a field weather station, equipped with such equipment as thermograph, hygrometer, photometer, and anemometer for obtaining the most pertinent meteorological information.

D. *Production of disease in controlled environments.* No study of epiphytology is complete without experiments in controlled environments, in which each important environmental factor is subjected to controlled variation while the others are held constant. Since the development of the Wisconsin constant soil-temperature tanks, numerous types of constant environment equipment have been described, varying from small cabinets to large rooms or greenhouses in which temperature, air moisture, soil moisture, amount and type of light, composition of the soil (often sand cultures with measured nutrient), genetic composition of the host and pathogen, quality and movement of the air, and even other factors are all controllable within narrow limits (Fig. 189). Knowledge of the rôle of each of these factors, alone and as modified by others, is today considered essential in a thoroughgoing study of parasitic disease, and this knowledge is being put to good use in interpreting the cause of disease in the field and in providing a basis for control measures. (See discussion of soil temperature and cereal scab in the following chapter.)

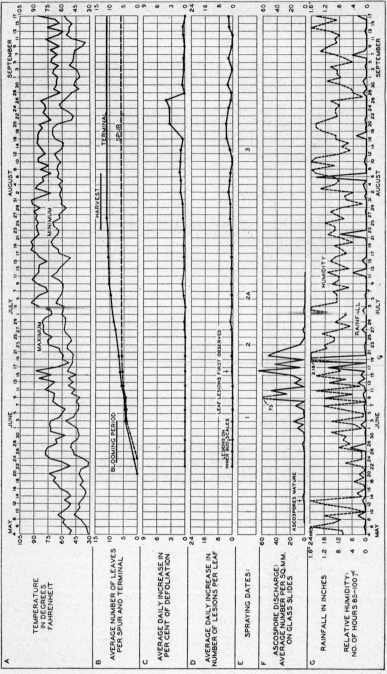

Figure 188. A graphic summary of certain records relating to the epiphytology and control of cherry leaf spot, Sturgeon Bay, Wis., 1935. (*Reproduced from Wis. Agr. Exp. Sta. Res. Bull. 132 with permission of G. W. Keitt.*)

E. *Artificial epiphytotics.*   In determining the varietal resistance or susceptibility of crops toward disease, and in
studying the conditions that bring about epiphytotic
spread of disease, it is sometimes desirable to induce
artificial epiphytotics on a small scale.   This is done in

Figure 189.   Equipment for studying plant disease under controlled
conditions of temperature, humidity, and light.   (*Reproduced by permission
from the Annals of Applied Biology.*)

various ways.   With cereal rusts and mildews in the
greenhouse, epiphytotics can be initiated by introducing
inoculum, and every few days enclosing the bench of
plants under a canvas cover over night after watering the
plants and the canvas.   In the field the inoculum may be
introduced by setting infected plants at frequent intervals,
and supplementing moisture with an overhead spray

system. Spore-production may be stimulated in the inoculum centers by providing them with cloth enclosures at frequent periods. Whether in greenhouse or field, a highly susceptible variety should occur at frequent intervals in the planting.

IX. **Studies on disease control.** The testing of control practices can be greatly facilitated by preliminary laboratory and greenhouse tests before proceeding to tests on a field scale. For example, The United States Rubber Co. submitted a thousand chemical by-products to a plant pathologist in the hope that some one or two might be useful for seed disinfestation. It would have been out of the question to test all of these in the field. By use of a laboratory technique described below, it was found that about 10 of the 1000 had fungicidal value. Eight of the 10 were rejected because of poor adherence, excessive cost, safety hazard, seed injury, or other reasons. There remained two, "Spergon" and "Spergonex." These two were then extensively tested in the field in comparison with other seed treatments and with untreated seed, and their place in disease control was established.

A. *Laboratory tests of fungicides.* Out of many trials in devising methods for the assay of fungicides, standard methods have been developed chiefly through the studies of Horsfall and Heuberger and of McCallan and Wilcoxon in New York. The standard methods described by Horsfall ("A design for laboratory assay of fungicides," Phytopath. 30: 545–563. 1940) are as follows:

The fungicide, at known dilution, is sprayed with a precise atomizer, delivering a known amount of spray per second, at a target consisting of a microscope slide coated with cellulose nitrate, placed 30 inches from the atomizer, and protected from wind currents by a tube, 4 inches in diameter. The entire equipment is placed inside a hood where humidity can be controlled. The time interval of spraying is regulated by a shutter and the amount of spray per second by the size of the atomizer outlet hole. After spraying the slides, two drops of fungus spore suspension are placed on each slide with a standard pipet. The suspension is of conidia of the fungus *Macrosporium sarcinae-forme*, grown under standard conditions, and at a concentration of 5000 spores per c.c. After incubating 16 to 20 hours, 50 spores in each drop are counted and recorded as germinated or not germinated. The results are plotted, and expressed in terms of the "LD50" (lethal dose for 50 per cent of the spores), and compared in fungicidal value with standard LD50 Bordeaux mixture. The fungicidal value of the material is then expressed as the:

Bordeaux coefficient

$$= \frac{\text{LD50 deposition of copper in Bordeaux}}{\text{LD50 deposition of toxicant in fungicide X.}}$$

Determining the adherence of seed-treatment dust fungicides is accomplished by thoroughly mixing a given weight of seed with an excess of fungicide, screening off the excess dust, and determining the weight of the dust adhering to the seed (difference in weights of undusted and dusted seed).

B. *Greenhouse and field tests of control practices.* Before embarking on a series of field tests, exposed to the viscissitudes of weather and other field hazards and irregularities, it is customary to undertake greenhouse tests of control practices, where plants can be protected and the environment can to a large extent be controlled. The greenhouse is adapted for small scale tests of seed-treatments, soil treatments, spraying and dusting, and varietal resistance. If the disease is a dangerous one that might escape to disease-free areas if studied in the field, the greenhouse may be the only place where it can be safely studied. In the field an attempt should be made to secure a site and a planting as uniform as possible, relatively free from one-sided effects or gradients of moisture, soil, shade, wind exposure, or other factors that might make comparisons unreliable between plants in one and another part of the plot. The plot should be as level as possible, free from ditches, or terraces, and should be square or in a broad rectangle rather than in the form of a long narrow strip. In the greenhouse, center benches are better than side benches where accurate comparisons between treatments must be made.

1. *Culture.* The plants should be grown as normally as possible except for the variations involved in the experiment. In the greenhouse, sterilized soil may be used, and unless the test refers to seed treatments, it is well to use suitably treated seed to avoid complications of seedling disease. The plants should be kept free of insects and of diseases other than the one under study. If possible the plants should be of genetically pure lines, and seed cleaning, grading, or culling of inferior plants is desirable to insure having normal plants in regular stands.

2. *Infestation.* For testing control methods the infestation should be as heavy as it is feasible to make it. Soil in which total losses have occurred in the past, highly susceptible plants as controls, and in many cases artificial epiphytotics or heavy artificial soil or plant inoculations, are all useful. To the plant pathologist an epiphytotic or a uniformly heavy infestation of a crop is indeed a "find," since if a control practice proves effective under these conditions its merit is established. Such a situation compares with the brutal testing grounds for automobile tires.

3. *Statistical significance of disease control experiments.* Experiments on disease control are nearly always quantitative experiments. We are interested in knowing, not merely that one practice is good and another poor, but just how much better one is than another. We cannot use the expression "this is significantly better than that" as a loose generalization. There is a measuring scale in common acceptance, by which we may determine how much weight we may attach to a difference between the results of two treatments. In fact, some scientific journals will not accept reports on research unless quantitative results have been mathematically analyzed and found to be statistically significant.

The basis of statistical significance lies in the variability of living things in nature.   If one tree is sprayed and another is not, and the sprayed tree produces more fruit than the unsprayed tree, the increased crop may be due to the spraying, or it might be due to genetic differences in the two trees, soil differences, age, or some other point of difference.   Since in field experiments we can never have two plants in identical condition for comparison, we fall back on the principle of odds.   If we spray enough trees under enough conditions, the odds will be so great that the spraying increased the crop that the results approach certainty, and are acceptable to critics.   Statistical analysis tells us what the odds are that our results are reliable, or conversely, how many trees we must spray in order to have the odds 19:1 or 99:1 that our conclusions are correct.

There is a natural tendency to conclude that the larger the plots the more reliable the results, and growers particularly find it difficult to understand that a well-arranged field experiment with many short replicated rows will give much more reliable information than the obvious plan of treating one acre and leaving an adjacent acre untreated.   In many types of field experiments the most desirable length of individual rows is 3 to 10 feet (vegetables), 1 rod (small grains), or 50 to 100 feet (cotton, corn, sorghums), and if these are properly arranged and replicated, little is to be gained by more extensive plantings in the same location.

Replications (repetitions of the same planting) are necessary to increase significance of results and to permit measuring the experimental error.   Three to five replications of each variant in the experiment are commonly used.   The variants of each replication must not be arranged in the same order in relation to the directions of the field.   For example, if 1, 2, and 3 represent 3 treatments and 4 is the untreated check, the following regular arrangements would be undesirable because in "A" the check, 4, would regularly be in poorer soil than

1, 2, 3, while 2 would be at a fertility disadvantage to 1,

	A					B			
1	2	3	4	1	2	3	4		
1	2	3	4	2	3	4	1		
1	2	3	4	3	4	1	2	Direction of
1	2	3	4	4	1	2	3	prevailing wind

→Decreasing fertility→

and 3 to 2 and 1, while in "B," treatment 2 would regularly be on the protected side of 1 and on the exposed side of 3. We assume that there is a gradient in fertility from one side of the field to the other and that the prevailing wind is in the direction indicated. Most environmental influences follow such gradients. The wind blows principally from one direction; soil, moisture, and elevation all tend to decrease progressively across a plot; and the ideal plot without such gradient is rarely if ever found. To eliminate such error, either a random arrangement or a latin square arrangement is commonly used. One useful way of obtaining a random arrangement is to number a series of poker chips, and write down the order of the numbers as they are drawn out a box. The latin square is regular only to the extent that each member appears only once in each row, horizontal and vertical.

Random				*Latin square*			
2	4	3	1	3	1	4	2
4	3	1	2	2	4	3	1
3	2	4	1	1	3	2	4
1	3	2	4	4	2	1	3

If there are several replications of the experiments, each replication should be independently randomized.

It is common observation that the marginal rows of a plot or field and the plants on ends of rows are often more vigorous or less vigorous than the remainder of the field, and in the greenhouse, the pots at the edge of a bench show the same relation to pots in the center.

This is "border effect." Plants showing border effect cannot be compared with plants in the center of the plot without introducing serious error. The main causes of border effect in the field are one-sided exposure of the border rows, greater availability of moisture and nutrients to the border rows, and less competition than the other plants. In the greenhouse, border effect is commonly due to a drying out of the plants on the edges of benches, or to temperature effects close to the greenhouse walls or steam pipes. Border effect is eliminated by planting two or three extra rows (buffer rows) around the experimental plot.

Once an experiment is set up so as to be favorable for statistical analysis, the results can be analyzed (analysis of variance) and from this analysis it is possible to determine in a scientifically acceptable manner, which experimental results are significant. For a brief discussion of the methods of analyzing variance see the manual by Riker and Riker, cited at the end of the chapter, which also contains references to more detailed treatments of this subject.

X. **Literature review.** In any thorough scientific study a student or research worker must be familiar with the literature bearing on the problem at hand, must know of the methods and experimental results of others who have worked on this and similar problems, in order to avoid endless repetition of experiments that have already been adequately performed and the embarrassment of announcing a "discovery" that may have been made by some other worker long ago. The literature of plant pathology is vast, scattered through thousands of American and foreign scientific journals, bulletins, circulars, and books. Fortunately, we have a number of very useful guides to this literature so that the problem is not as baffling as it first seems.

Let us suppose that your problem concerns the speckled leaf blotch disease of wheat, caused by the fungus *Septoria tritici*, and that you are interested in tracing down all of the papers dealing with earlier studies on this disease. You would first turn to certain journals that have well-indexed lists of pathological papers, and through their indexes locate and record the titles of the papers concerned. In the indexes you would search for reports of the disease under five key headings:

Wheat: *Septoria tritici*

Wheat: Speckled leaf blotch

Triticum (the scientific name of wheat): *Septoria tritici*

Triticum: Speckled leaf blotch

Septoria tritici.

The most useful indexing journals for this purpose would be the "Experiment Station Record," "Biological Abstracts," "Review of Applied Mycology," and the "Agricultural Index." The first three of these give not only titles of papers but also short abstracts of the content of the papers. If the original paper is available in a nearby library, you should not be satisfied with reading only the abstract, although this will be useful in indicating whether the original paper should be consulted. Many departments of plant pathology also maintain card indexes of plant disease literature that will be particularly helpful, as they are ordinarily more up-to-date than the indexing journals. The scientific papers you consult will usually have limited bibliographies included, from which further titles on the problem may be gleaned. Your bibliography is best kept on filing cards, one card for each title. Each title should present complete information on the source, as in the titles of references at the end of each chapter in this book.

Guided by your bibliography you can now turn to the papers and bulletins themselves. In searching a library for technical papers you will find that these are rarely listed in library card catalogues by author or subject. Instead you must search for a file of the journal or bulletin concerned, then turn to the proper volume and page. From each article you will want to record data on methods, experimental results, and conclusions, at greater or less length according to your interest in each phase of the problem. Your notes may be recorded on the filing card bearing the title of the article concerned. To help in later organization of the information, you may enter on the card symbols indicating the phases of the problem covered in that article. Later on, the entire body of information may be arranged in an organized fashion, one of the most useful of which is the Cornell outline of a plant disease study, which is given below in slightly modified form:

1. Hosts
   a. Plants affected
   b. Varietal susceptibility
2. Disease
   a. Names
   b. History and range
   c. Importance
   d. Symptoms and signs
   e. Etiology
      a'. Name, history, and classification of the pathogen
      b'. Pathogenicity
      c'. Life history (including pathogenesis and sapro-genesis)
   f. Epiphytology
3. Control
   a. By regulation
   b. By the use of host resistance
   c. By cultural methods
4. Bibliography

REFERENCES

1. Chamberlain, C. J.   Methods in plant histology.   Ed. 5.   Univ. Chicago Press, Chicago, 1932.
2. Johansen, D. A.   Plant microtechnique.   McGraw-Hill Book Co., New York. 1940.
3. Rawlins, T. E.   Phytopathological and botanical research methods.   New York. 1933.
4. Riker, A. J. and R. S. Riker.   Introduction to research on plant diseases.   Plano-graphed.   John S. Swift Co., St. Louis.   1936.
5. Sass, J. E.   Elements of botanical microtechnique.   McGraw-Hill Book Co., New York.   1940.
6. Trelease, S. F. and E. S. Yule.   Preparation of scientific and technical papers.   Williams and Wilkins Co., Baltimore.   1936.
7. Whetzel, H. H. et al.   Laboratory outlines in plant pathology.   Ed. 2.   W. B. Saunders Co., Philadelphia.   1925.

Chapter 16

ENVIRONMENT AND PARASITIC DISEASE

For contagious disease to occur in plants it is not enough that a susceptible host and a virulent pathogen come in contact. *No disease can result unless the environment favors its development.* Rust spores are present in every field of susceptible wheat, but only under a favorable set of environmental conditions can an epiphytotic result.

It was not long ago that growers and scientists alike ascribed each plague or crop failure to environment alone,—to soil deficiencies, to poor seed or degenerate seed stocks unable to cope with their environment, to errors in cultural practices, or to drought, rain, heat, or cold. All these are vastly important; alone they account for many plant troubles, and as they present the complex of conditions necessary to host and pathogen they set the stage on which the tragedy of pathogenic plant disease can be enacted. The record of plant disease is far more than a record of pathogenic organisms, with their formidable latin names; it is a record of the excesses of these pathogens under the influence of environmental syndromes that permit and encourage their most devastating spread and destructiveness. The geographic distributions of plant diseases,—late blight of potatoes in the North, root knot in the South, Texas root rot in the Southwest, and *Igniarius* heart rot from the arctic circle to the tropics, all bear telling witness that plant disease can become rampant only if virulent pathogen and susceptible host find themselves in an environment that will permit the one to flourish at the expense of the other. Even more striking evidence of this is seen in those enphytotic diseases that are always present in trifling amount, but that at long intervals, when the many necessary factors of an exacting environment combine, burst forth in almost unaccountable fury. Hardly a plant disease, of even the most benign and negligible behavior can be trusted when we recall the isolated but overwhelming epiphytotic of the powdery mildew of clover in 1922—never approached in severity before or since—, or the unique situation in 1941 when *Septoria tritici*, ordinarily an inconspicuous pathogen of wheat in the early spring alone, advanced up the jointing stems until, over a vast section of the wheat belt, half or more of the food-making foliage had irreparably succumbed.

The environment may favor the development of disease:

1. *By its effects on the parasite* (moisture to permit spore ejection and germination; wind to distribute inoculum; temperatures at which the parasite flourishes, etc.).
2. *By its effects on the vector.* (Diseases that depend largely or entirely on insect vectors, as bacterial wilt of corn and curly top of sugar beets are dependent for their annual occurrence on the geographic distribution of the vector, which in turn is limited in its prevalence and distribution by environmental factors.)
3. *By its effects on the host* (favoring either susceptibility to infection or the subsequent development of the disease, as by promoting succulence, extending the period of exposure, devitalizing it, etc.).

The effect of environment on disease is a complex one consisting of many factors (temperature, moisture, nutrition, light) *interacting with one another and affecting both parasite and host simultaneously.* For example, the temperature producing most rapid development of the parasite will not necessarily produce the greatest amount of disease. The environmental background producing most destructive disease is often intermediate between the optimum for parasite development and the optimum for host susceptibility. The optimum level of any single environmental factor in producing disease may vary considerably with the changing level of some other factor.

These principles describing the effect of environment on parasitic disease are brought out in the following examples:

Effect of temperature on parasitic disease.

1. *Gibberella seedling blight of cereals* (the seedling-blight stage of cereal scab). Studies were made by Dickson in Wisconsin of the effect of soil temperature on seedling blight.

Wheat and corn plants were grown in watertight pots, immersed in tanks of water, with thermostatically controlled temperature. The effect of temperature on the fungus alone in pure culture was observed in constant temperature incubators. The results are indicated in Figure 190.

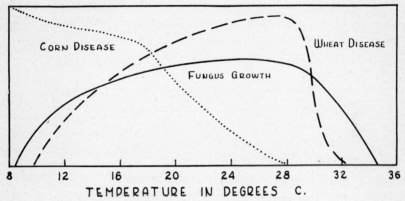

Figure 190. Relation between soil temperature and development of seedling blight in wheat and corn. (*After Dickson.*)

Observations:

a. The fungus grows best at high temperatures.

b. The most severe blight in *corn* occurs at low temperatures which are least favorable for either the growth of the fungus or the usual growth of corn.

c. The most severe blight in *wheat* occurs at higher temperatures which favor the fungus but are least favorable for the normal growth of wheat.

Conclusions:

a. The greatest amount of disease is not necessarily at the temperature which is most favorable to the fungus (cf. corn).

b. In this case the effect of temperature is primarily on the host plant, rather than on the fungus, unfavorable temperatures for normal plant growth predisposing the plants to disease.

c. The disease may be controlled in either crop by planting at a date when the soil temperature is best suited for the normal growth of the crop, i.e. planting wheat in cool soil, planting corn in warm soil.

2. *Bunt* (*covered or stinking smut*) *of wheat.*
   Observation:

For the disease to occur, the bunt spores on the seed surface must germinate at the time that the seedling is sprouting. Bunt spores germinate best in the range 43° to 50°F., fairly well up to 61°, and poorly or not at all above 63°F. Wheat develops best at 61° but will germinate at soil temperatures as high as 81°F.

Conclusions:

In this case the effect of temperature is primarily on the parasite. Bunt will be most serious when infested seed germinates in cool soil, favorable to the best wheat development. Bunt can be entirely avoided by planting in early fall when the soil is quite warm (65°F. or higher). This explains why early-planted wheat often escapes the disease, but planting in warm soil is not recommended for bunt control, since warm soil does not favor the best wheat growth, increases Hessian fly damage, and predisposes the plant to seedling blight and foot roots. Instead, for the best yields, plant the grain in cool soil even though this favors bunt infection, and control the bunt by one of the highly effective and inexpensive seed treatments.

Effect of moisture on parasitic disease. Moisture simultaneously affects both host and parasite and in this joint effect exerts a profound influence on the development of disease. Fungus spores require moisture, often condensed, for germination. Some spores are forcibly ejected only in presence of high moisture. Bacterial pathogens require water droplets for spread. Once a pathogen has gained the interior of a plant it becomes relatively independent of external moisture, the internal moisture of plant tissues sufficing for development of the organism. Abundant moisture favors rank, succulent development of the host which in many cases predisposes the host to infection. At the same time, abundant moisture in dry land areas may so stimulate plant growth that the damaging effects of disease are obscured. (Example: Rust years are wet years, in which the increased production due to adequate rainfall disguises the losses from rust.)   The effects of excess moisture are also seen in the destructiveness of contagious diseases in dense, overplanted stands which result in moist air about the plants, and in culture under irrigation or in wet climates, where rusts, powdery and downy mildews, and other diseases often become the deciding factor in production.   Deficient moisture after infection has occurred, as in wilt diseases or stem rust, may greatly aggravate the suffering of diseased plants.

Effect of wind on parasitic disease.   Wind is of chief importance in spreading inoculum of disease (spores, bacteria in wind-driven rain, wind blown leaves, infested insect vectors), and as such is highly effective.   (Recall that rust spores regularly initiate infections and epiphytotics after having been blown for hundreds of miles in the upper air, from Mexico to Canada in the spring and back in the fall.)   Wind is also of importance in influencing disease by its effect on moisture and temperature (accelerating evaporation), and by producing whipping injuries that permit infection by wound parasites.

Effect of light on parasitic disease.   Insufficient light often predisposes plants to disease by increasing the succulence or decreasing the vigor of plants, as is seen in the prevalence of powdery mildews, root decays and other contagious diseases in the greenhouse or in blanched or etiolated crops.   Most parasites are relatively independent of light, fungus spores, for example, usually germinating equally well in light or darkness.   The day and night alternations in spore production or mycelium spread seen in brown rot of stone fruits and agar cultures are usually due to diurnal temperature fluctuations rather than to variations in light.

Effect of soil on parasitic disease.   Many examples will be recalled of infectious diseases which occur only in certain types of soil, or which may be controlled by changing certain of the soil properties.

1. *Fertility.*   All contagious plant diseases fall into two groups, those which attack the most vigorous hosts (rusts, powdery mildews, virus diseases) and those which can attack only weakened plants (dry-land foot rot of wheat and numerous other root rot, canker, and leaf spot diseases.   The organisms that attack only vigorous

plants are usually obligate parasites, dependent on living cells for support. Many bacterial diseases flourish in rapidly-growing tissues and slacken their development in hosts that are weakened by soil deficiencies of any sort (e.g. fire blight of apple and pear).

2. *N-P-K ratio*. Excessive nitrogen in general lengthens the vegetative period which often increases the destructiveness of contagious disease by lengthening the period of susceptibility (stem rust). In some cases the reverse effect results, the longer growing period enabling the plant to make additional growth to compensate for that lost through disease (potato late blight). Phosphorus shortens the vegetative period, and with potassium stimulates the development of strong mechanical tissues in contrast to the succulent tissues resulting from nitrogen fertilization. Thus, by their own action, or in counteracting the effects of nitrogen, phosphorus and potassium in fertilization often afford effective control of those diseases that are favored by high nitrogen. Exceptions to this rule include the bacterial blight of stone fruits, which is conrolled pratctically by applications of readily available nitrogen, rust of flax, a crop which is very dependent on phosphorus for normal growth, and suffers most from rust in soils with a low N/P ratio on this account, and seedling-infection smuts in which high nitrogen promotes such rapid growth that the growing point grows away from the smut mycelium and produces healthy heads.

Cotton wilt is an outstanding case of a parasitic disease so dependent on potassium deficiency in the soil that applications of potash are a major feature of the control program (Fig. 68).

3. *Soil reaction (pH)*. Plant parasites vary in their pH requirements just as higher plants, and there is no logical classification of plant diseases according to pH requirements of the pathogens. Within the same genus are found acidophilic species (*Fusarium vasinfectum*—cotton wilt) and basophilic species (*Fusarium nivale*— snow mold root rot of wheat). Examples of pH requirements in certain diseases are given in Figure 191.

There is a long list of contagious diseases favored by acid soil, including:

Cotton wilt (possibly because potassium is less available in acid soils),

Tomato wilt (which decreases with rising soil pH),

Rhizoctonia root rot (controllable by physiologically basic fertilizers),

Club root of crucifers (see Figure 191.   A classic case of a disease
which is completely controlled by liming acid soils to raise the soil
pH to 7.0–7.5).

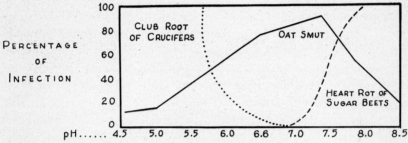

Figure 191.   Relation of the development of three diseases to pH of the soil.   (*After
Gaümann.*)

On the other hand, numerous other contagious diseases are
favored by alkaline soil reaction, e.g.:

Texas root rot (which occurs on every soil type in Texas but is
most severe on calcareous soils and to some extent can be combated
by soil acidification).

Potato scab (a classic case in which the disease increases as the pH
value drops from 8.5 to about 5.7 and then falls off sharply, so that a
pH of 5.2–5.4 is quite unfavorable to the disease.   It is practically
controlled in slightly acid soils by further soil acidification with 300
to 500 lb. of sulphur per acre).

Practically, diseases such as these are restricted to acid or alkaline soils and are often controllable by altering the soil reaction, but
actually little is known of the mechanism of this relationship.
Thus, adding lime to soil might affect disease in many ways, such as
altering the availability of other elements influencing disease,
affecting either host or parasite directly, disinfesting the soil,
changing its physical properties, and others.

4. *Soil texture*.   Many plant diseases are characterized by restriction to light or heavy soils.   In root knot, for example, the lighter
soils favor the migration of the pathogens from one plant to another.
In other cases heavy soil, through its retention of water or exclusion
of oxygen, influences disease largely by changing the susceptibility

of the host plant.   An example is bacterial blight of cotton which, in dry-land areas, is most destructive on plants in the heavier soils, since these soils are more retentive of water which favors the succulent type of growth most susceptible to the blight bacteria.

REFERENCES

1. Foister, C. E.   The relation of weather to fungous and bacterial diseases.   Bot. Rev. **1:** 497–516.   1935.
2. Jones, L. R., J. Johnson, and J. G. Dickson.   Wisconsin studies upon the relation of soil temperature to plant disease.   Wis. Agr. Exp. Sta. Res. Bull. 71.   1926.
3. Melhus, I. E. and G. C. Kent.   The influence of environment on plant disease. Chap. 6 *in* Elements of plant pathology.   Macmillan Co., New York.   1939.
4. Humphrey, H. B.   Climate and plant diseases.   *In* "Climate and Man," U. S. Dept. Agr. Yearbook 1941: 499–502.
5. Wilson, J. D.   Environmental factors in relation to plant disease and injury: a bibliography.   Ohio Agr. Exp. Sta. Tech. Ser. Bull. 9.   1932.

Chapter 17

ETIOLOGY AND EPIPHYTOLOGY OF DISEASE

Etiology

In connection with attempts to control a plant disease, it is often helpful to study the cause of the disease; if the disease is due to a pathogen, to work out its habits and cycle of activities. This study of the agencies which cause disease is called *etiology* (Greek: *aitia* = "cause").

A. **The names of pathogenic organisms.** Just as the common names of flowering plants vary in different regions, so the common names of diseases vary from one locality to another, and often confuse one disease with another. Most pathogens have no common names; instead, scientific names, uniform the world over, are used in their designation. An example is *Phymatotrichum omnivorum* (Shear) Duggar, the pathogen causing Texas root rot. *Phymatotrichum* is a genus of sclerotia-forming imperfect fungi, the name coming from two Greek roots, *phymato* = tubercle + *trich* = hair, evidently referring to the mycelium and sclerotia. The species name, *omnivorum* ("feeds on everything"), refers to the very wide host range of this fungus. When first discovered this fungus was found in a sterile form, without spores, and was placed in the genus *Ozonium*, a genus of non-spore-bearing imperfect fungi, by its discoverer, Shear, whose name, according to custom, thereafter followed the scientific name, *Ozonium omnivorum* Shear. But when the spore mats were discovered the pathogen was placed in a spore-forming genus of imperfect fungi, *Phymatotrichum*. Shear's name is retained in parenthesis to show that he was the one who originally described the fungus and gave it its present species name, while this is followed by the name of Duggar, the man who discovered the spore mats and gave the fungus the name it now bears, *Phymatotrichum omnivorum* (Shear) Duggar. In elementary textbooks and

459

other non-technical publications the name of the authority who originally described a pathogen is usually omitted, as has been done in the preceding chapters. But in scientific papers each technical name of a pathogen must include the authority, whose name is ordinarily abbreviated, e.g. *Puccinia graminis* Pers. [Persoon] or *Puccinia triticina* Eriks. [Eriksson].

Large and complex species are often subdivided into structurally or physiologically distinct varieties which are also given names, such as *Puccinia graminis* variety *tritici* (stem rust of wheat), *P. graminis* variety *avenae* (stem rust of oats), and *P. graminis* variety *hordei* (stem rust of barley). In fungi which show physiologic specialization the species or variety is further subdivided into numbered forms or races, as *Puccinia graminis* variety *tritici*, race 56 or the bean anthracnose organism *Colletotrichum Lindemuthianum*, form 3.

B. **The history of pathogenic organisms.** The history of a *disease* (crop injury) and the history of its *pathogen* (fungus, bacterium, etc.) may coincide if the pathogen and disease were discovered at the same time and studied by the same persons. But in many cases the history of the organism and that of the disease are entirely distinct. Thus the history of stem rust, the disease, goes back to epiphytotics in Bible times, while the history of its pathogen, *Puccinia graminis* begins with the discovery and naming of the fungus by Persoon in 1797. Conversely the honey mushroom, *Armillaria mellea*, has been known as a fungus at least since 1821 and its history, as a fungus, dates from that time or earlier, but the history of the root rot disease caused by *A. mellea* only goes back to its pathological study beginning about 1874. And even at the present time the history of a pathogenic organism, as such, and that of the disease it causes are progressing in different directions. That of the pathogen is concerned with its structure, habits, physiology, and classification, while the history of a disease has to do primarily with the effects on the host and on the crop, its epiphytology, and control.

C. **The life-history of a pathogenic organism** is the story of all of the activities through which it passes. Many pathogens spend part of their life cycle as parasites and part as saprophytes.

The stage during which the organism is parasitic is called *pathogenesis*, while its period of saprophytic life is termed *saprogenesis*. The sum of all activities during these two periods constitutes the life history of the pathogen.

1. *Pathogenesis* is the period from the time at which inoculum is first deposited on the host plant until the final reaction of the host, the death of its tissues, and the beginning of a saprophytic existence of the pathogen on the dead remains of the host. Pathogenesis consists of several stages:

a. *Inoculation* is the transfer of *inoculum*, (spores, fragments of mycelium, seeds, eggs, or any other reproductive body) from its source to an *infection court*, any place where infection can occur on the new host. The transport of inoculum from a diseased plant to a healthy one is *dissemination* and is accomplished by an agent of dissemination or *vector*. Dissemination may be either by *continuous spread*, the disease progressively passing from one plant or field to the next, or *discontinuous*, travelling in a long jump from one part of the world to another.

Continuous spread is accomplished by various types of vectors, the leading ones being:

Wind. This is by far the most important vector in the case of spore-borne fungous diseases. While wind is the principal agent of continuous spread as in the case of rusts, leaf spots, mildews, smuts, and numerous other types of fungous diseases, it can also act as an agent of discontinuous spread, as has been shown in the trapping of viable fungous spores from airplanes over the North Polar regions (Charles Lindbergh), and the Pacific Ocean (F. C. Meier). (Cf. Figure 187.)

Wind-driven rain is the most important agent of continuous spread of bacterial diseases, such as bacterial blight of cotton. It has been shown by Faulwetter that the droplets from a splashing raindrop will drift as much as 20 feet in quiet air, and even a light breeze will greatly increase effectiveness of this type of spread.

Water in the form of irrigation, surface runoff, streams, and public water supplies, is often instrumental in the spread of the typically soil-borne disease organisms, such as the root rot and damping-off fungi, and nematodes, and also in the case of bacteria, e.g. those which cause alfalfa wilt.

Insects, and other animals play a large part in the dissemination of virus, bacterial, and fungous diseases, and sometimes are the only natural means by which a disease

Figure 192. Sugar beets on land severely infested with nematodes following one year of barley. This field well illustrates how nematode infestation is spread in the direction of irrigation and cultivation. (*Photo by U. S. Department of Agriculture, Bureau of Plant Industry.*)

may be spread. Examples are the transmission of sugar beet curly top by the sugar beet leafhopper, fire blight of apple and pear by bees, the Dutch elm disease by bark beetles, and mistletoe by birds.

Agricultural machines are an important agency of spread of diseases by movement of contaminated soil on wheels, or by carrying the organisms of disease as on the blades of a mower. For this reason, diseases often spread most rapidly in the direction of cultivation (root-rot diseases; alfalfa wilt; nematode diseases: Fig. 192).

Contact of plants is often necessary in the spread of disease fungi which produce no spores but spread by slow mycelial growth from one plant to the next, as in the case of Texas root rot and *Rhizoctonia* root rot of many plants.

Wind-blown leaves at times may become efficient vectors of continuous spread. Rolfs has shown that cotton leaves carried by a whirlwind can effectively spread bacterial blight over a distance of one half mile or more.

Man himself can be a very efficient vector in his operations of handling plants. In picking beans when the vines are wet, the hands distribute the bacteria of bean blight so effectively that the greater part of the crop may be lost through this practice. Likewise the handling of tobacco or tomato plants in operations of transplanting, pruning, staking, and hand pollinating is often followed by 100 per cent infestation with tobacco mosaic.

Discontinuous spread is largely due to the activities of man, who is responsible for the transport of disease from one part of the country or world to another by shipments of *infested seed* (smuts, ergot, dodder, wheat nematodes, bean blight and mosaic), *or other propagating parts* (viruses and nematodes in potato tubers or flower bulbs; various diseases of nursery stock and cuttings), of *botanical specimens or experimental material* (as in the introduction of the gypsy moth to America), of *cut flowers and plants*, and of disease-infested *agricultural products*, such as cotton lint and binders, or elm tree burls which brought the Dutch elm disease from Italy to America. In recent years the development of modern transportation with the extensive use of the automobile and airplane, has favored the discontinuous spread of disease both by carrying disease organisms for long distances on such vehicles, and by increasing the difficulty of preventing the dissemination of infested plant material by inspection and quarantines.

b. *The incubation period* extends from the moment at which inoculum is deposited in the infection court until the moment of the first observed reaction of the plant to the pathogen. It may be very short, a matter of a few hours in the case of storage rots and some bacterial diseases, or very long, as in the case of wheat bunt, extending from harvest time, when the spores come to rest in the brush or crease of a healthy seed, through the dormant period of storage during the summer, on through the period of infection of the seedling and the development of the wheat plant, until the first symptoms of the bunt disease appear, nearly a year after inoculation took place.

But although symptoms have not yet appeared, the pathogen is passing through stages of activity during the incubation period.

If the inoculum is a spore, germination must occur, and the germ tube or infection hypha must penetrate its way to the interior of the host plant, and establish feeding mycelium. These processes vary greatly with different pathogens and hosts. Host plants are protected by a variety of chemical and mechanical barriers (cuticle, cork, etc.) through which the infection thread must pass. Some pathogens make use of natural openings in penetrating the host, stomata, lenticels, water pores, and glands, others such as the soft-rot bacteria, depend on scratches, insect stings, and other wounds, for entering the host tissues, while the most aggressive parasites force their way in through the uninjured cuticle by mechanical pressure, often aided by enzymes that dissolve away the protective layers of the host. Figure 13 illustrates this method of forceful penetration, the infection thread expanding to form a disk-like sucker or appressorium that attaches the hypha to the host, and through which is forced a needle-like peg that drills its way down through the cuticle, and then broadens out as a feeding hypha.

The processes of germination and penetration are highly dependent upon external factors, especially moisture and temperature, and in some cases the host itself secretes attractive or stimulatory chemicals without which the pathogen would be unable to infect. Some fungous spores will not germinate except in the presence of an extract of host tissues.

c. *The infection stage* is the period during which the host responds, symptoms appear, and the disease develops. It extends from the first response of the host until its final reaction to the pathogen. It may be very short, as in brown rot of peaches, potato late blight, or soft rot of vegetables, in which cases destruction may be complete within a few days, or it may extend for periods up to several years as in the wood diseases of trees. During the infection stage, lesions of disease appear and enlarge, secondary symptoms follow, the pathogen multiplies and begins non-sexual reproduction. This is the active period of infection and if death does not occur, it is usually followed by a decline in activity; the lesions cease to enlarge and the host either recovers or becomes invaded by secondary organisms that further its destruction. The decline in activity may be due to healing processes in the host (as walling off the lesions by cork or periderm), to a change in the environment so that the disease is no longer favored, or to the accumulation of waste by-products of the parasite that ultimately restrict its further development. Under the influence of alternating temperatures or light intensities, periods of high activity may occur intermittently, producing zonate, target-board, or "frog-eye" types of lesions.

In the invasion of new tissues the pathogen may be intercellular, feeding upon materials that are present or released between the cells or in the case of some fungi, such as rusts and powdery mildews, the intercellular mycelium may send absorbing organisms (haustoria) within the living cells as shown in Figure 13. Some pathogens, such as the club-root organism live entirely within the host cells.

Pathogens often excrete powerful enzymes that break down the plant constituents and render them available for nutrition of the pathogen, cellulase which breaks down cellulose, lignase, pectinase, proteinase, and many others. Or potent poisons may diffuse outward from the pathogen, killing cells in advance of its progress, so that the pathogen follows as a scavenger, feeding on the dead and dying cells that have been destroyed by its toxins. This may lead to a response in the plant far in advance of the area occupied by the pathogen.

2. *Saprogenesis* is the period during which the pathogen is no longer associated with the living host. The pathogen may be actively feeding and developing, living a saprophytic existence, largely on the decomposing remains of the host, as in the case of apple scab and numerous other diseases in which the sexual development occurs on the debris of the crop, or it may be largely or entirely dormant in the period of saprogenesis. The pathogen is often dependent on the residue of its natural host for its saprophytic existence, which in part explains the value of rotation in controlling plant diseases. Pathogenesis may be a fixed and more or less necessary part of the life cycle (apple scab, cereal scab) or may be only rare and incidental to a saprophytic existence. Thus, *Rhizopus nigricans*, the black bread mold, is ordinarily a saprophyte, but readily parasitizes sweet potatoes and strawberries in storage. Saprogenesis is lacking in nature in the case of obligate parasites such as rusts, powdery mildews, and viruses, while with other pathogens, such as the smuts, and leaf curl fungi, saprogenesis is wanting in nature but may be experimentally produced on culture media in the laboratory.

Epiphytology

Despite the presence of a pathogen, its efficient dissemination, and a susceptible host, plant diseases rarely "make the headlines" by becoming so disastrous that there is enormous crop loss, suffering, or even famine. But occasionally this occurs and the disease is then said to be *epiphytotic* (epi-phyton = "among plants," corresponding to "epidemic" in human disease or "epizootic" in animal disease). In contrast, diseases such as the wilts of tomato, flax, and watermelon, which are always present in a locality in relatively uniform amount, are called *enphytotic* (cf. endemic, enzootic). A disease is called *sporadic* if it only occurs occasionally and does not involve a large number of individuals, as in the case of root knot in the northern states, where it is relatively unimportant in most years and locations, but occasionally becomes locally prevalent.

Various combinations of circumstances may produce epiphytotics, as is shown in the following examples.

1. Epiphytotics due primarily to weather conditions. *Stem rust of wheat* is normally enphytotic, but occasionally, as in 1878, 1904, 1916, 1935, and to a lesser extent in 1937, it has broken out in epiphytotic proportions, the 1935 outbreak destroying one-fourth of the American crop. The factors that conspire to produce this destructiveness include:

a. A mild winter that permits the rust fungus to over-winter abundantly in the growing wheat of Texas. The milder the winter, the farther north in Texas this will occur.

b. Moderately cool temperatures during the growing season, especially during the period from emergence of the heads to full bloom.

c. Persistent humid, dewy, misty, or foggy weather during this period.

d. Extension of these temperature and moisture conditions over a wide wheat-growing area.

e. A large acreage of susceptible wheat.

f. A period of hot dry weather just before harvest. This aggravates the water-loss due to rust. In addition it shortens the period to maturity. In one way this may be an advantage, as it may reduce loss from lodging; on the other hand, late maturity will sometimes favor a rusted crop by allowing a longer period of photosynthesis.

Bacterial wilt (*Stewart's disease*) of corn becomes epiphytotic regularly when winter temperatures are unusually mild in the regions where susceptible varieties are grown.

Leaf rust of wheat was epiphytotic in 1938, the factors involved resembling those affecting stem rust except that leaf rust is dependent on somewhat cooler temperatures and a longer period of moist weather, extending throughout the growing season up to the heading stage.

2. Epiphytotics due primarily to unnatural culture. Many diseases that are relatively unimportant in the mixed plant associations of nature, become serious when the host is grown in an unnatural manner by the planting of large areas with a single susceptible species of plant.   An example is:

Phacidium blight of conifers.   This is a fungous disease of young trees that spreads directly from plant to plant under the snow. It is native in the maritime provinces of Canada, where it has been unimportant, since in a native forest, young susceptible trees are widely scattered and do not afford extensive contact with one another.   With the growing drain on northern forests for the paper industry, reforestation became necessary, and for this purpose, vast nurseries of coniferous seedlings were established.   Under these unnatural conditions, *Phacidium* blight ran rampant through the nurseries, destroying great quantities of the young trees.   Ultimately the disease has become controlled by an application of lime-sulphur spray before snowfall.

Other diseases which were unimportant until the host was cultivated in huge acreages are the downy mildew or "blue" "mold" and the white rust of spinach in Texas.

3. Epiphytotics due primarily to the introduction of disease in some part of the world where it has not previously existed.

a. *Late blight of Irish potatoes.*   Almost 300 years after the potato had been introduced into Europe, the blight fungus became established in European potato fields.   The native home of the host appears to be the Andes mountains of South America, but there the native potatoes show no material tolerance for the fungus and it is believed that the disease is native to Mexico, where most of the wild potato species are resistant to or immune from blight.   During the centuries of domestication and breeding of the potato in Europe, whatever tolerance of the fungus it may have had disappeared, and when the fungus was introduced, presumably on some solanaceous plant from Mexico, it came into contact with extensive plantings of a highly susceptible host.   The inevitable result was the great epiphytotic of 1843–1845 with famine and migration following in its train.   (See pages 3–5.)

b. *Chestnut blight.*   The American chestnut had never been exposed to its epiphytotic pathogen, when the fungus was brought from the Orient on infected ornamental plants.   In

China, its native home, the chestnut is relatively resistant to the blight fungus, which causes an inconsequential disease. The American chestnut proved highly susceptible and the epiphytotic beginning in 1904 advanced without hindrance until it has practically exterminated the chestnut from its extensive North American range.

c. *Dutch elm disease.*   This also appears to be native in Asia, if one may judge by the resistance of the elms in that part of the world.   It appeared in Europe about 1922 when it soon produced such a destructive epiphytotic on the highly susceptible European elm, that great areas were depleted of this species.   About 1930 or earlier it was brought to America in shipments of elm burls (galls of beautiful grain, used for cabinet making).   From New York it spread out radially into Connecticut, Pennsylvania, and New Jersey, destroying many thousands of trees.   A few cases occurred in Ohio but these were quickly eradicated.   The American elm epiphytotic differs from that of the chestnut blight in that the well-established Bureau of Plant Quarantine was able to initiate an extensive inspection and eradication program at the outset, with the result that this epiphytotic has not swept with unimpeded force through the range of the American elm.

4. The grand cycle of disease.   When a disease is first introduced into a new area it may rapidly increase to epiphytotic propor-

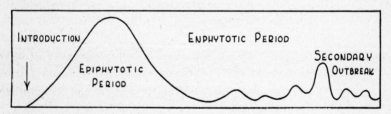

Time in years. The height of the curve indicates destructiveness.

Figure 193.   The grand cycle of disease.   Explanation in the text.

tions.   Unless the host species is completely wiped out, as time goes on, the crest of the epiphytotic is passed and the disease subsides to a moderately low level, and continues to be enphytotic except as this is interrupted now and then by conditions that favor a transient epiphytotic, such as weather, the introduction of a new host, the development of a particularly aggressive strain of the pathogen, or abnormal methods of culture. This sequence of events, diagrammed in Figure 193 constitutes the grand cycle of disease.

The recession of the disease, after the height of the epiphytotic is passed is due to:

a. *Reduction in the population of available host plants.*
b. *The development of resistant populations.* During the epiphytotic, thousands or millions of the most susceptible individuals succumb. A few of those having some natural resistance may survive, and propagate their kind, the more resistant individuals surviving each generation, until the resistance has become ingrained in the species.
Man can speed up this developing resistance in the population:
a'. By painstaking search for resistant survivors, protecting them from loss due to other natural hazards, and aiding in their propagation under conditions that subject them to repeated exposure to the pathogen and thus foster natural selection of the more resistant individuals of each generation.
b'. By introducing into the epiphytotic new genetic types secured through hybridization of resistant species with commercial or native varieties, thus increasing the numbers and types of survivors in the epiphytotic.
c'. By a combination of these two practices, and this is the background of man's greatest successes in combating epiphytotics.
c. *Natural control.* The recession of an epiphytotic may often be due in some measure to increasing difficulty on the part of the pathogen to maintain itself in the presence of antagonistic microorganisms.
a'. *Hyperparasitism.* Some plant pathogens are in turn parasitized by other organisms (*hyperparasitism*). For example, the blister-rust fungus is less destructive in Europe than America, because in Europe there is a hyperparasitic imperfect fungus, *Tuberculina maxima,*

which feeds on the blister-rust spores and destroys them. Similarly, the cereal rust fungi are hyperparasitized by the imperfect fungus *Darluca filum*, an obligate parasite on the pustules. Plant parasitic nematodes are frequently attacked by other, predatory nematodes or by nematode-trapping fungi (see Figure 166). Even pathogenic bacteria are subject to parasitism by the virus, bacteriophage, which has been shown actively to destroy colonies of the bacterial pathogens in crown gall and wilt of corn.

b'. *Antibiosis (competition).* In other cases a pathogen is held in check by its struggle to secure food, grow, and reproduce in the presence of other organisms competing for the same food or space. This is particularly true when a pathogen enters saprogenesis, and finds itself in competition with true saprophytes that may be better adapted to saprophytic life than the pathogen. The abnormal abundance of a pathogen during an epiphytotic cannot long be maintained in the face of natural competition with other organisms, and ultimately these will bring about a reduction in the pathogenic population and thus contribute to the recession of the epiphytotic. In a very limited way, man can sometimes put antibiosis to good use as in the control of Texas root rot by soil amendments of organic fertilizers that encourage the growth of soil saprophytes at the expense of the root rot fungus (Cf. Figures 81 and 82).

5. The origin of plant diseases. The questions are often asked: Why are new plant diseases continually appearing; where are they coming from; why are there so many more diseases than years ago? The principal reasons are:

a. *Wider distribution of old diseases.* The increased introduction of diseases into new localities, where they are viewed as "new diseases," is largely due to the progressive broadening of plant commerce. More facile and varied means of transportation, the use of refrigeration, the demands for exotic and unseasonable fruits, vegetables, and ornamentals consequent on improved standards of living, and the tendency toward larger and larger units of agricultural production and marketing, have all conspired to raise the production of nursery stock, plant foodstuffs, flowers, and seed from local undertakings for satisfying local demands to meet national or even international markets.   As the products have entered new areas their diseases have accompanied them.

b. *Increasing proportion of susceptible hosts in the population.*   The horticulturist, agronomist, and plant breeder are constantly striving to produce new selections or hybrids with more desirable aesthetic or utilitarian qualities.   In selection or breeding for these qualities it is easy to lose other qualities at the same time, among them the resistance to disease characteristic of the ancestral species.   This loss of resistance with improvement along other lines is especially char- acteristic of vegetatively propagated crops that have been in domestication for many centuries, such as the potato, and crops like sorghum in which the better varieties have resulted from extensive synthetic breeding.   With the loss in resist- ance from this cause, there follow the ravages of diseases to which the ancestral species were tolerant or resistant.

c. *Intensification of agriculture.*   As civilization progresses and populations increase, demands for food are greater, and it becomes necessary to produce more on less land.   This leads to intensified agriculture, such as characterizes the market garden areas around cities or the agriculture of European countries.   A disease causing a 5 per cent loss in a field crop with a value of $20.00 per acre ($1.00 loss) might be con- sidered negligible or too small to warrant the expense of control measures.   It might even be cheaper to offset this loss by increasing the acreage by 5 per cent than to go to the expense of controlling it.   With intensified agriculture the value of the crop might be $100.00 and of the loss $5.00 or even much more, since the plants are grown closer together, and well watered, which could materially increase the per- centage of loss.   Under these conditions the disease assumes importance which it did not have previously; it might even be regarded as a "new disease."

d. *Improved recognition of diseases.*   Plants in a field become yellow
or wilt and die.   Thirty years ago this would probably have
been attributed to drought, poor soil, alkali spots, or unfavorable weather.   At that time there were few trained men who
could identify the cause of the trouble; plant pathology was
just coming into being.   Today the yellowed plants are
examined and the trouble is demonstrated due to a virus
disease, root decay, or a vascular infection.   We may call
it a "new disease," but it is new only to science, it may have
been present for hundreds of years but never recognized as a
contagious disease.   In 1939 a field of cotton was found in
which 30 per cent of the plants were dead from *Fusarium* wilt.
The farmers in the community regarded it as a "new disease,"
it had never been called to their attention before, but the
older growers said that these fields had always had "dead
cotton," and they had always regarded the trouble as due to
soil or weather conditions or poor seed.

e. *Authentic new diseases.*   Nearly all so-called "new diseases"
are of the preceding types.   Occasionally but rarely a disease
may not only be new to science but actually new to nature.
This may be due to the production, by hybridization or
mutation, of new physiologic races of pathogens, or strains
with exceptionally high virulence, transforming a benign and
relatively harmless disease into a dangerous one.   Or a
pathogen on a wild host may produce a strain with a wider
host range, capable of passing to a cultivated crop and
producing serious disease.   This would be aided by man's
introduction of new crops in areas where they had not been
previously grown.

6. The prediction of epiphytotics. If it were possible to
predict epiphytotic outbreaks of plant disease in sufficient time to
allow intervention of precautionary measures, enormous losses
might be averted.   Because of the many requirements which must
be met before a disease can become epiphytotic, in particular the
unpredictable weather, there are few diseases in which such predictions are possible.   There are notable exceptions however, particularly in cases in which the majority of antecedant requirements

are regularly met, and where one or two observable antecedant circumstances will turn the balance in favor of epiphytotic outbreaks. As examples we have the cases of:

a. *Bacterial wilt (Stewart's disease) of sweet corn.* The corn-wilt bacteria overwinter chiefly in hibernating adult flea beetles, and whether because the survival of these vectors is in turn dependent on winter temperatures or because of some not yet recognized factor, the appearance of the disease in the northeastern states is correlated with winter temperatures. In 1934, Neil Stevens advanced the hypothesis that wilt only becomes destructive following a winter with a temperature index above 100, and that intermediate conditions follow winters with indexes between 90 and 100, the "winter index" being a simple sum of the mean temperatures for December, January, and February. For six years, experimental forecasts of wilt destructiveness, based on these indexes and issued in time for revision of the planting program, have been closely correlated with the amount of wilt actually experienced in the seasons following the forecasts.

b. *Keeping quality of cranberries.* Stevens also regularly forecast the keeping quality of cranberries grown on Cape Cod from 1928 to 1932. He based his predictions on the weather during the growing season, a cool, late spring plus dry weather in July and August favoring good keeping qualities. The forecasts, which were issued in time to avoid undue loss, proved accurate in all cases except for the late berries of 1929.

c. *Smuts of the blossom-infection type.* In these diseases, such as loose smut of wheat, infection occurs a year before symptoms appear and several months before planting time. The amount of infection depends largely on the amount of inoculum in the field and moderate moisture at blossom time. A study of the field conditions at that time gives a sound basis for predicting loose smut incidence a year in advance, in ample time for the use of the preventive hot water seed treatment.

d. *Apple scab.* Here the primary inoculum consists of ascospores discharged from overwintered leaves. Examination of these leaves in the spring to determine the moment of ascospore discharge coupled with an analysis of existing temperature and moisture conditions, serves as the basis for radio spray warnings in certain apple-growing areas. These warnings result in the most effective spray programs.

REFERENCES

1. Foister, C. E.   The relation of weather to fungous and bacterial diseases.   Bot. Rev. 1: 497–516.   1935.
2. Humphrey, H. B.   Climate and plant diseases.   *In* "Climate and Man."   U. S. Dept. Agr. Yearbook.   1941: 499–502.
3. Jones, L. R.   Essential factors in destructive plant disease development.   Proc. Int. Cong. Pl. Sci., Ithaca: 1284–1298.   1926.
4. Keitt, G. W. et al.   The epidemiology and control of cherry leaf spot.   Wis. Agr. Exp. Sta. Res. Bull. 132.   1937.
5. Leach, J. G.   Insect transmission of plant diseases.   McGraw-Hill Book Co., New York.   1940.
6. Link, G. K. K.   Etiological plant pathology.   Phytopath. 23: 843–862.   1933.
7. Stevens, N. E. and R. B. Stevens.   Recent developments in plant diseases in the United States.   Bot. Rev. 7: 714–736.   1941.
8. Stevens, N. E. and J. I. Wood.   Recent fluctuations in plant diseases in the United States.   Bot. Rev. 3: 277–306.   1937.

Chapter 18

PRINCIPLES AND PROCEDURES IN THE CONTROL OF PLANT DISEASES; CONTROL OF PLANT DISEASES BY REGULATION

In attempting to control a plant disease, the object is to prevent economic loss. It is often neither desirable nor possible to exterminate the pathogen, the function of control being to reduce the losses to a low level at the least expense. *To be most desirable and effective the use of control practices should be guided by these principles:*

1. Control practices are desirable only when the cost of control will be materially less than the loss from disease.
2. Control measures must not be too complicated, difficult, dangerous, or unpleasant for use by the average grower, else they will not be adopted for farm use (cf. the farm use of concentrated sulphuric acid in cotton seed delinting).
3. Control practices must be worked out as individual problems in each location, and the best control methods will differ from one farm or area to another, according to weather conditions, peculiarities of the site, type and condition of the crop, methods of culture, and value of the crop.
4. Wherever possible the program should include control of several diseases or diseases and insects in one operation. A control program should be worked out considering all kinds of loss.
5. Where control practices are opposed to other desirable practices, a compromise program should be worked out which will give the greatest return, all things considered. (cf. the problem of burning crop debris to destroy pathogenic organisms *versus* the fertilizer value of this organic material.)
6. Control should have a definite purpose Spraying, dusting, or any other control practice without a concrete purpose is wasteful and may even be harmful to the crop.

Control procedures.   When a plant disease threatens a crop, the following procedures may be followed:

1. *Excluding the disease by regulation* through the use of embargoes or quarantines enforced by an inspection service empowered to disinfest, eradicate, or condemn diseased plants or plant materials to prevent them from becoming sources of infection in disease-free areas.
2. *The development and use of disease-resistant crop varieties.*
3. *Cultural practices that enable plants to escape or resist disease*, the term being used in its broadest sense to include the use of uninfested or disinfested seed and soil, desirable methods of caring for the crop, the removal of undesirable plants, and the protection of the crop with sprays and dusts.
4. *Abandonment of the crop* may be the only recourse if the disease is serious and all other methods fail.   This is a regular procedure in banana culture once the Panama disease (*Fusarium* wilt) becomes prevalent.   It was the fate of watermelon and flax culture in North America in the days before the development of varieties resistant to the wilt diseases attacking these crops.

Of the control methods, chemical treatments have hitherto been looked upon as most important.   Actually they are most costly and often least satisfactory, while the other cultural methods and the use of disease-resistant varieties afford the best and least expensive control in the long run.

Control of Plant Diseases by Regulation

In nature, plants are in equilibrium with pathogens and insects; through centuries of exposure the more susceptible individuals have succumbed, and the surviving species is usually highly tolerant of its pests.   Man has upset this equilibrium by introducing diseases to new localities and producing new, but unfortunately more susceptible types of crops.   The consequence has been disastrous plagues of disease and insects.   Although the damage had been done, in the case of the chestnut blight, the irreparable loss from that introduced disease was a strong element leading to the passing in 1912 of the Federal Plant Quarantine Act, at that time directed at the dangers of pine blister rust, potato wart, and the Mediterranean fruit fly. Quarantines for protection against other diseases and insects soon followed, until today there are 20 foreign and 18 domestic federal plant quarantines or restrictive orders in force. Meanwhile the individual States were becoming more active in promulgating quarantines restricting the movement of diseased or infested plant materials from one state to another, so that by 1936 there were 219 state quarantines directed at 29 insect pests and 23 plant diseases.

A. **The biological aspects of quarantines.** For a quarantine to be effective it must be intelligently devised and adequately enforced. Intelligent legal control requires knowledge of:

1. *The nature of the pest or disease*, its life history, and particularly its means of dispersal. Is it spore borne? How resistant are the spores to cold, heat, drying, and ageing? Is it wind- or insect-borne or transmitted mainly by man? Is it spread with seed or through vegetative reproduction or in agricultural products, or only in living plants? Is it restricted to one or few cultivated hosts or is it widespread on native plants?

2. *The present distribution of the pest or disease.* Is it already established in the area to be protected?

3. *The probability that the pest or disease will be introduced in the absence of regulations.* Only where a pest or disease is carried by man in plant materials is there any ground for attempted control by regulation. For example, no useful end would be served by restricting the movement of seed from areas of Texas root rot infestation, because the disease is not carried by this means.

4. *The probability that the pest or disease will become established and important if introduced.* Many cases might be cited of diseases which remain within a limited area despite countless chance introductions into new areas. The distribution of Texas root rot, for example, has undergone no essential change for 50 years or more, yet infested plants and soil have doubtless been transported to new areas many times. Even when root rot infested soil is deliber-

ately transplanted for experimental purposes under the most favorable circumstances, it is difficult or impossible to establish the disease in the new location.   If there exists satisfactory evidence that the disease could not establish itself in a new area, because of unsuitable environmental or other causes, a quarantine against the disease imposes needless barriers to trade, is wasteful in its enforcement, and accomplishes no useful end.

5. *The probability that the quarantine will effectively prevent or delay the introduction of the pest or disease into protected areas.* Where man is the principal agent of dispersal and the activities of man can be regulated, a quarantine has promise of proving effective. But many pests and diseases are spread by other agencies, particularly wind. In such cases, only if the infested and protected areas happen to be separated by natural, geographical barriers such as mountains, oceans, and deserts, is a quarantine likely to succeed. "In districts with similar conditions and separated neither by natural barriers nor great distance, quarantine methods for the exclusion of pests and plant diseases are hopeless and without permanent value except as an adjunct to eradication . . . " (Smith et al.).

While the need for a complete knowledge of the biological basis for a quarantine is obvious, there are cases in which it would be disastrous to wait until this knowledge is available before undertaking the quarantine.   An example is the bacterial ring rot of potatoes which first began to attract attention about 1937, and within a year or two was recognized as a very serious disease problem in this crop. Rejections of affected stock, in effect quarantines of the strictest sort, were at once put into operation.   Little was known of the nature of the disease, but the danger was considered so great that a temporary quarantine appeared to be justified as an emergency measure.   Any quarantine, and above all an emergency quarantine of this sort, should be reconsidered periodically and modified as the pathological or economic picture changes, or rescinded entirely once the danger or the cause for the quarantine no longer exists.

B. The economic aspects of quarantines.   Any quarantine is a restriction of trade.   Even if it is intelligently conceived and effectively enforced, so that needed pest control is accomplished, there are bound to be individual growers and buyers of produce who will suffer economic loss from such a quarantine.   If, as is sometimes the case, a quarantine is enacted primarily as a trade barrier for the purpose of protecting a local industry, or as a retaliatory act of one state or country against another, disguised as a pest-control measure, except for the protected minority, the gross economic loss may be even greater, besides arousing prejudice against legitimate disease regulation.

In any legitimate quarantine, part of the gain resulting from pest control is offset by the lost markets of the growers within the quarantined area and the expense of enforcing the quarantine.   For the net result to be beneficial to the people as a whole, the gain from such means of pest control must be an important one, i.e. the pest must be a serious menace to crops, and the loss in markets and cost of enforcement must not be so great as to overbalance the gains. This clearly means that quarantines must frequently represent compromises with some sacrifice of the efficiency of the quarantine to avoid undue hardship on the grower and the consumer.

The more important items on the balance sheet of a quarantine measure are given in Table 12.

TABLE 12.—BALANCE SHEET OF QUARANTINES

Debit	Credit
Cost of enforcement.	Freedom from losses due to the depredations of the pest (which may be partly offset by higher prices for the reduced crop if no quarantine is employed).
Loss of markets.	
Condemnation and abandonment of crops (which may be partly offset by government reimbursement in some cases).	
Waste in adjustment to new types of agriculture.	Freedom from the cost of direct control measures against the pest.
Losses from retaliatory measures.	Trade advantage of growers outside the quarantined area.

Each of these items is important in itself and may have far-reaching secondary effects.   It goes without saying that the economic repercussions of a quarantine are so forceful that no permanent quarantine should be enacted until a thorough analysis, both biological and economic, by competent and unprejudiced authorities, establishes the basis for quarantine laws that will accomplish the desired purpose with the least possible hardship to growers and consumers.

C. **The mechanism of plant quarantines.** If a quarantine law is worth having, it is worth enforcing, and quarantines which cannot be adequately and effectively enforced should never be enacted. The method of enforcement varies with the disease problem and the methods of trade.

1. *Embargoes.* An embargo prohibits any movement of susceptible or affected plant materials from a quarantined area into protected areas. Examples are the present United States embargo against elm trees or wood from Europe on account of the Dutch elm disease, and that against Australian wheat on account of the danger of introducing flag smut.

Figure 194. The function of nursery inspection in providing growers with healthy nursery stock. Left, a state inspector examines a planting with the owner, pointing out the stock that is sound and suitable for sale, and that which should be culled. Right, a pile of cull apple trees. Conscientious and careful culling, aided by state inspection, is a regular part of good nursery practice. (*Courtesy of J. Reese Dews, Okla. State Nursery Inspector.*)

2. *Inspection at the point of destination.* Many plant propagating materials entering the United States are regularly inspected at the customs ports, and allowed entry only after having been declared free of injurious insects and diseases.

3. *Inspection and certification at the point of origin.* Certain plant propagation materials from abroad such as bulbs, may

enter the United States if a permit is secured certifying that the materials were inspected in the shipping country and found free of injurious insects or diseases. Inspection and certification at the point of origin is the basis of interstate shipments of certified seed and nursery stock and to be fully effective should include inspection of the seed crop while growing (Fig. 194).

4. *Disinfestation* of entering plant materials may be required either at the point of origin or at the port of entry. This applies, for example, to citrus seeds from abroad.

5. *Special permits.* Plants and plant products for scientific and breeding work, botanical specimens, and exhibit plant material may be brought into the United States under special permit, even though a quarantine prevents commercial shipments of the product.

6. *Unrestricted shipment.* Where no important disease pest is involved, plant materials of importance in world trade may be shipped from one country to another without disinfestation, or other restrictions, although they are subject to occasional inspection.

These regulations apply to international shipments, and many similar regulations govern the shipment of plant products from one state to another, under either state or federal law.

D. **Present day quarantines.** The following are among the more important quarantines at present in effect:

1. *Federal quarantines affecting international trade.*
   a. *Embargoes or special quarantines govern the importation of:* pines and gooseberries from all countries (blister rust), Irish potatoes from all countries but Canada (potato wart), cotton seed from all countries, sugar cane, alligator pears, citrus nursery stock, raw corn and related grains, sweet potatoes and yams, banana plants, bamboo propagation materials, seed rice, wheat from many countries, raw sorghums, and elm materials from Europe.
   b. *Entry under permit with inspection,* and, as provided, disinfestation, governs the entry of flower bulbs, propa-

gating materials of fruit and nut crops, tree seeds, rose propagating materials, and seeds of woody and perennial ornamentals.

2. *Federal quarantines affecting interstate trade* have to do with diseases or insects that are established in some part of the United States but as yet have not spread to other parts.

Figure 195.   Application of common salt in eradicating barberry, alternate host of the stem rust.   Ten pounds is sufficient to kill an average sized bush with a diameter of about 12 inches at the base.   (*Courtesy of the Colorado Agr. Exp. Sta.*)

The principal insects concerned are the *gypsy and brown tail moths* in New England, the *Japanese beetle* in the eastern states, and the *Mediterranean fruit fly* in Florida.   The diseases involved are *white pine blister rust* (no interstate movement of 5-needle pines or currants and gooseberries), *stem rust* (no movement of susceptible barberry bushes into the protected northern middle-west section), the *Dutch elm disease* (no movement of elm trees or wood out of the infested area around New Jersey), and the *Woodgate rust* (no movement of susceptible pines from New York State). The quarantines are augmented by extensive eradication programs in the cases of stem rust, blister rust, and the Dutch elm disease (Fig. 195).

3. *State-imposed quarantines affecting interstate trade.* Quarantines of the state departments of agriculture are aimed at excluding from a state those insects and diseases that occur in other states. The state quarantine laws vary so widely from one state to another that a serious problem faces the shipper who deals in many states. Large seed concerns and nurserymen sometimes must maintain a special organization to handle the tagging and permits required for meeting all of the various state quarantine regulations. The problem of state quarantines is further complicated by the common practice of retaliatory quarantines and fees on the principle that "if you tax us, we'll tax you, and if you quarantine our crops, we'll quarantine yours." Attempts are being made to encourage the states to adopt more uniform quarantine laws based on strictly biological principles.

While it is beyond the scope of this book to discuss in detail the various state quarantines, these may be summarized as follows:

The number of state quarantines varies greatly. The states having some protection from the Rocky Mountains have the greatest numbers: Oregon, 20; California, 18; Washington, 14; Idaho, 14; and Arizona, 12. This may be justified on the grounds that these states are free from a number of diseases and pests occurring east of the mountains, while mountains afford a natural barrier to aid in disease control by regulation. Less understandable are the 22 quarantines of Texas or the 12 of Mississippi, states that have no such natural advantage. Other states have 10 quarantines or less, with the fewest in the North Atlantic States.

In order of decreasing numbers of quarantines, the following are the leading plant diseases, and pests subject to state quarantines: European corn borer with 32 state quarantines; alfalfa weevil, 25; citrus diseases (canker and brown rot) and pests, 19; potato diseases and pests, 18; peach virus diseases, 17; sweet potato diseases (stem rot, black rot, etc.) and pests, 15; and raspberry virus diseases, 11.   Other plant diseases which are subjects of quarantines in 5 or fewer states are: chestnut blight, strawberry yellows, cotton wilt and anthracnose, eastern filbert blight, Texas root rot, downy mildew of hops, apple and pear scab, azalea disease, crown gall of bramble fruits, cranberry false blossom, pink root of onion, and root knot.

That some of these state quarantines are useless or in sore need of revising is seen in the following two cases; many others might be cited.   One Corn Belt state has a quarantine against chestnut blight in spite of the overwhelming evidence that no quarantine is effective against this disease, and the fact that this state is almost outside the range of the American chestnut, i.e. has very little chestnut to protect in any case.   Three of the Cotton Belt states regulate the introduction of cotton seed from other states by quarantine, for fear of introducing wilt and anthracnose.   Both diseases are already thoroughly established in all three of the "protected" states, and one of them, wilt, is rarely if ever disseminated by cotton seed.

State certified seed.   Many of the states maintain Crop Improvement Associations, or other similar agencies delegated to oversee the production of disease-free certified seed of many crops.   While this may not be directly governed by state law and may have no disciplinary power beyond allowing or disallowing certification, its effect is similar to that of other regulatory measures in aiding to keep disease-infested seed out of commerce.   Other states recognize this, and certified seed is exempt from some of the restrictions imposed by law on ordinary seed.

E. The efficacy of quarantines.   Authorities disagree as to the value of quarantines.   On the one hand there are those who have watched the ceaseless spread of chestnut blight, the gypsy moth, the boll weevil, the Japanese beetle, and stem-rust, despite costly quarantines enacted to check this spread.   The veteran pathologist, H. H. Whetzel expresses this school of thought in saying:

"No less than sixty distinct quarantines have been promulgated to date, and great sums of money have been expended in their attempted enforcement.   The net result of the program in protecting us from diseases and pests is negligible so far at least as definite evidence to the contrary is available.   It has, however, acted as an all but absolute tariff wall to exclude many plants and plant products heretofore imported at prices many times less than we must pay for home grown products of the same kind and often of inferior quality and more affected with diseases of various kinds.   The narcissus bulb situation may be cited as a glaring example of one of the many cases in point."

There is some reason to feel disappointed in the results of quarantines in some cases at least.   But there are also well authenticated instances in which significant and important pest control has resulted from quarantines.   The notorious wart disease of potatoes was stamped out of Sweden and Canada and kept under control in Pennsylvania by means of vigorous and prompt quarantines.   With the Dutch Elm disease in the East, and peach mosaic in Colorado, combined quarantines and eradication have been followed by the finding of smaller and smaller numbers of diseased trees each year after the program got under way.   Citrus canker, a bacterial disease that was discovered in 1915, seriously endangered Florida citrus growing.   Combined Federal, state, and private efforts in a $2,500,000 eradication campaign were successful in stamping it out. Other quarantines have not prevented the spread of plant pests, but have slowed down the spread and this has been a benefit in giving growers in the path of the spread time to readjust their systems of agriculture without serious losses.

The truth is probably intermediate between the more extreme views of the attackers and the defenders of quarantines.   Some quarantines have been costly and useless, others have been abused and used as purely economic measures, but in numerous cases where regulatory laws have been skillfully and intelligently devised and adequately enforced, it appears that the protection against plant pests has well repaid the cost and effort expended.

REFERENCES

1. Anon.   List of current quarantines and other restrictive orders and miscellaneous regulations.   U. S. Dept. Agr., Bur. Ent. & Pl. Quar., Serv. and Regul. Announcements 128: 144–150. 1936. (See also current numbers of these announcements, a file of which will be available in all agricultural libraries.)
2. Anon.   Nursery stock, plant, and seed quarantine.   U. S. Dept. Agr., Bur. Ent. & Pl. Quar.   Notice of Quarantine 37.   Reprinted 1936.
3. Buchholz, A. B. and P. M. Eastman.   The inspection, certification, and transportation of nursery stock in the United States, New York State, other States and Canada. N. Y. Dept. Agr. & Markets Cir. 569.   1938.
4. Liming, O. N. et al.   Some aspects of the plant disease eradication and control work of the Bureau of Entomology and Plant Quarantine.   Pl. Dis. Rep. Supp. 99. 1937.
5. Smith, H. S. et al.   The efficacy and economic effects of plant quarantines in California.   Cal. Agr. Exp. Sta. Bull. 553.   1933.   (Extensive bibliography on quarantines.)
You should also examine copies of the quarantine and certification regulations of your own and neighboring states, usually available from the State Board of Agriculture, Agricultural College, or State Agricultural Experiment Station.

Chapter 19

CONTROL OF PLANT DISEASE
BY INDUCING RESISTANCE

I. THE ECONOMIC SIGNIFICANCE OF THE DEVELOPMENT OF DISEASE RESISTANT CROP VARIETIES.

The pioneer in breeding plants for disease resistance, W. A. Orton, has pointed out: "Nature has been breeding disease-resistant plants since the world began." When a population of plants is exposed to the ravages of a killing pathogen, natural selection for disease resistance begins to operate. The more susceptible genotypes are destroyed. Only those individuals that possess some degree of resistance survive and reproduce, transmitting their semi-resistance to their progeny. These in turn are again exposed to the disease which again culls out the most susceptible types, and thus in each succeeding generation the level of resistance is raised until relatively non-destructive equilibrium between host and pathogen is reached.

In nature this is a slow and gradual process. Plant breeders and pathologists can greatly accelerate the process by selecting, caring for, and propagating the more resistant individuals of a large population, by hybridizing plants and producing a greater variety of genotypes on which natural or human selection can operate, and by exposing the plant populations to such extreme disease attack that the great bulk of non-resistant individuals are soon destroyed.

The development of disease resistance in plants extends back only to about 1900, but in these 40 years great advances have been made. Coon's estimates of 1937 show that now disease-resistant varieties of 17 farm crops are adding between 60 and 70 million dollars a year to the American farm income, that with a number of crops the resistant varieties are yielding a 25 or 50 per cent benefit to the grower, that more than half the acreage of a number of crops is planted with resistant varieties, and that in certain crops, notably flax, sugar cane, and asparagus, practically the entire national acreage is planted with disease-resistant varieties. Some crops such as watermelons, cantaloupes, and flax could not be successfully grown today were it not for varieties resistant against their leading diseases. Few undertakings in science or industry have paid such huge dividends in comparison to the original cost.

Figure 196. The breeding of cabbage for resistance to *Fusarium* wilt ("yellows") is a notable example of achievement. In this experimental planting the center row is of a yellows-susceptible variety. The rows to left and right of it, and several other rows at the right are of resistant varieties. (*Courtesy of O. A. Reinking, N. Y. Agr. Exp. Sta.*)

The only cost of disease control through varietal resistance is the original cost of developing the varieties, and even though resistant varieties must be replaced by new ones from time to time, this is a decided advantage over the more costly practices of disease control by quarantines or by physical or chemical treatments. The economy, the labor saving, the ease of widespread adoption, the absence of risk through errors, are the reasons why resistant varieties represent the best of all forms of disease control.

II. SOME BASIC CONCEPTS OF PLANT IMMUNOLOGY.

The committee on technical words of the American Phytopathological Society (Phytopath. 30 (1940): 363–365) ascribe essentially the following meanings to terms used in discussing disease resistance in plants:

Immunity is freedom from disease because the qualities necessary for development of the pathogen are lacking in the plant. Immunity may be *natural* (or congenital) due to qualities inherent in the plant, or *acquired* during the life of the plant as a result of exposure to a non-fatal attack by a pathogen.

Resistance is the ability of a plant to withstand, lessen, or overcome the attack of a pathogen.

Susceptibility, the opposite of immunity and resistance, includes the presence of qualities that permit the development of the pathogen, and the inability on the part of the plant to overcome or withstand the injurious effects of the pathogen.

Immunity is absolute, resistance and susceptibility are relative, that is, a plant is immune or not immune from a pathogen, but it may be more or less susceptible or resistant; so, for example, we may say "slightly susceptible," "moderately resistant," extremely susceptible," but not "moderately immune" or "highly immune."

Escape or *klendusity* is the ability of a susceptible plant to avoid infection because it possesses some quality (such as earliness) that prevents successful inoculation. It must be clearly distinguished from resistance.

Tolerance is the ability of a plant to endure the invasion of a pathogen without much symptom expression or damage.

Practical resistance is a degree of resistance great enough so that no serious economic loss results, although considerable invasion by the pathogen may be sustained. Kawvale wheat, for example, is resistant to leaf rust for practical purposes, in that little loss results from the rust, although plants may become heavily rusted as they approach maturity.

Hypersensitiveness is such a violent reaction of a plant to an obligate parasite that the invaded tissues are quickly killed, which prevents further spread of infection. In essence it is extreme susceptibility, but its practical effect, so far as crop loss is concerned, amounts to extreme resistance.

The various degrees of susceptibility and resistance are seen if a number of wheat varieties varying in their susceptibility are inoculated with leaf rust. Five degrees of reaction are distinguished:

"0". No symptoms, indicating a very high degree of resistance. The plant is not immune, for the fungus initiates an infection, which, however, does not develop beyond an early stage.

"1". A small necrotic spot marks the site of infection.   As the cells are destroyed, the fungus cannot develop beyond this point, and for practical purposes the plant is highly resistant.   No spores are produced.

"2". Infection develops to the point where small uredinial pustules are produced, surrounded by bright yellow rings, indicating a considerable degree of resistance on the part of the host.

"3". Large, productive uredinial pustules are produced but a pale yellow halo around the pustule indicates slight resistance in the host.

"4". Large, productive uredinial pustules with little or no chlorosis surrounding them, indicating a high degree of susceptibility.

For practical purposes types 0, 1, and 2 are classed as resistant reactions, types 3 and 4 as susceptible, since in the first three types there is little injury to the plant and little opportunity for the rust to multiply.

The different degrees of susceptibility displayed by plants must not be regarded as fixed and absolute. They are profoundly modified by the environment. In the case of leaf rust again, the reactions described are best expressed at temperatures near 65°F. If the plants are inoculated at 65°F., incubated for one day at that temperature, and then incubated at a high temperature, even the most susceptible plants becomes so highly resistant that no symptoms appear; the infections lie latent, until the plants are brought back to cooler temperatures, after which normal susceptibility is displayed.

The observed degree of susceptibility in any case is a product of many interacting factors of which the inherent susceptibility of the plant is only one. The degree of virulence of the pathogen, the age and condition of the plant, and the environment with its many effects on both host and pathogen, all must be suitable before susceptibility can be expressed. Infection has been compared with the operation of a complicated lock: every tooth and tumbler of the lock must be in its proper alignment before the lock will open, and as the failure of a single correspondence between lock and key will entirely prevent the act of unlocking, just so the failure of any of the many factors required for disease expression will entirely inhibit the infection.

It follows that susceptibility of a plant to a pathogen is a rare phenomenon in nature. An apple tree is bombarded with bacteria and spores of countless species of fungi, spores of corn smut, of alfalfa rust, of potato late blight, of wood decay fungi, molds, and mildews. Not one spore in a thousand may be of a species of pathogen to which the tree is susceptible, and even in the rare case in which the spore is constitutionally capable of attacking the tree, it must fall in a suitable infection court, at a suitable time of year, and under suitable environmental conditions For every spore that accomplishes infection there are millions that fail to do so, either because the conditions for infection are not fulfilled or because every plant is immune or resistant to the vast majority of the pathogens with which the air is laden. Resistance or immunity is the law of nature, susceptibility the rare exception. Why is it that the alfalfa plant is susceptible to only one species of rust fungus? What is there about the plant which prevents the attack of any other of a thousand species or rusts? In a word, what is the mechanism or basis of resistance and immunity in plants?

III. THE NATURE OF DISEASE RESISTANCE AND IMMUNITY.

The armament of a plant against its enemy pathogens can be compared with that of a modern army. It includes mechanical defenses, each plant being a fortress enclosed within teguments of tough and chemically resistant cutin, lignin, cork, and cellulose, often bristling with spines or hairs, or coated with an impervious and repellant bloom of wax. The armament of the plant also provides chemical weapons of defense and offense, its inner economy may not include foodstuffs that are needed by the pathogen, or may include acids, alkaloids, tannins, and other substances that are toxic to the pathogen. Again, as in modern warfare, the plant may elude the pathogen to which it is susceptible by developing or functioning in such a way that susceptible and vulnerable infection courts are not available at the time the pathogen is active.

A. Mechanical defenses:

1. *Epidermis and cuticle* represent the first-line mechanical defenses of plants. These vary in structure, and in some cases this serves as a mechanism of protection. Barberry species vary, for example, in their reaction to stem rust, some being susceptible, others resistant. The resistant varieties are found to have a thicker epidermis than the susceptible ones.
2. *Stomata* differ in size, number, and form in different plants, and this influences infection by pathogens that enter through the stomata. They are unusually small in Kanred wheat, and this is advanced as a part of the reason for Kanred's rust resistance.
3. *Hairiness* of leaves or fruits is held to have some protective value.
4. *Waxy coating* of stems in certain varieties of raspberries is correlated with their resistance to stem canker.

B. Chemical defenses:
Little is known of the chemical defenses of plants; a rich and fascinating field of discovery lies ahead. We can envision the complexity of the situation by considering the rust fungi. Their need of a delicately adjusted substrate for development is shown in the fact that they are obligate parasites, and must have living cells from which to obtain their nourishment. No one of the thousands of non-living media that have been tried will support their growth. And not just any living cell will suffice. All of the rusts are distinguished by their narrow host ranges, attacking only one or two species of all they encounter in nature, or even developing on only a few varieties of a single species, or paradoxically, developing only on two widely different species of plants, as the barberry and wheat, or the pine tree and goldenrod. What is there lacking in all other kinds of plants, that is present only in the pine and the goldenrod, or what combination of defenses protects all species of plants from this rust save only the wholly unrelated pine tree and golden rod?

The physiologic specialization of the rust fungi gives further testimony of the delicate chemical adjustment between host and pathogen. There are more than 150 races of the variety of stem rust that affects wheat. These races are indistinguishable in appearance but each has its own peculiar conditions for life, different from those of the other races, since each race finds itself able to develop on a group of wheat varieties different from the wheats that will support any of the other races. What is there about Ceres wheat that defends it against most of the common races of stem rust but permits race 56 to invade it? It is not mechanical defense, for the infection thread of any rust race enters resistant and susceptible wheats alike, develops a small mycelium and begins to draw nourishment from the wheat cells. But at this point the resistance of the resistant wheat expresses itself; the mycelium develops no farther, and the rust dies.

Whatever these factors of resistance may be, they obviously relate to a complex chemical relationship between host cells and those of the pathogen, a chemical relationship so specific that it can occur not oftener than once in a thousand combinations of suscept species and rust species.

It is easy to see why the subject of chemical defense in plants is still in its infancy. Of the few cases in which the details of the chemistry of resistance are known, Walker's experiments with the onion smudge fungus stand out as noteworthy.

J. C. Walker of Wisconsin, first observed that the smudge fungus, *Colletotrichum circinans*, normally attacks only white onions, not those with red or yellow papery scales. But if he removed the colored scales the colored onions then became susceptible to smudge. Acting on the assumption that the red or yellow pigments of the scales were in some way associated with the resistance of the colored onions, he extracted the pigments with water and found that the spores of the fungus would not germinate normally, and that the fungus would not grow in extracts of the pigments, although it developed normally in similar extracts of white-scaled onions. The extracts of red and yellow pigments were analyzed by Link and Angell and the toxic substances found to be protocatechuic acid and catechol. These substances were also found to protect the colored onions from certain other diseases.

Brown and his students in England have been intensively studying the chemistry of disease resistance and have concluded that in the case of potato tubers attacked by certain fungi, susceptibility depends largely on the chemical action of the tuber in permitting the fungus to produce a type of pectinase with specific ability to digest the potato cell walls.

In other cases resistance has been ascribed to unsuitable food supplies or to inhibiting acids, oils, esters, and tannins in the host tissues, but the evidence in these cases is very limited.

C. Functional defenses. Plants frequently avoid disease not by virtue of any defensive structure or product, but because they grow or are grown in such a way as to escape attack, even though quite susceptible. Early-maturing varieties are commonly used to avoid late-season diseases, such as early wheats which are not as severely attacked by rust as midseason and late varieties, or early cowpeas which avoid wilt and rootknot. This is not true resistance, and if such early varieties are made to mature later, as by late planting, they are usually badly attacked. Other forms of functional defenses include the habit of some plants of opening their stomata for only short periods of the day, or the development of an upright, well-ventilated plant body that avoids pockets of moist air in which pathogens might rapidly develop (correlated with gray-mold resistance in lettuce).

Another use of the principle of escape is seen in the practice of planting at excessive rates, on the assumption that even with a high mortality in the crop enough plants will survive to yield a profitable return. This has long been a standard practice in cotton, an extravagant planting rate being used to avoid losses from seedling blight, and in the culture of canning tomatoes in curly-top areas it has been found that setting two plants per hill in most cases allows one to escape even though the other is destroyed by the curly-top virus.

Still another related phenomenon is seen in the escape of plants from diseases carried exclusively by insects in those varieties that are repellant to the insect vectors. The plants may be fully susceptible but are not infected in nature since the vectors avoid them. A case in point concerns the "resistance" against mosaic of the raspberry variety "Lloyd George."

It is important to distinguish between true disease resistance and disease-escaping (klendusity), for a disease-escaping or klendusic plant may be destructively attacked by disease when grown under conditions that do not allow the escape function to operate.

D. Hypersensitivity refers to the reaction of plants against obligate parasites in which the first cells attacked soon die, thus cutting off the pathogen from access to living cells and preventing its further development. It is best seen in the type "1" reaction of plants toward rusts. A rust infection represents a delicately balanced equilibrium between pathogen and host in which the success of the infection depends on the host's having enough susceptibility to allow the fungus to nourish itself and reproduce, but not too much susceptibility, else the cells will die at once and with them the fungus. It is important to distinguish hypersensitivity and true resistance in breeding for disease resistance, since a cross between a resistant parent and a hypersensitive parent (both appearing resistant, although one is in reality excessively susceptible) might produce extremely susceptible offspring.

E. Acquired immunity. Much of modern-day medicine is based on acquired immunity of animals. A patient recovers from scarlet fever; his blood contains antibodies that destroy the pathogen; he has acquired an immunity from scarlet fever such that he will not again take the disease, and that his blood serum may be used to prevent or cure scarlet fever in other patients. Once a child is inoculated or vaccinated with the virus of cowpox, a mild form of smallpox, he suffers a mild disease, and as a consequence of this he acquires immunity from the more virulent smallpox. Do plants have the same ability as animals to recover from one attack of disease and thereby acquire an immunity against subsequent attacks of the same disease? And can we make use of this in plant disease control?

Much thought has been given to these questions, but as yet there are few clear-cut instances of acquired immunity in plants. The best evidence available concerns the virus diseases of plants as brought out in the case of tobacco ringspot.

Ringspot is a virus disease that produces severe necrosis of the leaves of young tobacco plants. If a diseased plant is protected and allowed to continue growth, the severe phase of the disease passes, the new leaves produced show less and less necrosis, until finally leaves are produced that are entirely normal in appearance.

If these leaves are again inoculated with ringspot virus, no further disease will develop; the plant has acquired immunity from ringspot (Fig. 145).   Cuttings may be taken from the recovered parts of such plants and from these cuttings new plants may be produced. These appear entirely normal and they are immune, as they cannot again be made to show symptoms by inoculation of the virus. They still contain the virus; if juice from a normal-appearing "recovered" plant is inoculated into a normal plant, the latter will come down with typical ringspot.   These recovered plants are like the notorious "Typhoid Mary," who recovered from typhoid fever, developed immunity thereby, yet continued for many years to pass on the disease to those with whom she came in contact.   Moreover, as in animal medicine, the immunity is specific.   The recovered ringspot plant is immune from ringspot but not from mosaic or any other disease, just as the patient who has recovered or been vaccinated against smallpox is immune from that disease but not from any other type of human disease.

Plants, then, do in some cases recover from plant disease and display specific acquired immunity as a consequence.   The next question concerns the uses to which this knowledge can be put.

Acquired immunity in plants has proven a useful tool in the difficult field of classifying the viruses.   Many viruses show variation and occur as distinct strains or races each strain producing distinct symptoms on test plants.   A hundred or more such strains have been detected in tobacco mosaic alone.   It is important to know which viruses are strains of the same type virus and which are entirely distinct viruses, in connection with quarantine laws for example.   The recovered plant is immune from the various strains of the same type of virus but not from distinct but similar appearing viruses, and so the immunity test has come to be a valuable aid in determining the identity of viruses.   By means of this test, for example, it has been shown that celery mosaic and lily mosaic are both strains of cucumber mosaic, and that peach yellows and little peach viruses are strains of the same virus.

So far little has been done in using acquired immunity for the practical control of plant diseases, although some progress has been made along this line on potato viruses in England.   The greatest possibilities concern plants that are vegetatively propagated, since in such plants a single "vaccinating" inoculation will be carried on to all vegetative progeny, or in plants that are extensively handled in culture, such as tobacco or tomato, in which the "vaccinating" inoculation of mechanically transmissible viruses could be automatically performed by having the operator keep his hands wet with attenuated virus juice during transplanting or some other handling operation.

F. Complexity of the factors that determine resistance.   As a general rule, the defense mechanism of a plant, as that of an army, does not depend on any one structure, product, or function, but is a combination of many types of armaments.   For a plant to be susceptible to a pathogen a long list of requirements must be fulfilled. In the average case of resistance, several of these requirements may be lacking.   This is the reason for the difficulty in determining the exact nature of resistance in given cases, yet we must learn what we can of the nature of resistance to give us guidance in using this resistance in breeding for disease control.

IV. THE CONTROL OF PLANT DISEASES THROUGH THE USE OF RESISTANT VARIETIES.

A. The need for this type of disease control.   It has been pointed out that control by resistant varieties is, in the long run the best and cheapest method of disease control.   More than this, there are many diseases that can be controlled in no other way, in particular those caused by persistent soil-dwelling fungi.   Such diseases as watermelon wilt, flax wilt, tomato wilt, sugar cane mosaic, and curly top of sugar beets gravely threatened or even destroyed great agricultural enterprises before disease-resistant varieties of these crops became available, as no other effective control measures are known.   Other crops are today regularly suffering important losses from diseases that cannot be controlled by any known means, and probably will not be controllable until resistant varieties have been developed.

B. Requirements for an acceptable resistant variety.   Fortunately many plant diseases are so host-specific that only certain varieties of a species or certain species of a genus are subject to a given pathogen.   By crossing the resistant species or varieties with susceptible ones it is often possible to obtain hybrids that combine the desired disease resistance of the one parent with desirable commercial or cultural characteristics of the other parent. It is not enough to secure disease resistance alone; many other characters must be combined with disease resistance before a variety is acceptable to growers and consumers. In Florida, for example, there is a project for breeding watermelons resistant to *Fusarium* wilt. While wilt resistance takes first place among the objectives of the work, consideration is also given to many other melon characteristics, including resistance to other diseases and insects, vigor, earliness, prolificness, shape, size, color, rind-thickness, and texture, flesh color and texture, uniformity, flavor, sugar content, seed size, color, and number, and market preferences. The melons that are sought in this project are those which will be substantially wilt-resistant but which must at the same time possess a majority of desirable characters of the types listed, for grower and market preferences are so strong that even in the face of heavy wilt losses it may be almost impossible to have a good resistant variety accepted by growers if it varies in any important degree from the type of susceptible melons which they have been growing.

Granted that a resistant variety is of an acceptable type, its resistance must meet rigorous requirements. It must hold up under widely varying growing conditions, and under conditions of heavy infestation. It must be genetically stable so that progeny of resistant parents will also be uniformly resistant. If more than one strain or race of the pathogen is prevalent the variety should carry resistance to all pathogenic strains to which it is likely to be exposed. In the face of these rigid requirements it is indeed astonishing to consider the accomplishments of breeding for disease resistance which have occurred within a period of only forty years.

C. Accomplishments in the development of disease resistant varieties. Chronologically, asparagus rust was one of the first plant diseases to be combatted by means of resistant varieties. The disease appeared in previously healthy American fields in 1896 and within six years had spread from coast to coast. It was everywhere destructive and no success was obtained in attempts to control it by dusting and spraying. It was observed that some varieties were more subject to rust than others, and J. B. Norton of the federal Department of Agriculture imported numerous foreign asparagus varieties in a search for a truly rust-resistant one. Among these was one from England, "Reading Giant," which was most rust-resistant of all.   It was variable in type but pure lines selected from hybrids of this and other varieties have given us such improved rust-resistant varieties as "Mary Washington" and "Martha Washington" which now dominate asparagus growing in America.   Thus the problem of asparagus rust was solved within five years.

In 1895 the wilt disease of cotton was becoming alarmingly destructive in the area where Sea Island cotton was grown.   A farmer, E. L. Rivers, encouraged and aided by Erwin F. Smith and W. A. Orton of the federal Department of Agriculture, began selecting the more resistant individuals in his fields and in two years had secured a tolerably wilt-resistant strain, of inferior fiber quality however.   Better resistant strains were sought, as it became evident that no other control measure would succeed.   By 1902, Rivers had succeeded in isolating and multiplying a good quality, wilt-resistant strain which was distributed as the new "Rivers" variety, while Orton had found another desirable resistant type which was soon widely cultivated as the "Centerville" variety.   Meanwhile the disease was becoming important in upland cotton, and Orton continued selecting from a partially wilt-resistant variety, "Jackson Limbless," eventually producing "Dillon," the first upland wilt-resistant cotton developed by systematic methods.   Its other characters were unsatisfactory, however, so the search continued, with the result that "Dixie," a much better quality cotton, was secured. Each of these had been produced by selecting a resistant individual, planting its progeny in a single row, and reselecting until the resistance became stabilized.   Now the importance of hybridizing was recognized, and Dillon and Dixie were crossed with other desirable but susceptible varieties to produce a number of new resistant varieties, chief of which were "Dixie Triumph," "Dixie Cook," and "Cook 307-6."   Continued selection and breeding has given us a number of high-quality wilt-resistant varieties which are widely grown today, such as "Stoneville 2-B," "Rowden 5056," "Roldo Rowden 40–2–9," "Coker Clevewilt," and "Rhyne Cook."

In attempts to control the destructive wilt of watermelons, Orton crossed the watermelon with the resistant citron, producing

the synthetic variety "Conqueror," a poor quality but wilt-resistant melon, the forerunner of a long list of desirable melons of various types, represented by such varieties as "Hawkesbury," "Klondike R-7," "Stone Mt. 5," "Kleckley 6," "Blue Ribbon," "Iowa King," "Iowa Belle," and "Pride of Muscatine."

It is not necessary to multiply instances of the efforts on many fronts to provide agriculture with more and better disease-resistant

Figure 197. Another of the noteworthy achievements in breeding for disease resistance was the production of powdery-mildew resistant cantaloupe No. 45 by the United States Dept. of Agriculture. The resistant variety is seen in the two rows in the foreground bordered on both sides by rows of susceptible cantaloupes in which this destructive disease has largely defoliated the plants. (*Photo by Bureau of Plant Industry, U. S. Dept. of Agriculture*).

varieties of crops.   Successful efforts have given us rust- and smut-resistant small grains, wilt-resistant tomatoes, alfalfa, flax, sweet corn, cabbage, and cowpeas, mosaic-resistant sugar cane and legumes, blight-resistant potatoes, root-rot resistant soybeans and tobacco, and many others.

D. The genetics of disease resistance in plants.   The earliest attempts at producing disease-resistant varieties consisted of selecting resistant individuals from susceptible populations, multiplying these individuals, and reselecting until pure resistant lines were obtained.   Later and more effective efforts have been directed at deliberately producing resistant varieties by crossing resistant with susceptible parents, selecting from the hybrid generation, and backcrossing the selected individuals with the more desirable parent, until desirable, homozygous, resistant lines have been secured. It has been seen that disease resistance is a genetic character as regularly inherited as any other genetic factor, however the genetic behavior of resistance differs from one case to the next.

Resistance to one disease is not necessarily correlated with resistance to another. Thus Thatcher wheat, our best stem rust resistant commercial variety, is so highly susceptible to leaf rust that it needs replacement on that account, some of the wilt-resistant sweet corns are highly susceptible to smut, and numerous wilt-resistant cottons are nematode-susceptible.

Simple monohybrid inheritance of resistance, depending on a single gene with a 3:1 Mendelian ratio, has been observed in numerous instances, as in the resistance of cabbage to yellows, of lettuce to downy mildew, and of peas to wilt. In these cases resistance behaves as a dominant character. Simple monohybrid inheritance of resistance with resistance recessive is seen in resistance to powdery mildew of barley, smut of sorghum, and speckled leaf blotch of wheat. Two-gene segregation (ratios 9:3:3:1, 15:1, 9:7, 3:13, or 12:3:1) appears to be involved in resistance to wilt and mosaic of beans, and is one type of inheritance in certain of the cereal rusts. Again, the resistant genes may be either dominant or recessive. Three gene segregation (27:37) is seen in bean anthracnose, in a variety of beans which is resistant to three of the four races of the anthracnose fungus, resistance to each race being governed by a separate gene. Polymeric genes (number unknown) for resistance have also been found as in the resistance of cucumbers to powdery mildew, of cotton to wilt, of tobacco to root rot, and of corn to scab and smut. Finally, instead of two allelomorphic genes for resistance of susceptibility there may be several allelomorphs giving a complex series of resistance relationships when several parents are studied.

In relation to physiologic specialization of the pathogen, a single gene for resistance may apply to but one race of the pathogen, as in the case of bean anthracnose above, or a single gene may carry resistance to several pathogenic races as in the resistance of wheat and oats to stem rust. Moreover a given gene for resistance may

function only at a certain period in the development of the plant or only under certain environmental conditions.   This is well seen in the cereals, where rust resistance commonly applies to the mature plant, the seedlings of resistant varieties often being highly susceptible.   Such a situation indicates that there are two *types* of resistance to cereal rusts, each inherited differently and controlled by different genes.   This can be seen even when the two types of resistance appear at the same time in the disease cycle, in which case they may be differentiated by temperature or some other environmental variable as in cabbage yellows and tomato wilt.

E. The limitations of breeding for resistance.   Breeding for disease resistance may be impossible or only partly effective for a number of reasons:

1. *There may be no source of resistant genes.*   Breeding is usually most successful in dealing with a pathogen of narrow host range, where some resistance is found within the genus or species of crop concerned.   There are exceptions to this rule, however, as in the case of tobacco root rot where success has been obtained in breeding root rot resistant tobacco in spite of the wide host range of the pathogen, *Thielavia basicola*. With a pathogen of very wide host range, such as that of Texas root-rot, breeding for resistance may be unsuccessful because there is no starting point, no variety or species of cotton or alfalfa that manifests the least resistance to the pathogen.   Miraculous as the work of the breeder appears to be, he must still have genes for resistance to start with.

2. *The source of resistant genes may be too distantly related to the crop.* In bacterial blight of cotton a high degree of resistance is found in certain Asiatic cottons such as *Gossypium cernuum*, but these are so distantly related to American upland cotton that fertile hybrids between the two cannot be obtained. Intermediate cottons must be used and the genes for resistance slowly and step by step passed from the resistant species to the desirable but susceptible one.

3. *It may be difficult to combine disease resistance with the other desirable characters.*   At times the breeder encounters a genetic correlation between susceptibility and some other desired char-

acter so that he must take his choice between resistance and the other character; he cannot have both in the same plant. This has been a limitation in breeding smut-resistant corn since susceptibility and vigor are correlated and vigor is essential in field corn.

4. *It may be necessary to develop resistance against many pathogenic races at once.* It has been seen that the genes conditioning resistance to one pathogenic race may be distinct from those governing resistance to other races. To secure a variety that is practically resistant under field conditions it may be necessary to incorporate many genes into the variety until it is protected against all races to which it may be subjected. Remarkable accomplishments along this line have marked the progress of breeding rust- and smut-resistant cereals, but even here, the unexpected appearance of a new or unrecognized race may nullify the breeders' efforts. The appearance of new stem-rust races marked the downfall of Kanred wheat and its successor Ceres. Such races are constantly appearing, and this means that new resistant varieties must constantly be developed to replace old ones. If the breeder can keep a few years ahead of the disease that is all that can be expected; there is no time to sit back and rest on the laurels of an accomplishment in breeding for resistance. Even while a new resistant variety is being distributed, its successors must be in the early states of development.

5. *Increased host resistance promotes increased virulence of the pathogen.* The development of a disease-resistant crop variety is often followed by its widespread cultivation. In cases such as that of powdery mildew of cantaloupe in California, corn wilt in Iowa, and tomato leaf mold in Ohio, the introduction and general adoption of disease-resistant varieties has been followed by apparent loss in resistance. On a resistant variety only strains of the pathogen that are highly virulent can survive. The resistant variety filters the strains of low virulence out of the pathogen's population, leaving only the most highly virulent strains. This raises the general level of virulence of the pathogen, and accelerates the pace with which variation in the pathogen and natural selection of the

most virulent races will ultimately overcome the resistance of the host.

6. *The problem of cross fertilization.* Once a resistant variety is developed it may be relatively easy to maintain its genetic purity if the plant is close pollinated. But in dealing with a plant such as cotton where cross pollination is the rule, every effort must be made to protect the new variety from genetic contamination, else the work of the breeder will be lost. "Meade" cotton, while it was not wilt-resistant, had other fine characteristics and commanded a premium price. By 1920–1922 it was planted on 10,000 acres and was becoming a striking success, but mixing of seed, and planting close to other varieties so contaminated it that the fiber was rejected by the trade and by 1928 the variety was largely abandoned.

REFERENCES

1. Brown, W. Mechanism of disease resistance in plants. Trans. Brit. Mycol. Soc. **19:** 11–33. 1934.
2. Coons, G. H. Progress in plant pathology: control of disease by resistant varieties. Phytopath **27:** 622–632. 1937.
3. Orton, W. A. The development of disease resistant varieties of plants. IV Conf. Intern. de Génétique, Paris: 247–265. 1911.
4. Price, W. C. Acquired immunity to ring spot in Nicotiana. Contr. Boyce Thomps. Inst. **4:** 359–403. 1932.
5. Stevens, N. E. How plant breeding complicates plant disease problems. Science **95:** 313–316. 1942.
6. U. S. Dept. of Agriculture. Yearbook of Agriculture, 1936 (on improvement of field crops by breeding), and 1937 (on improvement of horticultural, forage and cover crops by breeding). Washington.
7. Walker, J. C. Disease resistance in the vegetable crops. Bot. Rev. **7:** 458–506. 1941.
8. Walker, J. C. Disease resistance to onion smudge. Jour. Agr. Res. **24:** 1019–1039. 1923.
9. Wingard, S. A. The nature of disease resistance in plants, I. Bot. Rev. **7:** 59–109. 1941.

Chapter 20

CONTROL OF PLANT DISEASES
BY CULTURAL METHODS

Production of disease-free crops involves care and forethought at every step from the selection of the land on which the crop is to be grown until the final use of the harvested crop. It includes the planting of non-infested seed in non-infested soil, care and protection of the growing crop, and extends through the various steps of harvesting, storing, transporting, and marketing.

Non-infested Soil

Non-infested soil does not necessarily mean sterile soil nor soil that is free of all plant pathogens, but is soil that is relatively or entirely free of destructive pathogens capable of attacking the particular crop to be grown. Root knot nematode-infested soil may be looked upon as non-infested insofar as grain crops and this pest are concerned. Non-infested soil may either be naturally free from dangerous pathogens (uninfested) or may be pathogen-free by virtue of treatments that have destroyed pathogens originally present (disinfested).

A. Uninfested soil.

1. *New land* that has not been cultivated within recent times is often a desirable source of uninfested soil and in the past has been the only such source for crops affected by certain of the soil-borne wilt diseases (flax, banana). But even new land may be dangerous if, as sometimes happens, the wild native flora is harboring pathogens capable of attacking the cultivated crop. Thus, newly-cleared oak land is a regular source of the fungus causing shoe-string root rot of orchard trees, and in the Southwest recently-cleared land often contains the Texas root-rot organism which is endemic as a

506

gens are dependent, and to bury spores.   This cannot be done in all cases, for other than pathological reasons, e.g. in areas subject to wind erosion.

C. Soil amendment is a large element in disease control in some instances, as in the dry land foot rot of wheat, in which weathered or undernourished plants are most subject to disease. Specific soil amendment practices are indicated in the cases of cotton wilt (potassium), potato scab (sulphur), club root of crucifers (lime), bacterial blight of stone fruits (nitrogen), and all mineral deficiency diseases.   In those diseases favored by succulence in the host (e.g. rusts and many bacterial diseases) excessive nitrogen fertilization predisposes the plants to disease, and this can be avoided by preventing such fertilization and by applications of potassium and phosphorus to offset the nitrogen.

D. Seeding.

1. *Time of seeding* has an important bearing on disease control in many cases, as in dry land foot rot of wheat which may be entirely prevented by proper date of seeding, or early spring seeding in dealing with diseases such as root knot or Texas root rot which prevail only in the hot summer months.   The effect of time of seeding is usually directly related to temperature influencing disease, as is strikingly seen in the case of bunt (inhibited by soil temperatures above 70°F.).

2. *Rate of seeding.*   Those fungous diseases that are favored by excessive humidity develop most destructively in the moist conditions accompanying excessive rates of seeding (cereal rusts and mildew; damping-off).   However, where heavy seedling loss from disease characterizes a crop, as in cotton, such losses may be averted by excessive seeding rates to compensate for seedling mortality.

3. *Depth of seeding.*   Deep planting often favors damping-off and other soil-borne fungous diseases by lengthening the susceptible seedling stage.   In addition it may lead to root asphyxiation as also in the burying of plants with soil deposited by wind or water.

E. Water supply.   Where the water supply is controllable, it is often a leading factor in disease control.   Excessive watering favors those pathogens that are dependent on moist air and soil, and in the case of bacterial diseases often aids in the spread of the pathogen.   On the other hand there are occasional cases where flooding serves as a disease control measure, as in the case of root-knot. An unusual case is that of cranberry leaf-drop, a disease due to asphyxiation of the plants under water, which is controlled by flooding the beds in winter, allowing a crust of ice to form, then draining away the water beneath the ice to permit aeration under the ice crust. So important is water in relation to plant disease that the entire pathology of a crop may be profoundly altered under irrigation and in planning irrigation projects this potential hazard should be seriously considered.

F. Handling. In crops such as tobacco, tomatoes, and fruit trees requiring frequent handling (transplanting, grafting, pruning, staking, disbudding, hand pollination, etc.) the act of handling in itself is often a means of spreading disease as in the well-known case of tobacco mosaic. Special precautions are often necessary to avoid this spread, such as disinfestation of tools and hands, and whenever possible the adoption of methods that reduce handling to a minimum.

G. Harvesting. The proper time of harvesting is of vital importance in reducing storage diseases, as is strikingly seen in potatoes. The danger of harvesting when the crop is wet with rain or dew is well illustrated in bacterial blight of beans and bacterial wilt of alfalfa, where this is the principal agency of spread of these diseases.

H. Storing. In all types of crops prompt and proper storage is necessary to avert destructive losses. In this the peculiarities of each crop and each disease must be considered especially as regards temperature and aeration. In general cool temperatures and good ventilation, sometimes preceded by curing, are the requisites for storage disease control, but even here there are exceptions, as in the case of gray-mold neck-rot of onions which is most destructive in cool storage and is inhibited by heat or by storage barely above freezing. The combination of warm temperatures and inadequate ventilation is responsible for a variety of physiological disorders, such as apple scald and potato black-heart, troubles that are combated by well ventilated cool storage and in the case of fruits by oiling the fruits, packing them in oiled paper shreds, or wrapping them in individual oiled wrappers (Fig. 176).

Removal of Undesirable Plants or Plant Parts

A. Weed control by clean culture aids in the control of those diseases that are favored by low vigor in the host plant insofar as the competition afforded by weeds weakens the host. Also the humid air and poor circulation in rank weedy undergrowth is a factor favoring those disease organisms that are dependent on ample moisture. In rare cases toleration of weeds may function in disease control, as in the case of heat canker of flax where the shading value of weeds may be of greater importance than their competition effect.

B. Eradication of wild hosts. There are many cases in which weeds and other uncultivated plants are reservoirs of disease affecting nearby cultivated plants, as the harboring of potato and tomato viruses in wild *Solanaceae*, of grain diseases in wild grasses, and of fruit diseases in wild or neglected fruit trees. Volunteer plants from a harvested crop are often the means of carrying a disease from one crop season to the next as is true of the cereal rusts and some of the spinach diseases. In these cases eradication of the wild plants often constitutes an important element of disease control.

C. Eradication of alternate hosts of rust diseases, in some cases contributes to the control of the disease (stem rust of wheat in the Great Plains), and in other cases may be fully efficient in complete control of the rust (stem rust in protected valleys, cedar-apple rust, pine blister rust). Eradication of the uredinial host is usually more effective than eradication of the aecial host, since the aeciospores are unable to reinfect the host producing them, and in general are shorter-lived than uredospores.

D. Rogueing, or the destruction of individual diseased crop plants as soon as they appear, is the only effective control method for the virus diseases of stone fruits and is a valuable accessory control measure for the virus diseases of potatoes, cowpeas, and beans, anthracnose of melons, and numerous other diseases. In these and other crops, rogueing is worthy of more extensive use.

E. Removal of infected plant parts is of greatest importance in connection with tree surgery and winter pruning of fruit trees. Even where the value of individual plants is much less, it is possible that prompt excision of infected parts might be used to advantage. In Asia Minor, under conditions of extremely low standards of living, highly effective disease control is associated with the practice of hand picking individual diseased leaves of garden crops to salvage them for human or stock consumption. Here additional protection results from the burning of excreta and manure for fuel before using it as a fertilizer. While such extremes are not warranted under American conditions of living, they illustrate the efficiency of sanitation as a disease-control measure.

F. Removal of the body or reproductive parts of the pathogen. In a few instances, where the pathogen is large and conspicuous and the value of the host is considerable, a limited control value attaches to removal of the pathogen or its reproductive parts by hand. This applies in the removal of cedar-apple rust galls from ornamental cedars, of conks from fruit or ornamental trees, and the leafy mistletoe. Corn smut deserves more attention in this connection.

Protection of the Growing Crop with Fungicides

Sprays and dusts are used to protect growing crops against disease, and are of little value once infection has occurred. Their principal function is to inhibit germination of fungous spores largely by means of their metallic ions which are highly toxic to the infection threads. Bacteria are less susceptible to such applications. In rare instances, the mechanical protection or shading effect of sprays and dusts is used to advantage as in the control of tip burn of potatoes. In certain crops regular fungicidal spraying or dusting is essential to good culture (tree fruits, potatoes and peanuts in the East), in others it is not indispensible but helpful. As intensification of agriculture progresses and cheaper and more efficient chemicals become available, a large field is opening in the further development of spraying and dusting.

A. Spraying versus dusting. Both are widely used, even on the same crops, and each has advantages not pertaining to the other.

1. *Advantages of dusting.*
   a. On tree fruits dusting is five times more rapid than spraying.

b. Less labor is required in dusting.

c. In dusting there is no need for hauling water.

d. Less motive power is required to haul dusting equipment.

e. On an acreage basis dusting equipment is cheaper than spraying equipment.

f. Dusts are less likely to burn foliage than sprays.

g. Dusting equipment can be used when the soil is soft and spray rigs would bog down.

h. Dusts can be applied by airplane (Fig. 206) which is cheapest on large acreages, faster and hence more timely, and avoids trampling of the crops.

2. *Disadvantages of dusting.*

a. Dust materials cost more per acre treated than spray materials, however this cost is more than compensated for by labor savings.

b. Dormant dusts are not as efficient as dormant sprays.

c. Two machines are required for orchards, as a spray rig must be available for the dormant application in addition to the duster, and this spray rig could be used for the entire protection program.

d. Quiet air is necessary for efficient dusting, while spraying is not so dependent on atmospheric conditions.

e. There are fewer data available on the control of some diseases by dusting.

For growers who are experienced in spraying, dusting should be tried in an experimental way at first, until acquired skill and experience justify extensive use of the practice.

B. Sprays and spraying.

1. *Copper series.*

a. *Bordeaux mixture.* Since its discovery by Millardet in 1882, Bordeaux mixture has always been the leading fungicide for grapes, tree fruits, potatoes, and many other crops. Various strengths are used expressed by a formula, for example "Bordeaux 3–4–50" which consists of 3 lb. $CuSO_4$ + 4 lb. unslaked lime (90% CaO) or 6 lb. hydrated lime, in 50 gallons of water. Although ready-mixed Bordeaux can be purchased it is better to prepare quantities of stock solutions of one pound per gallon of each chemical, and make the desired mixture by adding one gallon of the stock solutions, which keep well, for each pound specified in the formula.   In mixing, strain the lime into the spray tank, add the water, and then pour in the copper sulphate, agitating well and using at once.

b. *Burgundy mixture* $(Na_2CO_3 + CuSO_4)$ and

c. *Ammoniacal copper carbonate* $(CuCO_3 + NH_4OH)$ are substitutes for Bordeaux mixture when spotting of the foliage is objectionable as on ornamental plants.   They are less effective than Bordeaux and more likely to burn the foliage.

d. *Insoluble coppers.*   A number of comparatively insoluble copper compounds which are relatively non-injurious to foliage on this account, are now receiving attention as substitutes for Bordeaux mixture.   The list includes copper oxides and hydroxides, copper oxychloride, copper ammonium silicate, basic copper sulphate, copper phosphate, copper resinate, copper stearate, copper zeolite, copper silicate, basic copper chlorides, and various mixtures containing colloidal copper.   While many of these are still in the experimental stage, very good results have been reported particularly in the case of red and yellow copper oxides as sprays for preventing post-emergence damping-off and for fungous diseases of various vegetables, fruits, and ornamentals.

2. *Sulphur series.*

a. *Elemental sulphur* (wettable sulphur) is a good fungicide and is less burning to foliage than some other spray materials.   It is usually used at the rate of 6 to 8 pounds of finely divided sulphur in 50 gallons of water, made wettable or miscible by adding a proprietary wetting agent or a "spreader" such as calcium caseinate, oleic acid, glue, diatomaceous earth, flour, dextrin, skim milk, or dry lignin pitch, or by processes of manufacture which produce hygroscopic forms of sulphur.   "Flotation sulphur" is

very finely divided sulphur with certain impurities; it is a
by-product of gas manufacture.

b. *Lime sulphur* is one of the most useful of fungicides and is
widely employed as an orchard spray except in hot
weather when it is more likely to injure foliage than wettable sulphur or Bordeaux mixture. It is commercially
available as a concentrated solution, used at the rate of 2
to 5 gallons of solution per 100 gallons of water for spring
spraying and at higher strengths for dormant spraying.
The concentrated solution may be prepared on the farm
by boiling quicklime (50 lbs.) and sulphur (100 lbs.) in
water (enough to make total of 50 gallons). Formerly,
"self-boiled lime sulphur," in which sulphur and lime are
combined in the heat of slaking, was widely used, but it is
now largely replaced by wettable sulphurs for summer
fungicides.

c. *Dry lime sulphur* is obtained by dehydrating lime sulphur
concentrate, with the addition of sugar as a stabilizer.
In appropriate concentrations it is used either as a summer
or as a dormant spray.

d. *Dry mix sulphur lime* consists of elemental sulphur to which
lime is added to prevent the burning of foliage that results
when sulphur alone is mixed with lead arsenate. Common formulas are 8 lbs. finely divided sulphur plus 4 to
8 lbs. hydrated lime plus ½ lb. wetting agent in 50 gallons
of water.

It should be noticed that these various sulphur-lime
compounds differ from one another in chemical composition according to the method of preparation, resulting in
differences in fungicidal effect and toxicity to the plant.

3. *Mercury series*. Mercury compounds are rarely used as
sprays, but do have a useful place as lawn fungicides, usually
in the form either of mercurous chloride (calomel) or organic
mercury compounds (e.g. "Nu-Green").

4. *Methods of application*. A long chapter could be devoted to
the subject of sprayers and the technique of spraying but
such a discussion is beyond the scope of this book. The
subject is fully treated in Mason, A. F. "Spraying, dusting

and fumigating of plants" (Macmillan Co., 1936) and
Anderson, O. G. and F. C. Roth, "Insecticides, fungicides,
and appliances" (Wiley Co., 1923). Sprayers range from
the hand atomizer through various types of hand and knapsack sprayers and barrel pumps up to large commercial

Figure 203. Small hand-operated sprayers and dusters.

Figure 204. Row sprayer applying Bordeaux mixture to potatoes at the
rate of 200 gallons per acre. (*Photos by Tenn. Agr. Exp. Sta.*)

power sprayers, and each has uses for which it is particularly
suited (Figs. 203, 204, and 205). The art of spraying
also includes knowledge of when and how to apply fungicides
in order to accomplish the desired end with a minimum of
cost and labor.

C. Dusts and dusting. There is a growing tendency to replace
spraying with dusting because of the advantages pointed out on
page 526. Sulphur is usually the material used, although some use
is also made of copper dusts.

1. *Sulphur and sulphur-lime.*   Sulphur alone or sulphur and lime mixtures are excellent fungicides.   The sulphur should be so fine that 98 per cent of it will pass through a screen with 300 or 325 meshes to the inch and this fineness is obtained either by grinding or by precipitating sulphur from solutions.   The finer dusts are less likely to burn foliage although there appears to be a limit of fineness beyond which nothing is

Figure 205.   A combination of rod and gun nozzles used in orchard spraying.
(*Photo by Tenn. Agr. Exp. Sta.*)

gained.   Sulphur alone rarely burns plants and may be combined freely with arsenical dusts without incompatibility. Sulphur dust is finding an important place in control of peanut leaf-spot, diseases of tree fruits, and powdery mildews of various crops.   It is effective in controlling cereal rusts, but as yet this use has not been developed on a commercial scale.

To maintain the fineness necessary in a good sulphur dust and prevent lumping, the dust is frequently treated with fillers or inert materials such as Fuller's earth, diatomaceous earth, talc, gypsum, hydrated lime, magnesium carbonate, or tri-calcium phosphate.   Such treated sulphurs are known as "conditioned sulphurs."

2. *Copper-lime dust.* This consists of very finely ground anhydrous copper sulphate (300 mesh) mixed with lime. It has proven quite injurious to foliage in warm climates but is useful as a substitute for Bordeaux mixture on tomatoes, melons, cucumbers, and other vegetables, and is used to a small extent on potatoes.
3. *Methods of application.* Dusts may be applied with hand and knapsack type dusters, or on a large scale with power

Figure 206. Applying sulphur dust by airplane, for protecting wheat from rusts. (*Courtesy of F. J. Greaney, Canada Dept. of Agriculture.*)

equipment. Recently airplane dusting has developed at a rapid rate in North and South America, this being a cheap method of application when large acreages are involved (Fig. 206). To be most effective the dust should be applied before rains, and when the air is calm.

D. Hazards of dusting and spraying. The usefulness of dusting and spraying is somewhat limited by dangers accompanying the practices. Chief of these are:

1. *Spray injury.*
   a. *Bordeaux mixture injury* appears as burns, shot-hole, yellowing, or defoliation of leaves, russetting of fruit, cankers and dieback of twigs, blighting of blossoms, and in severe cases general necrosis and death of the plant. Plants vary in their susceptibility to Bordeaux injury, the stone fruits being very susceptible, the pome fruits variable,

and the potato quite resistant. The greatest danger is at cool temperatures and when damp, foggy weather accompanies and follows the spraying. It is believed that the reason for the injury is excessive carbon dioxide emitted under shady conditions, which dissolves in water on the leaves to form carbonic acid, which in turn liberates free copper from the copper sulphate, this entering the cells and killing them. The danger of Bordeaux injury is reduced by avoiding excessive applications, unusually strong solutions, or excessive copper sulphate in relation to the lime present, use of the more resistant varieties, and substitution of lime-sulphur for early spring applications.

b. *Lime-sulphur injury* in contrast to Bordeaux injury, occurs chiefly in hot weather. Leaves are burned, especially at the margins and tips, and the leaves of stone fruits may become shot-holed. In potatoes the plants are stunted and their life is shortened. The chemical appears to act on the chlorophyll in such a way as to starve the plants, and in this way leads to premature fruit drop. For prevention of lime-sulphur injury, do not use lime sulphur on the most sensitive crops but substitute weak Bordeaux mixture or sulphur dusts, use the weakest effective concentration, spray moderately, with a fine mist, and if an arsenical is added it should be arsenate of lead, not calcium or sodium arsenate or Paris green.

c. *Incompatibility of sprays.* While it is economical to combine different spray materials in the same application to control several pests at once, not all spray materials can be mixed without producing ineffective or injurious mixtures. For instance, oil and sulphur cannot be safely mixed. For a full discussion of this subject see Anderson and Roth "Insecticides, Fungicides, and Appliances."

2. *Poisoning of useful insects.* Wide scale application of insecticides, particularly airplane dusting with calcium arsenate, may prove destructive to useful as well as harmful insects. Beekeepers in California complain about losses in their apiaries from such dusting and there is a likelihood that other beneficial insects are also destroyed by dusting.

3. *Poisoning of the soil.* In commercial orchards where intensive spray programs are followed year after year the problem of injurious accumulation of spray materials in the soil is a growing one. Already complaints of such soil poisoning have been heard in the apple-growing sections of Washington, Idaho, and New York, and in some cases it has become impossible to grow crops on such soils.

4. *Spray residues.* On crops such as fruits and greens, spraying or dusting with poisons can constitute a menace to health. The Federal Department of Agriculture has ruled (1938) that fruit may not contain more than .025 grains of lead or .01 grains of arsenic or fluorine per pound. Growers or marketers can be prosecuted under the Pure Food and Drug Act if their products contain greater amounts of these poisons. This danger can be avoided by the use of spray and dust materials which do not contain the heavy metals, by avoiding excessive or late applications, and in the case of fruit by washing off spray residues in an acid bath, a practice regularly followed in apple production.

E. Unusual fungicidal practices.

1. *Fumigation.* Although fumigants are usually directed against insects, there are cases where they are valuable aids in controlling plant diseases. The most notable case is the use of benzol vapor for the control of the very destructive downy mildew or "blue mold" in tobacco seedbeds. The beds are covered with sheeting and the benzol allowed to evaporate from a free surface, unheated. Paradichloro-benzene is also used for this purpose, the method of use being illustrated in Figure 207.

Sulphur vapor is also a good fungicide. In ordinary greenhouse practice it is customary to coat steam pipes with sulphur paste. The slow volatilization serves as an excellent preventative against such diseases as powdery mildew and black spot of roses. In much stronger concentration the vapor from boiling sulphur is used to fumigate sweet potato storage houses and other storage buildings. The vapor in this case is so highly injurious to plant tissues, that the storage house must not be in use at the time of fumigation. Formaldehyde is used for fumigation in a similar way.

2. *Fungicides in irrigation water.* Another downy mildew or "blue mold," that of spinach, creates a serious problem in the leading trucking sections. In cases where the crop is watered by irrigation the disease develops on the lower surface of the leaves in contact with the soil, where no spray

Figure 207. Fumigating a tobacco seedbed with paradichlorobenzene. Crystals of the chemicals are scattered over the regular seedbed cover, and then the bed is covered with a heavy cloth and wet down. (*Courtesy of J. A. Pinckard, Va. Agr. Exp. Sta.*)

could reach it. Preliminary work in Texas with control by adding fungicides to the irrigation water is giving encouraging results, and this opens the field for attempts at controlling other diseases of irrigated plants in the same manner.

3. *Eradicant spraying.* Spraying the ground around the bases of fruit trees to kill hibernating pathogens before primary infection of the trees in the spring is a new practice that appears very helpful in reducing the burden of orchard spraying during the growing season. This type of control is discussed in more detail in connection with apple scab on page 116.

Cure of Diseased Plants

In human medicine the great emphasis is on *curing* affected individuals (therapeutics). In plants, on the other hand the value of diseased individuals is usually small, and not worth the cost of curing. Here the emphasis is on *preventing* disease (prophylaxis). There are cases, however, in which the curing of individual plants may justify the cost either because of high value of the individuals or of low cost of the curative treatment, as in the following:

A. Heat treatments of plants for nematode control. Some types of nursery stock and greenhouse plants which are lightly infested with root-knot can be cured by heating the root systems in water at 118°F. for 30 minutes. Not all plants will stand this temperature without injury, but it has been used successfully with black locust, chinese elm, mulberry, cyclamen, begonia, and roses. In the case of large lots of nursery trees the cost of the treatment is about six cents per thousand. Many other plants affected with root-knot should be tested for their heat resistance, as there is a probability of extensive use of this control method in such stock. Heat treatments of this sort have also been used with success in protecting coffee nursery stock from the root lesion (meadow) nematode.

B. Heat treatments for viruses. Kunkel has shown that peach trees suffering from peach yellows and little peach may be cured by heat treatments. It is questionable whether this would be practical with entire trees, but the work indicates the possibility of thus disinfesting peach budwood which might be of great value in producing virus-free stock and in the virus-free distribution of peach propagating material from one part of the country to another. Although some virus diseases cannot be cured in this manner (e.g. peach rosette and certain potato viruses), the field of usefulness of this method is largely unexplored.

C. Therapeutic treatments of trees. Individual shade trees may in some cases be worth several hundred dollars, and their value justifies attempts at curative treatments. Tree surgery is a step in this direction, although the effect of surgery is usually to postpone decay, not to cure it. Many attempts have been made to find chemicals that might be profitably injected into trees. Most of these attempts have failed but there appear to be a few authentic cases of cure of contagious disease in trees by injections. An example is the bleeding canker of oak, beech, elm, and maple trees.

Here there is good evidence that injections of Helione orange, a basic yellow dye, destroys the fungus within the tree and effects recovery. In dealing with minor-element deficiencies in trees, injection of salts is a reliable method of cure, and is widely practiced in some areas in combating chlorosis. However in view of the abuse of the practice by wandering charlatans posing as tree experts, the tree owner should have due caution in the use of such treatments.

REFERENCES

1. Anderson, O. G. and F. C. Roth.   Insecticides and fungicides.   John Wiley & Sons, New York.   1923.
2. Burton, T. R.   Insecticides, fungicides, and weed killers.   Ernest Benn Ltd., London.   1926.
3. Haskell, R. J.   Progress in controlling plant diseases, 1914 to 1939.   U. S. Dept. Agr., Ext. Path. **43:** 43–48.   1940.
4. Martin, H.   The scientific principles of plant protection.   London.   1928.
5. Mason, A. F.   Spraying, dusting, and fumigating of plants.   Macmillan Co., New York.   1936.
6. Stevens, N. E.   Recent trends in plant disease control.   Trans. Ill. Acad. Sci. **33:** 66–67.   1940.

Many of the state experiment stations and extension services issue disease control circulars and spray bulletins and calendars, and on application to your college of agriculture you will be furnished these, for example:

Robinson, R. H.   Sprays, their preparation and use.   Oregon Agr. Exp. Sta. Bull. 393.   1941.

Some of the most extensive and detailed works on plant disease control unfortunately are not available in English.   One of the best of these is:

Appel, H. c. O. et al.   Handbuch der Pflanzenkrankheiten.   VI. Verhütung und Bekämpfung der Pflanzenkrankheiten.   Paul Parey, Berlin.   1937–1939.   (The parts thus far issued correspond to the subject matter in this chapter.   Future parts are intended to deal with control by breeding for disease resistance and by regulation.)

INDEX

The main discussion of a topic is indicated by italic numbers, illustrations by boldface numbers.

Powdery mildews, legumes, *136–137*
　　rose, *137–138*, **137**
Practical resistance, 490
Prediction of disease outbreaks, *308–309*
Preparing soil in relation to plant disease,
　　522
Preservation of specimens, *422*
Pressure sterilizers, 430, **431**, 510, **511**
Price, 334
Prickly pear, *Rhizopus* rot, 237–241
Privet, root knot, 370
　　"rust" (alga), 367
　　Texas root rot, 168
Promycelium, **26, 80**
Propagation. See also seed, grafting,
　　budding
　　materials as agents of disease dis-
　　　semination, 463
　　vegetative, and crown gall, 316
　　　and virus diseases, 328
　　wood, registered, 518
Prophylaxis, 535
Proteins, virus, 334
Protozoa, 18
Provenience, 411
Prune. See also stone fruits
　　fireblight, *291–295*
　　peach mosaic, 346
　　Rhizopus rot, *237–241*
　　shoestring root rot, 91
Pruning, *525–526*
　　and apple blotch, 214
　　　scab, 117
　　and black knot of stone fruits, 121
　　and brown rot of stone fruits, 143
　　and peach scab, 196
　　and rose cankers, 217
　　and virus spread, 327
Pseudomonas, 283
　　spp. See *Phytomonas spp.*
Pseudoperonospora cubensis, 229–230
Pseudopeziza, 199
　　medicaginis, *144–145*
Psorosis, citrus, 518
Puccinia anomala, 48
　　antirrhini, *55*, **56**
　　asparagi, **54**
　　dispersa, 48
　　graminis, *30*, 460. See also stem rust

Puccinia graminis, avenae, 32
　　secalis, 32
　　tritici, 32
　　malvacearum, *55*, **56**
　　peridermiospora, **49**
　　purpurea, 48
　　sorghi, 48
　　triticina, *43*, **44**, 460
Pull-down. See dodder
Pumpkin anthracnose, *202–203*, **202.**
　　See also cucurbits
Pure culture, *431–434*
Pycnidium, **22**, 117, **118**
Pycnium, **35**
Pycnosclerotium, 212
Pyracantha, Texas root rot, 168
Pythium aphanidermatum, 253
　　arrhenomanes, 274, *276–281*
　　debaryanum, *251–257*
　　ultimum, 253

Q

Quarantines, Act, 5, 478
　　alligator pear, 482
　　apple, 485
　　as trade barriers, 479, *480–481*
　　azalea, 485
　　balance sheet of, *480*
　　bamboo, 482
　　banana, 482
　　benefits of, 486
　　biological aspects of, *478*
　　bramble fruits, 485
　　bulbs, 482
　　cereals, 482
　　chestnut, 485
　　citrus, 482, 484, 485, 486
　　corn, 482
　　cotton, 272, 482, 485
　　cranberry, 485
　　crown gall, 485
　　currant, 483
　　economic aspects of, *480*
　　efficiency of, *478–479*, 485
　　elm, *125–127*, 482, 483, 484, 486
　　enforcement of, *481*
　　federal, *478*
　　filbert, 485

Quarantines, flower bulbs, 482
   gooseberry, 482, 483
   hop, 485
   interstate, *483–484*
   mechanism of, *481–482*
   natural barriers and, *479*
   onion, 485
   ornamentals, 483
   pea, 485
   peach, *435–439*, 486
   pine, 478, 482, 483, 484
   potato, 478, 479, 482, 485, 486
   present day, *482–485*
   raspberry, 485
   rescinding of, 479
   results of, 486
   retaliatory, 480, 484
   rice, 482
   root knot, 485
   rose, 483
   sorghum, 482
   state imposed, 478, *484–485*
   stem rust, 484, 486
   strawberry, 485
   sugar cane, 482
   sweet potato, 482, 485
   Texas root rot, 173, 485
   variation in, 484
   wheat, 69–70, 482
   yam, 482
Quince, brown rot, 139
   fireblight, 291
   root knot, 370
   rust, 50
   Texas root rot, 168

R

Radish. See also crucifers
   boron deficiency, 393
   club root, *244–250*
   root knot, 371
   Texas root rot, 168
   white rust, *234–236*
Rafflesia, 355
Rag doll germinator, 276
Ragweed, dodder, 357
Rain as agent of disease dissemination, *461*

Rainfall and epiphytotics, 467
Rape. See also crucifers
   club root, *244–250*
Raspberry. See also cane fruits
   anthracnose, *145*
   crown gall, *313–316*
   fireblight, 291
   mosaic, **321**, 495
   quarantine, 485
   root knot, 370
   rust, *53–54*
   shoestring root rot, 91
   Texas root rot, 168
   virus diseases, **321,** 485, 495
Rate of seeding in relation to plant disease, *523*
Ray, W. W., 267
Razoumofskya, 363, **365**
Reaction, soil, effect on parasitic disease, *456–457*. See also acid, alkaline soil
Recovery from plant disease, *496–497*
Red copper oxide. See copper
Red rot, sugar cane, 207
"Red rust." See "rust" (alga)
   cereals, 35. See wheat leaf rust
Redbud, leaf spot, **214**
   shoestring root rot, 91
   Texas root rot, 168
Registered propagation wood, *518*
   seed, *518*
Regulation, control of plant disease by, *476–487*
Removal of pathogens, 526
Replication, 446
Residues, crop, disease and, *507–508*
   oil well, *396*
Resistance to plant disease, *488–505*. See also susceptibility
   chemical, *493–495*
   complexity of, 498
   control of plant disease by use of, *488–505*
   cross fertilization and, 505
   definition, 490
   degrees of, *490–491*
   development of in nature, 488
   disease control by, *488–505*
      economy of, 489

Smuts, inoculation methods with, 435
    nature of, 58–59
    types of, 58
Smuttox, 521
Snapdragon, root knot, 370, **373,** 380
    rust, *55,* **56**
    Texas root rot, 168
Soapberry, Texas root rot, 168
Sodium cyanide for soil disinfestation, 515
Soft rot, bacterial, 289, 299
Soil, acid and plant disease, 155,. 165,
    173, 257, 267, *395, 456–457*
    alkaline and plant disease, 155, 165,
      173, 182, 267, *394–396,* **396,**
      456–457
    amendment, 523
    and physiogenic diseases, *388–401*
    -borne diseases, soil treatments for,
      506–516. See also soil disinfes-
      tation
    chemical excesses, *394–397*
    deficiencies, *388–394*
    disinfection. See soil disinfestation
    disinfestation, 257, *508–516,* **509,**
      511, 512, 515
    by chemicals, *513–516,* **513, 516**
    effect on parasitic diseases, *455–*
      458
    for club root control, 248–249
    for damping-off control, 257,
      508–516
    for root knot control, 378–381
    for Texas root rot control, 176–179
    for watermelon wilt control, 160
    in greenhouses, 508
    injury to soil, 509
    inoculation of, 435
    non-infested, *506–516*
    poisoning by sprays, 397, 534
    reaction, effect on parasitic disease,
      456–457. See also acid, alkaline
      soil
    sterilization, 255. See soil disin-
      festation
    sterilized, use in experiments, 445
    temperature and plant disease, *452–*
      454
    texture, effect on parasitic diseases,
      457–458

Soil, treatment for soil-borne diseases.
    See soil disinfestation
    type and Texas root rot, 175
    uninfested, *506–508*
    virgin, and plant diseases, *507*
    water-logged, *401–402*
Solanaceae, late blight. See potato late
    blight
Solutions, preserving, *422–423*
Sooty molds, 179, 265
Sore shin, cotton, 253, 258, 260, **261**
Sorghum. See also cereals
    anthracnose, *196–202*
    blasting, 400
    charcoal rot. See sorghum root and
      stalk rots
    covered smut, 58, 69, 502
    damping off, *251–257, 276–281*
    disease susceptibility in, 472
    downy mildews, *233–234*
    head smut, 58, 77
    Helminthosporium diseases, 190
    leaf spot, *305–306*
      streak, *305–306,* **305**
      stripe, *305–306*
    lodging. See sorghum root and
      stalk rots
    Milo disease, *276–281,* **277**
    mosaic, 328
    quarantine, 482
    root and stalk rots, **277,** *276–281*
    rust, 48
    seed treatment for, 69, 519, 520
    seedling blight. See sorghum root
      and stalk rots
    smut, 58, 69, 77, 502
    stalk rots. See root and stalk rots
    Texas root rot, 168
    weak neck. See sorghum root and
      stalk rots
Southworth, E. A., 259
Soybean. See also legumes
    bacterial blight, 298
    excess light, 415
    root knot, *369–381*
    scalding, 415
    Texas root rot, 168
Spartina pectinata, **49**

Specialization. See physiologic specialization

Specimens, botanical, as agents of disease
dissemination, *463*
collecting, *422*
laboratory examination of, *424–426*
preserving, *422*
shipping, *422*

Speckled leaf blotch, wheat, *217–219*, **218**,
448–449, 502

Spergon, 256, 443, 521

Spergonex, 443, 521

Sphaeriales, 106

Sphaeropsidales, 150
diseases caused by, *207–221*

Sphaeropsis malorum, 117

Sphaerotheca humuli, *137–138*
pannosa, *137–138*

Spinach, blue mold. See spinach downy
mildew
boron deficiency, 393
damping off, *251–257*
downy mildew, *231–232*, **230**, 468,
535
Heterosporium leaf disease, **230**
mosaic, 353
root knot, 369–381
Texas root rot, 168
white rust, *236–237*
smut, 58, 82–83

Spindle tuber, potato, 322, *337–338*, **338**,
341

Spiraea, fireblight, 291
Texas root rot, 168

Sporadic diseases, defined, 466

Sporangiophore, **21, 22, 238**

Sporangiospore, 21, **22**, 222

Sporangium, 20, 21, 22, **233, 238, 243**

Spore germination, **20**, *464*
fungicides and, 526
mat, **171**
methods of, **425**, *426*
traps, *438–439*, **439**

Spores, 20. See also aeciospore, ascospore, basidiospore, chlamydospore, conidium, oospore, pycniospore, sporangiospore, teliospore, uredospore, zoospore, zygospore, etc.

Sporidium, **26,** 58

Sporodochium, **22, 140,** 151

Sporulation, 28
inducing, 433–434

Spot blotch, barley, 179, *190–192*, **193**

Spot diseases. See leaf spot, boll spot,
black spot, etc.

Spotted wilt, tomato, 329

Spray(s), burning by, 115, *532–533*
compatability of, 529, 531, 533
copper, *527–528*
injury, 115, 142, 531, *532–533*
mercury, *529*
residues, *534*
soil poisoning by, 397, *534*
sugar in, 529
sulphur, *528–529*
warnings, 116, *475*

Sprayers, **530**

Spraying, *526–530, 532–535*
advantages and disadvantages, *526–
527*
combined purpose, *116–117*
dormant, *529*
equipment, **530**
eradicant, 116, *535*
for apple black rot, 118
blotch control, 213
scab, *115–117*
for bacterial blight of stone fruits, 296
diseases, 290
wilt of cucurbits, 313
for brown rot of stone fruits, 142–
143
for cherry leaf spot, 144
for fireblight of apple and pear, 294
for peach leaf curl, 148
scab, 196
for *Phyllosticta* leaf spots, 215
for plum pockets, 148
for potato late blight, 228, **530**
for tobacco downy mildew, 232–233
for tomato bacterial wilt, 300
ground, 116, *535*
hazards, 117, 142–143, *532–534*
methods of, *529*
warnings, 116, *475*

Spread of plant diseases. See dissemination

Wheat, anthracnose, *196–202*, **199**
black point, 181, **183**, 184
rust. See stem rust, leaf rust
blackheads. See loose smut
bunt, 58, *59–66*, **61**, 70, 71, 419, 454, 463–464, 517
common root rot, 181
covered smut. See bunt
crown rot, 180
damping off. See seedling blight
diseases, number of, 9
dry land foot rot, *179–193*, **183, 185,** 454
ergot, *127–132*
flag smut, 58, 59, *69–70*, 481
foot rots. See root rots
frost injury, 411
Fusarium blight, *106–110*, **107, 108,** 452–454, **453**
glume blotch, *219*, **220**
greasy stinking smut. See bunt
Helminthosporium blight, *180–193*, **183 185,** 454
leaf spot, **193**
high smut, 61
leaf rust, 34, *43–47*, **44**, 420, 467, 490–491, 502
lodging, 414
loose smut, 58, **61,** *70–76*, **74, 75,** 474, 516, 518
low smut, 61
mosaic, 328, *350–352*, **351**
nematode, *381–383*, **382**
orange rust. See leaf rust
powdery mildew, *132–136*, **134**
quarantine, 482
red rust. See leaf rust
root rot, 179, *180–193*, **183, 185,** 454, 456
scab, *106–110*, **107, 108,** 452–454, **453**
seed treatment for, *62–66*, **64, 65,** *72–76*, **74, 75,** 519, 520, 522
seedling blight, *106–110*, 181, 183, 452–454, **453**
Septoria diseases, *217–220*, **218, 220,** 448–449, 502
snow mold root rot, 456
speckled leaf blotch, *217–219*, **218,** 448–449, 502

Wheat, stem rust, 1–2, *30–43*, **33, 35, 43,** 455, 460, **483**, 484, 486, 493, 494, 502, 504
stinking smut. See bunt
stripe rust, 34, *47*
sulphur dusting, *42–43*, **43**, 46, 420
by airplane, **532**
Texas root rot, 168
white heads, 184
yellow berry, *389*
"White pickle," cucumber, *353*
White rusts, *234–237*
crucifers, *234–236*, **235, 236**
pigweed, 236
spinach, *236*
White smuts, 58, *82–83*
White spot, alfalfa, 400
White trunk rot, *86–91*, **87**, 451
Wind, as agent of dissemination of pathogens, *461*
-blown leaves as agents of disease dissemination, *463*
dissemination of diseases, methods of study, *438*
effect on parasitic disease, *455*
Wilcoxon, 443
Wild hosts of disease, eradication of, *525*
Willow, mistletoe, 363
root knot, 370
scab, 6
Texas root rot, 168
Wilt diseases. See also bacterial wilt, *Fusarium* wilt, etc.
bacterial, *306–313*
alfalfa, 289, *310–312*, **311**
corn, **Frontispiece**, 285, 286, 287, *306–310*, **307, 308, 309,** 452, 474
cucurbit, 287, *312–313*, **313**
Cephalosporium, 162–164
elm, *163–164*, **163**
persimmon, 6, *164*
Fusarium, 150–162
banana, 8, 162, 285, 477, 506
cotton, *151–157*, **153, 156,** 173, 289, 369, 389, 390, 456, 473, 485, 500, 502, 505
flax, 9, *160*, 498, 506
sweet potato, *160–161*, **161,** 485
tomato, *157–158*, 300, 369

Wilt diseases, watermelon, *8*, 14, 152, *158–
      159, **159,** 369, 498, 499, *500–501,*
      514
    Verticillium, 152, *164–165,* 173
    cotton, 152, 165
Winter browning, evergreens, *411–413,*
      412
    injuries, *411–413*
      alfalfa, cowpea, 205
      conifers, 412
      peach, **412**
      relation to stem rust, **31**
    killing, alfalfa, *411*
      cereals, *411*
      strawberries, *411*
Wisteria, root knot, 370
Witch's broom, potato, 322, 339
Wood decay, *84–91,* **87**
    fungi, **25**
Wood stain, 85
Woodgate rust, pine, 483
Wooly knot, apple, 314
Woronin, 244
Wounds and bacterial diseases, 286

X

X-bodies, 323
X-disease, peach, 6, 319
X-Fungus, 521
X-ray, effect on viruses, 334

Y

Yam, quarantine, 482
Yellow-berry, wheat, *389*
Yellow copper oxide.   See copper

Yellow dwarf, potato, 340
Yellow(s).   See also bacterial yellows
    alfalfa, **391**
    aster, 328
    blight, Western, tomato, 352
    cabbage (= *Fusarium* wilt), 162, **489,**
      502, 503
    diseases, 319, 321, **323**
    peach, 319, **323,** 327, 497, 536
    strawberry, 485

Z

Zinc, availability of, *394*
    chloride, for canker treatment, *295*
    deficiency, **390**
      apple, 391
      citrus, 391
      grapefruit, 395
      pecan, **390**
      tung oil tree, 391
    -lime spray for bacterial blight of
      stone fruits, *296*
    oxide, as bactericide, 290
      for seed treatments, 256, 257, *520*
    sulphate for brown rot control, *142–
      143*
Zinnia, damping off, **513**
    powdery mildew, 137
    root knot, 370
    Texas root rot, 168
Zoosporangium, **21,** 222
Zoospores, 20, **21,** 222
    inducing production of, *434*
Zygomycetes, **21,** *237–241*
Zygospore, 21, **22,** 222, 239
Zygote, **222**